Psychodynamic Perspectives on Sickness and Health

Psychodynamic Perspectives on Sickness and Health

Edited by Paul Raphael Duberstein and Joseph M. Masling

American Psychological Association • Washington, DC

Published by
American Psychological Association
750 First Street, NE
Washington, DC 20002

Copies may be ordered from
APA Order Department
P.O. Box 92984
Washington, DC 20090-2984

In the U.K., Europe, Africa, and the Middle East, copies may be ordered from
American Psychological Association
3 Henrietta Street
Covent Garden, London
WC2E 8LU England

Typeset in Palatino by EPS Group Inc., Easton, MD

Printer: Edwards Brothers, Ann Arbor, MI
Dust jacket designer: Berg Design, Albany, NY
Technical/Production Editor: Amy J. Clarke

The opinions and statements published are the responsibility of the authors, and such opinions and statements do not necessarily represent the policies of the American Psychological Association.

Library of Congress Cataloging-in-Publication Data
Psychodynamic perspectives on sickness and health / edited by Paul Raphael Duberstein and Joseph M. Masling.
p. cm.—(Empirical studies of psychoanalytic theories)
Includes bibliographical references and index.
ISBN 1-55798-668-1 (cb : acid-free paper)
1. Clinical health psychology. 2. Health—Psychological aspects. 3. Medicine and psychology. I. Duberstein, Paul Raphael. II. Masling, Joseph M. III. Series.
R726.7.P78 2000
616'.001'9—dc21 99-058549

British Library Cataloguing-in-Publication Data
A CIP record is available from the British Library.

Printed in the United States of America
First Edition

Contents

Contributors

Jamie Arndt is an assistant professor of psychology at the University of Missouri—Columbia. He has recently joined Jeff Greenberg, Tom Pyszczynski, and Sheldon Solomon in their publishing efforts.

George A. Bonanno is an assistant professor in the Department of Counseling and Clinical Psychology at Teachers College, Columbia University, New York. He has published empirical and theoretical articles on coping with grief and trauma, emotion, and memory for traumatic events. In addition to scholarly interests, he devotes as much of his free time as possible to painting and playing the *balafon,* an African precursor to the xylophone.

Robert F. Bornstein is a professor of psychology at Gettysburg College, Gettysburg, PA. He has written numerous articles and chapters examining the antecedents and consequences of dependent personality traits and unconscious determinants of personality, motivation, and affect. Bornstein wrote *The Dependent Personality* (Guilford, 1993), edited *Perception Without Awareness: Cognitive, Clinical, and Social Perspectives* (Guilford, 1992), and coedited with Joseph M. Masling Volumes 4–8 of the Empirical Studies of Psychoanalytic Theories book series. He received the Society for Personality Assessment's 1995 and 1999 Walter Klopfer Award for Distinguished Contributions to the Personality Assessment Literature.

Paul Raphael Duberstein is an associate professor of psychiatry and oncology at the University of Rochester's School of Medicine and Dentistry (Rochester, NY), where he is affiliated with the Center for the Study and Prevention of Suicide. He received his PhD in clinical–community psychology from the State University of New York at Buffalo in 1991 and completed a postdoctoral fellowship in late-life psychopathology at the University of Rochester. Dr. Duberstein's research examines the relationships between personality and both mental and physical health, with a special emphasis on personality, loss, and suicidal behavior in older adults.

Jamie L. Goldenberg is completing his postdoctoral work in psychology at the University of Colorado, Colorado Springs. He has recently joined Jeff Greenberg, Tom Pyszczynski, and Sheldon Solomon in their publishing efforts.

Jeff Greenberg is a professor of psychology at the University of Arizona, Tucson. With Tom Pyszczynski and Sheldon Solomon, he has been collaborating since they were all graduate students at the University of Kansas in the late 1970s. Together, they have published theoretical and empirical articles and chapters on a range of topics, focusing especially on self-esteem, meaning, anxiety, and defensiveness.

Melanie A. Greenberg is an associate professor in health psychology at the California School of Professional Psychology, San Diego. She received her PhD in clinical psychology in 1992 from the State University of New York at Stony Brook and completed a postdoctoral fellowship in health psychology at the Graduate Center, City University of New York. Her research has been funded by the Arthritis Foundation (New York chapter). Her awards include the Harry Crossley Fellowship, Sigma Xi research awards, and the Student Research Award from the American Psychological Association's Division 38 (Health Psychology). Her research focuses on how people's cognitive and emotional reactions to traumas and stressors can affect their physical health, the development of emotional disclosure and cognitive-processing interventions to enhance adjustment to life transitions and illnesses, and the roles of cognitive appraisal and emotion management in adaptation to chronic illness.

Stacey Kaltman is a doctoral candidate in clinical psychology at Catholic University of America, Washington, DC. She just completed her dissertation in traumatic grief and is currently completing an internship at the University of Maryland's School of Medicine in the behavioral medicine track.

Milton Kramer received his MD from the University of Illinois (Chicago) in 1954 and completed his internship and psychiatric residency at Cincinnati (OH) General Hospital in 1958. Currently, he is a clinical professor of psychiatry at the New York University School of Medicine. Formerly, he was a volunteer professor of psychiatry, University of Cincinnati, and a clinical professor, Wright State University, Dayton, OH. He was also the director of the Sleep Disorders Center at Bethesda Hospital in Cincinnati from 1984 to 1999. He has published extensively on the topic of dreams and sleep, and he has coedited three books, *Dream Psychology and the New Biology of Dreaming, Dimensions of Dreams,* and *The Functions of Dreams.*

Joseph M. Masling is an emeritus professor of psychology at the State University of New York at Buffalo. He has written numerous articles on interpersonal and situational variables influencing projective tests, and he has published widely on the empirical study of psychoanalytic concepts. Dr. Masling edited the first three volumes of the Empirical Studies of Psychoanalytic Theories book series (1983, 1986, 1990); coedited with Robert F. Bornstein the next five volumes, including *Psychoanalytic Perspectives on Developmental Psychology* (1996), *Empirical Studies of the Therapeutic Hour* (1998), and *Empirical Perspectives on the Psychoanalytic Unconscious* (1998); and received the Society for Personality Assessment's 1997 Bruno Klopfer Award for Lifetime Achievement in Personality Assessment.

Richard M. O'Neill is an associate professor at the State University of New York Health Science Center at Syracuse's Department of Psychiatry and Behavioral Sciences, an ABPP Fellow of the Academy of Clinical Psychology, a licensed systems-centered psychotherapist and group facilitator, an AGPA-certified group psychotherapist, and an Academy Award Winner (Best Student Documentary, 1976). A former president of the New York State Psychological Association, he has appeared on television over 175 times discussing psychological issues and has published numerous scientific and professional articles regarding individual and group survival, development, and transformation. His professional practice includes consulting to organizations and individuals about enhancing performance in work, home, and sports. He notes that ever since his mother gave him $1 for each *A* he earned in second grade classes (including physical education), he has been interested in the psychology of healthy achievement.

Tom Pyszczynski is a professor of psychology at the University of Colorado, Colorado Springs. With Jeff Greenberg and Sheldon Solomon, he has been collaborating since they all were graduate students at the University of Kansas in the late 1970s. Together, they have published theoretical and empirical articles and chapters on a range of topics, focusing especially on self-esteem, meaning, anxiety, and defensiveness.

Joshua M. Smyth is an assistant professor of psychology at North Dakota State University, Fargo, and a research scientist at the Neuroscience Research Institute (Fargo, ND). His interests include the development and application of psychological interventions in medical patients with chronic physical illness, emotional (non)expression, stress and coping processes, psychoendocrinology, and the physical and psychological sequelae of traumatic experiences. When not in the office, he is often on the golf course, desperately trying to achieve a single-digit handicap.

Sheldon Solomon is a professor and chair of psychology at Skidmore College, Saratoga Springs, NY. With Jeff Greenberg and Tom Pyszczynski, he has been collaborating since they all were graduate students at the University of Kansas in the late 1970s. Together, they have published theoretical and empirical articles and chapters on a range of topics, focusing especially on self-esteem, meaning, anxiety, and defensiveness.

Introduction: Psychoanalysis and Health Psychology

Paul Raphael Duberstein and Joseph M. Masling

As individuals and as a species, humans precipitate and accelerate their own diseases and deaths (at the same time seeking to cure and prevent diseases) at a rate unparalleled in any other animal. Warfare and completed suicide may be the most obvious examples of self-destruction; fratricide and infanticide may be the

We thank Robert Ader and Nancy Talbot for their comments on an earlier version of this Introduction. Work on this book was financially supported in part by Public Health Service Grant K07-MH01135. We would like to acknowledge the following individuals for their suggestions, comments, or reviews of the chapters in this volume: J. Gayle Beck, Arthur Efron, Leonard Epstein, Mark Larson, Ross Levin, Michael Perlis, Dean Pruitt, Larry Seidlitz, Tara Spevack, and Nancy Talbot. Katie Graffrath and Karen Hoyer provided secretarial support.

most repugnant and, fortunately, least frequent. Relatively pedestrian behaviors, perhaps reflecting underlying personality traits, take the greatest toll on individuals, families, and society. Approximately 25–40% of cancer deaths (Doll & Peto, 1981) and 19% of all deaths in the United States (McGinnis & Foege, 1993) can be attributed to tobacco. Alcohol abuse accounts for roughly 5% of the deaths in this country (McGinnis & Foege, 1993); efforts to quantify its effects on physical morbidity and psychological suffering remain major public health challenges. Dependency on drugs affects not only the health and longevity of the users and their families but also the safety of others.

This volume of the Empirical Studies of Psychoanalytic Theories series, the ninth, is devoted to applications of psychodynamic ideas to problems of health and illness. Unlike previous volumes, which emphasize rigorous tests of specific psychodynamic propositions, this book has a broader goal: to view contemporary health psychology through a psychodynamic lens and to test the merit of a few psychodynamic ideas about the body. To a considerable extent, health psychology and psychoanalytic thought have not taken notice of each other. Psychodynamic theories focus almost exclusively on the fine nuances of mental life, rarely considering physical health at length. Health psychology incorporates some of the aims of psychosomatic medicine and seeks to decrease the adverse effects of health-damaging behaviors by identifying, promoting, and encouraging healthful lifestyles. With its somewhat blinkered view of the world derived primarily from self-report data, health psychology has steadfastly avoided the close investigation of people's fantasies and unconscious motivations.

The isolation of the two disciplines from each other has exacted a cost: Each is more provincial and parochial for the lack of cross-fertilization between the two. It is time to begin the business of constructing a health psychology that considers and integrates empirically validated psychodynamic insights and hypotheses about personality, wishes, intrapsychic conflicts, and unconscious motives. Such a task will not be easy. Many scholars may view the juxtaposition of psychodynamics and health psychology as a "fabulized" combination, to use the Rorschach term, a fairy tale at best. Some psychoanalysts dismiss empirical work as artificial, contrived, irrelevant to clinical practice, and essentially superfluous because clinical evidence is sufficient proof of the theory's merit. Tansey (1992), an authority on countertransference, admitted that he has "until now been singularly uninterested in, if not contemptuous of, anything that the 'number crunchers' have to say. . . . The phrase 'meaningful statistical data' was, to [him], an oxymoron of hilarious proportions" (p. 539).

Many health psychologists and biologists believe that psychoanalytic thinking is vague, unnecessarily mentalistic, and therefore inimical to scientific investigation, even when they do acknowledge that some elements of the theory are "right." For example, in his mass-market book on stress and disease, the physiologist Robert Sapolsky (1994) commented that many of Freud's ideas "just feel 'right.' But they are hard to assimilate into modern science, especially biologically oriented psychiatry. There is no way to study the correlation between norepinephrine receptor density and internalization of aggression" (p. 217). This criticism has little merit. The nine volumes of this series, the books by Fisher and Greenberg (1978, 1985, 1996), the volume by Barron, Eagle, and Wolitzky (1992), and seminal reviews published over the past decade or so (Bornstein, 1992; Epstein, 1994; Hardaway, 1990; Kandel, 1999; McClelland, 1989; Pyszczynski, Greenberg, & Solomon, 1999; Shedler, Mayman, & Manis, 1993; Westen, 1998) attest to the extraordinary number of interesting, insightful experiments generated by psychodynamic ideas. Despite the prevalent attitude held by so many, in both academic psychology and the wider community of scholars, psychoanalytic theory has probably inspired more research than any other theory of personality.

Health psychology takes its theoretical cues from stress theories and cognitive–behaviorism, not psychoanalysis. This book is premised on the assumption that a psychodynamically informed health psychology would be desirable. However, we do not mean to imply that psychoanalysis is the only alternative to stress theory or behaviorist approaches. Nor are we saying that health psychology is doomed to fail unless it acknowledges the significance of psychodynamic concepts. Instead, psychoanalytic theory is (in this era) a novel, interesting, underused, and empirically heuristic alternative. It is true that psychosomatic medicine long ago emerged from the shadow of psychoanalysis (Weiner, 1999), but it may be time now for clinicians and scholars who are interested in mind–body issues to return to psychoanalysis.

In the first section of this introduction, we review three themes in the psychoanalytic literature that give shape and form to a maturing psychodynamic health psychology: the invention of the concept of *todestrieb*, the rejection of the strong form of mind–body dualism, and the experience of treating patients with physical symptoms for more than a century. Second, we consider the barriers to the development of a psychodynamic health psychology. The doctrine of specific etiology, which inspired research on specific material causes of disease, began to dominate medicine by the end of the 19th century. Moreover, knowing how to treat physical illnesses and generating data about them increasingly required rigorous research, particularly "bench" science. The same could not be said of treating mental illnesses. The psychoanalytic establishment shrunk from science and thereby consigned itself to mental, not physical, illnesses. Attempts to accommodate psychoanalysis to prevailing notions of specific etiology were forced, misguided, and ultimately discouraging. But there is cause for optimism now. Health psychology along with other modern specialties, namely, cognitive neuroscience and social epidemiology, have begun to attack the strong forms of dualism and specific etiology on scientific grounds. Despite repeated assertions that psychoanalysis is dead and not amenable to science, investigators are increasingly turning to psychodynamic theory as the basis for research ideas. This interest may be the biggest cause of optimism for those wishing to integrate psychodynamics and health psychology.

A Latent Psychoanalytic Health Psychology

The Death Drive

Epidemiological data on the effects of alcohol, cigarettes, and drugs on physical health and mortality were not available to Freud. However, he did attempt to accommodate his theory to the unsavory facts of warfare (Freud, 1915/1957), which, along with his observations on the repetitive nature of self-destructive behavior, led-him to invent the concepts of repetition compulsion and *todestrieb* (death drive; Freud, 1920/1955).[1] In *Beyond the Pleasure Principle*, he wrote that

> the instincts of self-preservation, of self-assertion and of mastery . . . are component instincts whose function it is to assure that the organism shall follow its own path to death, and to ward off any possible ways of returning to inorganic existence other than those which are immanent in the organism itself. . . . What we are left with is the fact that the organism wishes to die only in its own fashion. Thus, these guardians of life were originally the myrmidons of death. (Freud, 1920/1955, p. 39)

Freud took care to differentiate between two similar forms of death: (a) a silent drive ("the aim of all life is death"; Gay, 1988, p. 401), seeking to reduce tension and impulse to quietude, and (b) overt, everyday aggression. Nonetheless, the concept of a death drive has remained one of Freud's most controversial ideas, which even some of his most ardent supporters have faulted. For example, Fenichel (1945) noted that "there are many possible objections[;] . . . the concept . . . is neither necessary nor useful" (pp. 59–60). Still, some theorists have been sympathetic to the idea (Abraham, 1925/1955; Bakan, 1968; Ferenczi, 1929; Jelliffe, 1933; Menninger, 1938/1985). Among his contemporaries, Abraham and Ferenczi may have been the most receptive,[2] and it is perhaps no accident

[1]Freud endured many losses in his later years. He first used the term *todestrieb* in his correspondence only 1 week after the death of his daughter, Sophie (Gay, 1988). Gay (1988) noted that "it is tempting to read Freud's late psychoanalytic system, with its stress on aggression and death, as a response to his grief of those years" (p. 394). In an ingenious study, Suedfeld and Bluck (1993) analyzed the integrative complexity of a random sample of letters written by famous people. Letters written around the time of a major negative event were more complex than those written during the postevent period.

[2]Freud (1926/1958) eulogized Abraham in the pages of the *International Journal of Psychoanalysis*: "Among all those who followed me along the dark paths of psycho-analytic research, his was so pre-eminent a place that only one other name could be set beside his" (p. 277). In his editorial footnote, Strachey informed the reader that he has "no doubt" that the "other name" was Ferenczi. Could it be a coincidence that the two men who embraced Freud's most controversial idea attained special status in his mind?

that both authors made numerous references to the interface of psychodynamics and physical health. In an article titled "The Unwelcome Child and His Death Instinct," Ferenczi (1929) wrote that

> children who are received in a harsh and disagreeable way die easily and willingly. Either they use one of the many proffered organic possibilities for a quick exit, or if they escape this fate, they keep a streak of pessimism and of aversion to life. (p. 127)

Abraham (1925/1955) noted that a tuberculosis patient may have "strong psychological reasons to resist [a] cure. His unconscious may exploit the organic disease to alienate him from life and gradually bring about his death" (p. 307). Menninger (1938/1985) extended Freud's concept, expanding the theme of inherent self-destructiveness and illustrating its relevance to daily life by leavening his text with case examples culled from his practice and stories taken from Midwestern newspapers. Still Menninger's (1938/1985) message, like Freud's, is too stark and, therefore, difficult for many to accept:

> Each man has his own way of destroying himself; some are more expedient than others, some more consciously deliberate than others. . . . Study of the personality often shows that "organic" disease is only a part of the total personality disease and fits into a pattern which seems to have the definite purpose of destroying the self. (pp. 312–313)

This claim alone could have formed the basis of a psychodynamic health psychology, but the world is not prepared to hear it.

Rejection of Mind–Body Dualism

Freudian psychoanalysis has never been exclusively about "minds" or minds distinct from bodies. It is about embodied minds and, more to the point, minds in a sexual body (Efron, 1985). The psychoanalytic rejection of dualism was consistent with the general view of 19th-century neurology. What distinguished Freud from his contemporaries was his emphasis on the sexual body and his allocation of primacy to psychology, not biology. Some scholars have attempted to interpret psychoanalysis from a dualistic framework and have literally removed the body from the theory (e.g., Schafer, 1976). But Freud's (1923/1961) belief that the ego develops largely through physical stimulation is quite clear: "The ego is first and foremost a body ego; it is not merely a surface entity but it is itself the projection of a surface" (p. 26).

Any number of psychoanalytic writers have commented on the primacy of bodily experiences as the foundation for later personality development. Edelberg (1957) suggested that a body ego is a constituent part of ego processes. Fisher and Cleveland (1968), who provided an excellent summary of Freudian views of this topic, cited Joan Riviere, the translator of Freud's article, as developing Freud's statement further: "That is, the ego is ultimately derived from bodily sensations, chiefly from those springing from the surface of the body. It may thus be regarded as a mental projection of the surface of the body" (p. 62). For Jacobson (1964), body image is shaped by infantile experiences and memories of both pleasant and unpleasant events. Greenacre (1958) speculated that the perception of the face and genitalia are particularly important in forming the body image.

Fenichel (1945) linked the perception of reality directly to bodily sensations:

> At first there is only the perception of tension, that is, of an "inside something." Later, with the awareness that an object exists to quiet this tension, we have an "outside something." One's own body is both at the same time. Due to the simultaneous occurrence of both outer tactile and inner sensory data, one's own body becomes something apart from the rest of the world and thus the discerning of self from nonself is made possible. The sum of the mental representations of the body and its organs, the so-called body image, constitutes the idea of I and is of basic importance for the further formation of the ego. (pp. 35–36)

In this form of psychoanalytic thought, it is apparent that the body is the bedrock of ideas about the self and the source of interactions with the world. Traumatic events in the world should be reflected in a form of bodily impairment.

> The first reality is what one can swallow. Recognizing reality originally means to judge whether something helps to gain

> satisfaction or whether it raises tensions, whether one should swallow it or spit it out. Taking-into-the-mouth or spitting-it-out is the basis for all perception, and in conditions of regression one can observe that in the unconscious all sense organs are conceived as mouth-like. (Fenichel, 1945, p. 37)

Freud's concern with the body in some ways precluded his interest in events occurring externally to the body. His description and naming of the various psychosexual stages illustrate how bodily processes influenced his beliefs about the way in which an infant grows to adulthood. The tasks to be mastered are organic and physical; the interpersonal aspects, particularly any needs for attachment to others, are relatively unexamined and remain for later writers (Bowlby, 1969, 1973, 1980; Scharf & Birtles, 1994) to describe more fully. Oral, anal, and phallic stages, named after body parts and functions, document the extent to which Freud's thinking was based on his medical school training. The central crisis in all human development, the resolution of the Oedipal complex, revolves around the presence or absence of a body part. Feelings engendered by the threat of the loss of that organ, or the wish to have one, is crucial to Freud's theory.

Treatment of Patients With Physical Symptoms

Perhaps the best indicators of a latent psychodynamic health psychology are the hundreds of case reports of patients with puzzling physical symptoms. Following Breuer's (Breuer & Freud, 1893/1955) initial success with Anna O., Freud treated many patients with hysterical ailments. From his observations of hypnotic techniques, he had witnessed how words can both initiate and remove physical symptoms. In 1910, he first discussed the concept of *nonpsychogenic* symptoms (Freud, 1910/1957), ailments resulting from unconscious gratification of a bodily organ or its purpose. He held that it was possible to remove some of these ailments solely by verbal insight. In perhaps his most famous case, Freud (1918/1955) ascribed the "Wolf Man's" constipation and diarrhea to various unresolved conflicts, and he conjectured that neurasthenia is caused by "excessive" masturbation and anxiety neurosis by coitus interruptus (Freud, 1898/1962). Of course, the data gathered in psychotherapy sessions are correlational—the patient discusses both previous psychic conflict and present ailments—leading Freud and many other analysts to conclude that the former caused the latter, when no such conclusion can be legitimately reached.

Confronted with the need to treat patients who had unexplained physical symptoms, the first few generations of psychoanalysts and psychoanalytically informed physicians had nothing more reliable to guide them than their inchoate theories of personality. The original conflict is repressed; its energy is channeled into symbolic bodily symptoms. When conflict remains unconscious, its energy can find overt expression in physical symptoms that represent a compromise between the unacceptable impulse and the ego's defenses against it. Psychic energy is thus transformed into somatic symptoms. As Brenner (1982) put it, "if a patient has many prominent somatic symptoms of psychic origin, by definition conversion of psychic conflicts into somatic manifestations plays a role in the dynamics of those symptoms" (p. 81). Fenichel's (1945) position is quite similar: "In conversion, symptomatic changes of physical functions occur which, unconsciously and in a distorted form, give expression to instinctual impulses that previously had been repressed" (p. 216).

Writers after Freud have agreed that physical symptoms can follow from unresolved conflicts. Unfettered by data, analytic writers have relied on nothing more substantial than reasoning by analogy to explain a number of physiological functions and disorders. For example, Fenichel (1945) declared that the respiratory system could reflect signs of unresolved conflict and that asthma is "a cry for help directed at the mother" (p. 251). This type of proposition is based on reasoning by analog: "Inhaling the same air as another person means to be united with him, while exhaling means separation" (p. 251). Peptic ulcers occur in people "with a chronically frustrated oral-receptive demanding attitude who . . . are unconsciously permanently 'hungry for love'. . . . This permanent hunger makes them act like an actually hungry person does" (p. 245). Even myopia was subject to this form of interpretation.

> Constant use of the eye for libidinous gratification of scoptophilic impulses may cause it actively to strain in the direction of objects in order psychically to incorporate them. It is con-

> ceivable that this may finally result in a stretching of the eyeball. (p. 256)

Barriers to Psychodynamic Health Psychology

In the absence of scientific information, the early analysts embraced ideas that were fanciful, poetic, dramatic ("organic suicide"), vague, and, at times, silly. Worse, many of their ideas were not amenable to scientific methods. "Engaged in a titanic, subterranean struggle between the urge to speculate and the need for discipline" (Gay, 1988, p. 768), Freud knew that some of his constructs, like *todestrieb*, would be extremely difficult to operationalize. But that left him unperturbed. Unlike Freud, scholars influenced by logical positivism have taken seriously only those hypotheses and constructs with clearly defined and observable behavioral referents. Whereas vague language precluded the development of the concept of *todestrieb*—and psychodynamic health psychology more broadly—there were other, more insidious obstacles: the prominence of the doctrine of specific etiology and mind–body dualism in 20th-century medicine, resistance to data within the psychoanalytic establishment, and psychological resistance to psychoanalytic ideas.

The Doctrine of Specific Etiology, Koch's Postulates, and the Institutionalization of Mind–Body Dualism

As Freud was launching his career, two of his contemporaries, Louis Pasteur and Robert Koch, were revolutionizing medicine by establishing scientifically that specific germs caused specific diseases—an idea now called the "doctrine of specific etiology." Koch, who won the 1905 Nobel Prize for his discovery of the bacillae that caused tuberculosis, had also identified the bacillae that caused cholera. Earlier, he had articulated general principles and methods for establishing that a particular bacterium caused a specific condition, which came to be known as "Koch's postulates." Based on elegant and carefully controlled studies, these ideas conferred great status to medicine, and status was important. Whereas links between psychological and bodily states were the stuff of folklore and everyday speech (e.g., fire in the belly, faint hearted, lion hearted, lily livered, no stomach for, gutless, does not have the balls for, toothless tiger, foot in mouth), there was little room in the new medicine for psychology. Abraham (1925/1955) decried "academic medicine," particularly its "superior, skeptical attitude . . . [and] . . . preconceived objections to the notion that unconscious psychological factors exert upon the origin, course, and cure of organic disease" (p. 307). Alexander (1933) preferred to analyze the problem:

> Long experience has shown that it is by no means a popular task to give an address on psychoanalysis to a group of physicians. . . . The aversion to the introduction of psychological factors in medicine is due to the fact that it reminds the physician of those very remote days in which medicine was sorcery, and therapy consisted of expelling the demons from the body. Medicine . . . tries to . . . emphasize its exact nature in keeping out of field everything that seems to endanger its scientific appearance. Indeed, among the exact sciences medicine became more Pope-like than the Pope himself. (p. 469)

By comparing psychosomatic specificity to microbial specificity, Alexander (1950), among others, tried to reconcile psychodynamics with Koch's postulates. Each illness or dysfunction was said to have resulted from specific unresolved needs. In retrospect, these strained attempts to link a specific personality trait or psychosexual conflict with a specific symptom, syndrome, or disease represented misguided efforts to force the square pegs of psychodynamics into the round holes of specific etiology. The lack of empirical support for the specificity hypothesis may have been a major reason why a coherent psychodynamic health psychology never emerged and may have contributed to the marginalization of psychodynamics in medicine.

While psychodynamic scholars challenged the concept of mind–body dualism, organized medicine and the academy embraced it during the 20th century. Medical schools and professional medical organizations separated the mind from the body, symbolized best perhaps by the split between neurology and psychiatry. Immunology charted a separate course; the notion of an integrated mutually influencing immune system and nervous system had no theoretical or empirical basis. In universities, psychology was carved from biology and philosophy. As psychology departments evolved, experimentalists and clinicians grew apart, with psychology as a social science viewed as somehow different from psychology as a natural science; specialists in affect distinguished themselves from specialists in cognition. Both in medicine and in psychology, subdisciplines evolved and grew more differentiated. As envisioned by Weber (1922/1946), these subdisciplines and associated professional organizations became increasingly bureaucratized and rigid, developed new language forms that outsiders could not readily understand, and attended to member versus nonmember boundaries, meanwhile conferring financial security and credentials to each other (cf. Meehl, 1998).

Small wonder, then, that theorists and clinicians who rejected dualism paid a price. Despite "ridicule, skepticism, and contradiction" (Menninger, 1938/1985, p. 311), Jelliffe (1933) held to his view that skin disease is associated with emotional conflict. Of all Freudian thinkers, Wilhelm Reich took most seriously the problem of how body and personality interact (Efron, 1985). His concept of character as armor of the personality has been particularly important. In this view, character is formed as the ego hardens (Reich, 1973), much as simple organisms harden themselves for protection against the environment. Furthermore, different character types develop different physical and psychological reactions to changes in life circumstances, so that "compulsive" characters manifest different body types than "hysterical" characters. Character types show unique psychological aspects (character armor) with unique physical components (muscular armor). The therapeutic goal is to break through this armor to allow the impulse to be identified and expressed. Reich also advanced a number of potentially testable hypotheses concerning the relationship between cancer and sexuality, but little came of these (Reich, 1948). Generally disparaged and scorned by the medical, psychological, and psychoanalytic establishments, he was jailed for defying a court order that prevented him from sending one of his Orgone accumulators (the Orgone box) across state lines. He died alone and alienated in a U.S. penitentiary in 1957 (Greenfield, 1974), his work suppressed and many of his books and journals destroyed by order of the U.S. government (Arthur Efron, personal communication, January 23, 1999).

Resistance to Data Within the Psychoanalytic Establishment

The failure of psychoanalysis to adopt the scientific method contributed to its alienation from mainstream medicine, which became increasingly enamored of science after the successes of Pasteur, Koch, and other 19th-century pioneers. This self-imposed exile from science made it impossible for psychoanalysis to contribute to knowledge of physical health and disease.

It is instructive to contrast the extent to which psychoanalytic theories have changed in the 100 years since 1900—when *The Interpretation of Dreams* (Freud, 1900/1965) was published—with the changes in such sciences as physics, astronomy, biology, and chemistry. Even the arts—music, painting, poetry, literature—have undergone dramatic alterations in form, method, and content in the last century. Psychoanalysis remains essentially as it was 100 years ago, despite the many schools of analytic thought that have split off from Freud's original position. Looking at the many divisions within the analytic house, a psychoanalyst might see enormous changes, but most dispassionate observers would find the differences between schools so minute to be detectable only by vigilantes in opposing camps. Sadly, the many schisms within psychoanalysis speak to nothing more substantial than one group of analysts claiming their clinical ideas and experiences are superior to those of another group. None of these splits developed as a result of empirical data. Clinical experience, as formulated by some charismatic but personally and professionally biased leader, seems to have produced many of the major shifts within psychodynamic theories. A physicist living in 1900 would not understand a modern lecture in physics, but Freud would easily comprehend a current psychoanalytic text.

The cost of remaining static in a dynamic, turbulent world is to risk becoming a fossil, a quaint historical curiosity. The signs of the decline in psychoanalytic theory's popularity are easily found. The popular press and professional journals contain frequent attacks on psychoanalysis (Crews, 1994; Grunbaum, 1984), psychoanalytic treatment is losing favor to drug and cognitive–behavioral forms of therapy, and the number of clinical psychologists whose primary theoretical orientation is psychodynamics has fallen from 35.0% in 1960 to less than 20.0% in 1995, whereas 24.0% of clinical psychologists now prefer cognitive treatment methods—a therapeutic modality unknown in 1960 (Norcross, Karg, & Prochaska, 1997). Citations to psychoanalytic literature have been declining since 1994 (Friman, Allen, Kerwin, & Larzelere, 1993). Psychoanalysis no longer dominates training in psychiatry, and departments of psychiatry are rapidly becoming agents for pharmacological treatment.

The loss in popularity and influence was both predictable and avoidable. Until quite recently, psychoanalysis, in the name of clinical confidentiality, denied access to its primary data, the psychoanalytic session, to researchers. Happily, that unfortunate situation has recently been changed, so that qualified researchers can now examine verbatim exchanges between analyst and analysand. No other serious form of intellectual inquiry held out so long against external study, arguing in the face of criticism that the world should accept its adherents' claims for the merits of the enterprise. Furthermore, the gatekeepers of psychoanalysis have maintained that empirical inquiry is unnecessary because the clinical method is sufficient to establish the validity of psychoanalytic treatment and psychoanalytic theory. Eissler's (1969) remarkable comment summarizes this attitude well: "The psychoanalytic situation has already given forth everything it contains" (p. 469). It is impossible to imagine a physicist, chemist, or geneticist making such an absurd claim, but the neuroscientist Eric Kandel (1999) appealed to Eissler's authority to support his own attempt to help psychoanalysis "re-energize itself" (p. 505). However, Kandel did not acknowledge that Eissler's myopic vision, shared by so many others, contributed to the marginalization of psychoanalysis from mainstream medicine.

The belief that the clinical method of collecting data is so valid that it obviates the need for independent confirmation of its hypotheses can be traced directly back to Freud, who produced generalizations without making available his raw data (Spence, 1994). As a result, "the psychoanalytic literature tends to minimize evidence at the expense of conclusion and maximize argument at the expense of evidence" (Spence, 1994, p. 30). The relatively static position in which psychoanalysis is held

> can be laid to two factors: reliance on an outmoded method of scientific data collection and a preference for fanciful argument over fact. . . . Most disturbing of all is the absence of data. Argument by authority stands directly in the way of the benefits, zealously guarded since the Renaissance, of an adversarial, critical, and dialectical tradition of investigation. (pp. 1, 3)

The faith in the analyst's (or patient's) record of the analytical hour as sufficient to support the entire enterprise of psychoanalysis is ill founded. Memory is so easily influenced by wish, defense, expectation, and experience that an account of an analytical hour by either of its participants is bound to be filled with omissions, alterations, and inventions. Any clinical supervisor can attest to the nonrandom differences between what a supervisee reports and what a taped record of the session reveals. Furthermore and more important, the therapist inevitably selects and shapes the contents of the patient's speech (Murray, 1956; Truax, 1966). By responding to some content and not to others, the therapist communicates to the patient what topics need to be explored and analyzed and what topics can be safely ignored (Masling & Cohen, 1987).

This implicit coaching explains why so many different schools of psychoanalytic thought—Kleinian, self psychology, object relations, intersubjective, Jungian, Freudian—can so easily produce evidence from their patients' speech that validates each position. To believe that everything the patient says emerges untutored and unshaped by the therapist is to mistake a mirror for a window. Inevitably, the patient's words and memories sometimes reflect both the therapist and patient. The controversy about recovered memories of sexual abuse in childhood demonstrates how easily therapists' expectations can produce distorted patient "recollections" (Loftus, 1993).

None of these remarks is intended to challenge the ability of psychoanalytic treatment to make profound changes in individuals' behaviors, lessening their misery, and helping them to lead easier, more meaningful lives. However, it is simply wrong to rely on a case history as exclusive support for the entire structure of psychoanalytic thought. Clinical evidence is rich with the stuff of human experience, but it is also susceptible to the unwitting influence of the therapist's personal and professional expectations. Alas, the same ore that yields psychoanalytic treasures also yields "fool's gold." Only careful, repeated testing of clinical evidence can separate the two. Good experimental data now support many of Freud's contentions. For the sake of brevity, we cite only two such instances. Freud's second theory of unconscious processes, that they have goals and purposes of their own (Weiss & Sampson, 1986), is consistent with much research. His idea that a personality is stable, enduring, and consistent over situations has also received considerable validation (Masling, 1986). However, some of his other ideas, equally plausible at the time of their writing, have fared less well when examined experimentally. For example, he maintained that women are more dissatisfied with their bodies than men, that their superegos are not as strong, and that every dream is an effort at wish fulfillment, but none of these has received consistent empirical confirmation.

Relatively few creative ideas about personality have come from the laboratory. The raw material of psychoanalytic thought has originated from interactions between therapists and patients and from persuasive, coherent case presentations. This method is limited. As Holt (1984) observed, "psychoanalysts must begin to face the fact that their primary and typical form of research, the uncontrolled case study, is devoid of scientific value *except* as a source of hypotheses" (p. 13, emphasis in original). Although experiments can be rigorous and are capable of being replicated, they are also subject to bias and other threats to validity. Neither cogent clinical presentations nor empirical data are sufficient to provide satisfactory evidence for the use of psychodynamic theories. A wise science would use both sources of knowledge.

Psychological Barriers

The history of ideas reveals the folly of efforts to separate theories, hypotheses, and constructs from the social and historical context in which they came into being. Pharmaceutical companies know that it is easier to sell pharmacological treatments for alcoholism in France than it is in the United States. Americans are more likely than the French to view alcoholism as a moral problem. Psychoanalytic institutes are not spread randomly throughout the United States but are instead concentrated in specific metropolitan regions. Becker (1973) observed that "the hostility to psychoanalysis in the past, today, and in the future, will always be a hostility against admitting that man lives by lying to himself about himself and the world" (p. 51). Is it possible that people who live in large metropolitan areas are simply more willing to believe that people lie to themselves? Freud himself recognized that some people would be morally or personally threatened by many of his ideas, perhaps none more so than *todestrieb* (Gay, 1988). That the instinct of self-preservation serves to assure a certain way of death is paradoxical at best, if not simply incoherent and illogical. Like the notion of the dynamic unconscious, the idea that we humans are inherently self-destructive seems inconsistent with our accomplishments and narcissistic notion of a privileged place in the animal kingdom. It also conflicts with many idealistic and romantic visions of life.

The notion that constitutional psychological factors and early life events increase risk for disease and death is inconsistent with egalitarian doctrine. All people are not equally vulnerable to bad things. To believe Shakespeare's maxim that the "past is prologue" (*The Tempest,* Act 2, Scene 1) may be construed by some as undermining free will or self-determination (Berlin, 1969). To implicate personality traits, fantasies, and motives in death's causal chain is considered rude, even bad medicine. For example, Angell (1985), a deputy editor of the *New England Journal of Medicine,* complained that

> the popular media, stirred by occasional reports in the medical literature, remind us incessantly of the hazards of certain personality types. We are told that Type A people are vulnerable to heart attacks, repressed people (especially those who have suffered losses) are at risk for cancer. . . . At a time when patients are already burdened by disease, they should not be further burdened by having to accept responsibility for the outcome. (pp. 1570, 1572)

A few years later, Rogers and Reich (1988) wrote an editorial in that same journal arguing that

> the physician owes it to the patient to point out the strengths of the human response rather than the susceptibilities that are often belabored in the media. Rather than emphasize the disruptive power of stress, the physician may do better to emphasize human resilience and the power of life. (p. 511)

The tension between discovery and doctoring, or science and medicine, is unavoidable, or so it seems. As long as a psychodynamically informed health psychology can be construed as threatening the egalitarian ideal, undermining self-determination, or blaming the victim, it will not be taken seriously, let alone thrive. Temperament theorists (Kagan, 1994) and molecular geneticists (Jacob, 1998) have deftly deflected the charge that they potentially undermine values so central to democracy, community, and civility. A psychodynamically informed health psychology can preempt and defuse such criticisms as well.

Time for a Psychodynamic Health Psychology?

Notwithstanding Angell's (1985) comments—and the scientists and clinicians who share her views—limitations of the doctrine of specific etiology and Cartesian dualism are widely acknowledged in a manner unimaginable to previous generations. Disciplinocentrism appears to be waning, and there is an emerging consensus that disciplinary boundaries are arbitrary, even "historical fictions that can restrict the imagination" (Ader, 1995, p. ix). Attempts to think rigorously about the meaning, strengths, and limitations of "disciplinarity" in all its forms, namely, multi-, inter-, and transdiscipline are ongoing (cf. Rosenfeld, 1992; Stokols, 1998). Researchers (Berkman, 1995; Wulsin, Vaillant, & Wells, 1999) have identified many socially and psychologically mediated determinants of longevity, which is consistent with the spirit, if not the actual content, of Freud's statements about a death instinct.

The field of health psychology is vigorous and flourishing. The *Annual Review of Psychology* published its first article on the topic in 1983 (Miller, 1983); six articles on the topic have subsequently been published (Adler & Matthews, 1994; Baum & Posluszny, 1999;

Cohen & Herbert, 1996; Krantz, Grunberg, & Baum, 1985; Rodin & Salovey, 1989; Taylor, Repetti, & Seeman, 1997), and many others have appeared on closely related topics (e.g., Ader & Cohen, 1993). Division 38 of the American Psychological Association (APA) was founded in 1978; it is now one of the fastest growing divisions in APA history, and its journal, *Health Psychology,* has the widest member and nonmember circulation of all APA-specialty journals ("Summary Report of Journal Operations, 1997," 1998). A number of other specialty journals, societies, and subspecialties have been launched over the past 2 decades.

The story of psychoneuroimmunology's dramatic rise is particularly compelling because it challenged the received wisdom in immunology. Generations of students were taught that the immune system is "autonomous," but both psychological and neurobiological research demonstrate the opposite: The immune system is inextricably linked to the nervous system. A landmark study shows that immune responses can be classically conditioned (Ader & Cohen, 1975), and other investigations document nervous innervation of lymphoid tissue (Felten & Felten, 1991). As a direct consequence of these discoveries, the journal *Brain, Behavior, and Immunity* began publishing in 1987, and the Society for Psychoneuroimmunology Research was founded in 1993. Although the psychological and physical consequences of neural–immune interactions are still not well understood, much progress has been made over the past decade (Ader, Felten, & Cohen, 1991, in press; Cohen & Herbert, 1996; Kiecolt-Glaser, & Glaser, 1992). A new multidisciplinary field of study has been built on a foundation of solid data.

From its inception, psychoanalysis sprouted rapidly and widely, with no disciplinary boundaries. It was soon enervated by its own antagonism toward empiricism. That situation is slowly improving, as more investigators turn to psychodynamic theory as the basis for research ideas. A previous volume of this series, *Empirical Studies of the Therapeutic Hour* (Bornstein & Masling, 1998), describes the efforts of numerous investigators, sophisticated in both psychoanalysis and experimental method, aimed at studying and identifying subtle processes occurring within the psychodynamic therapy session. Numerous important discoveries about the psychoanalytic hour have been reported in the last few years (Blatt, 1992; Crits-Christoph, Cooper, & Luborsky, 1988; Dahl & Teller,

1994; Henry & Strupp, 1994; Jones & Windholz, 1990; Luborsky & Crits-Christoph, 1990; Weiss & Sampson, 1986). As more evidence about the merits and limitations of psychodynamic hypotheses accumulates, it will become more difficult for the psychoanalytic establishment (i.e., in journals and training institutions) to ignore the relevance of these data for the theory and practice of psychoanalysis. It will also ease the task of integrating psychodynamics and health psychology.

Psychoanalysis in This Volume

This is the first volume in the series to target a readership outside psychology. Reflecting the multidisciplinary nature of health psychology, we hope that this volume will interest any scholar or clinician working at the interface of psychology and physical health. This book is not intended to provide comprehensive coverage of health psychology or behavioral medicine. Some major, multifaceted topics, such as cancer, are not covered here in any depth. This is not a deliberate omission but may reflect the extent to which behavioral, as opposed to psychodynamic, ideas have held sway in psychosocial oncology. Perhaps this volume will remedy that situation.

Over the past decade, Robert F. Bornstein has emerged as one of the world's leading authorities on the topic of psychological dependency. In chapter 1, Bornstein turns his attention to the manifold relations between dependency and health. He contends that dependency, perhaps more than any other personality trait, increases a person's risk for physical illness. It may also increase the likelihood that a person will seek treatment, while decreasing treatment delay and enhancing compliance. This may be of particular relevance to health services researchers. Bornstein is also careful to point out that certain institutional settings, such as nursing homes, may elicit dependency, with unintended negative consequences.

Richard O'Neill (chap. 2) marshals a carefully constructed argument in favor of a psychodynamic perspective in research on psychological aspects of heart disease. He notes that there are numerous similarities between the Type A behavior pattern and the anal character, bemoans the overreliance on self-report data in the cardiovascular psychology literature, and offers several directions for further research.

Sleep is often disturbed in sick people, but what about their dreams? Milton Kramer (chap. 3) addresses this question. Although sufficient evidence indicates that the content of dreams is altered in people who are acutely ill with psychiatric disorders, Kramer concludes that the evidence for a relationship between dreams and physical illness is equivocal. We hope that his thoughtful review will serve to move the field and inspire some imaginative research.

"Give sorrow words," pleads Shakespeare's MacDuff (*Macbeth*). Does writing about traumatic events have a positive effect on one's physical health? Joshua Smyth and Melanie Greenberg (chap. 4) address this fascinating topic that has captured the public imagination over the past several years, most recently with Smyth's article in the *Journal of the American Medical Association* (Smyth, Stone, Hurewitz, & Kaell, 1999). Their review, which bears the mark of authors who have conducted original research in this area—and have thought deeply about it—concludes with a qualified *yes.*

Should recently bereaved people be encouraged to dwell on their memories or advised to move on? In various forms, that question has been asked for centuries. George Bonanno and Stacy Kaltman (chap. 5) assert that classical psychoanalysis, a product of 19th-century thought, advocates "working through" old memories. Drawing on recent research on the architecture of memory and Bonanno's program of bereavement research, these authors argue that this psychoanalytic idea is not only antiquated but also misguided. Bonanno and Kaltman propose an empirically and clinically heuristic distinction between "working through the memory of a traumatic event" and the "construction of a new narrative meaning."

When Ernest Becker (1973) placed the denial of death first and foremost on the list of human motivations (and his book sailed to the top of Pulitzer's nonfiction list, winning the 1973 prize), he probably did not anticipate that several creative psychologists would launch a new field of study—terror management theory—and subject some of his ideas to rigorous experimental and empirical investigation. In chapter 6, Jamie Arndt, Jamie L. Goldenberg, Jeff Greenberg, Tom Pyszczynski, and Sheldon Solomon summarize their remarkably fruitful collaboration, drawing out the implications of their theory and data for understanding health-damaging behaviors, physical illnesses, and the somatic bases of mental illness.

Tales of spouses or lovers dying in rapid succession have long been told and may even constitute a timeless theme in literature. Reflecting the currency of stress theory, a modern version of this story holds that the death of the surviving spouse is mediated by stress-related suppression of immune function. In chapter 7, Paul Duberstein reviews the empirical literature on mortality following bereavement. Numerous methodological shortcomings preclude unambiguous interpretation, but Duberstein maintains that the stress paradigm itself represents an even more insidious obstacle. He argues for a shift to a life-course paradigm, one that acknowledges that the responses to loss cannot be understood apart from long-standing temperament traits and psychodynamic themes of dependency and help seeking, early loss, and ambivalence.

This lineup of contributors mixes seasoned clinicians and relatively junior researchers, people who have conducted original and programmatic research, and others who have spent much of their professional lives in clinical practice; some are steeped in the esoterica of psychoanalytic theory, and others are working in areas that only abut psychoanalysis. Some of the contributors place a greater emphasis on application, whereas others advance theory. It is exactly this sort of mixture that will be needed to nurture a nascent psychodynamic health psychology. We offer this volume not as a coherent and mature body of work but as a promissory note, illustrating how psychodynamics and health psychology can brim with ideas, be constrained by rigor, and influence each other to their mutual good.

References

Abraham, K. (1955). Psycho-analytical notes on Coue's system of self-mastery (H. Abraham & D. R. Ellison, Trans.). In H. Abraham (Ed.),

Clinical papers and essays on psychoanalysis (pp. 306–327). New York: Basic Books. (Original work written 1925)

Ader, R. (1995). Foreword. In B. E. Leonard & K. Miller (Eds.), *Stress, the immune system, and psychiatry* (pp. ix–xiii). Chichester, England: Wiley.

Ader, R., & Cohen, N. (1975). Behaviorally conditioned immunosuppression. *Psychosomatic Medicine, 37,* 333–340.

Ader, R., & Cohen, N. (1993). Psychoneuroimmunology: Conditioning and stress. *Annual Review of Psychology, 44,* 53–85.

Ader, R., Felten, D. L., & Cohen, N. (Eds.). (1991). *Psychoneuroimmunology* (2nd ed.). San Diego: Academic Press.

Ader, R., Felten, D. L., & Cohen, N. (Eds.). (in press). *Psychoneuroimmunology* (3rd ed.). San Diego: Academic Press.

Adler, N., & Matthews, K. (1994). Health psychology: Why do some people get sick and some stay well? *Annual Review of Psychology, 45,* 229–259.

Alexander, F. (1933). Functional disturbances of psychogenic nature. *Journal of the American Medical Association, 100,* 469–473.

Alexander, F. (1950). *Psychosomatic medicine: Its principles and applications.* New York: Norton.

Angell, M. (1985). Disease as a reflection of the psyche. *New England Journal of Medicine, 312,* 1570–1572.

Bakan, D. (1968). *Disease, pain and sacrifice: Toward a psychology of suffering.* Boston: Beacon Press.

Barron, J. W., Eagle, M. N., & Wolitzky, D. L. (Eds.). (1992). *Interface of psychoanalysis and psychology.* Washington, DC: American Psychological Association.

Baum, A., & Posluszny, D. M. (1999). Health psychology: Mapping biobehavioral contributions to health and illness. *Annual Review of Psychology, 50,* 137–163.

Becker, E. (1973). *The denial of death.* New York: Free Press.

Berkman, L. F. (1995). The role of social relations in health promotion. *Psychosomatic Medicine, 57,* 245–254.

Berlin, I. (1969). *Four essays on liberty.* New York: Oxford University Press.

Blatt, S. J. (1992). The differential effect of psychotherapy and psychoanalysis on anaclitic and introjective patients: The Menninger Psychotherapy Project revisited. *Journal of the American Psychoanalytic Association, 40,* 691–724.

Bornstein, R. F. (1992). The dependent personality: Developmental, social, and clinical perspectives. *Psychological Bulletin, 112,* 3–23.

Bornstein, R. F., & Masling, J. M. (Eds.). (1998). *Empirical studies of the therapeutic hour.* Washington, DC: American Psychological Association.

Bowlby, J. (1969). *Attachment and loss* (Vol. 1). New York: Basic Books.

Bowlby, J. (1973). *Attachment and loss* (Vol. 2). New York: Basic Books.

Bowlby, J. (1980). *Attachment and loss* (Vol. 3). New York: Basic Books.

Brenner, C. (1982). *The mind in conflict.* New York: International Universities Press.

Breuer, J., & Freud, S. (1955). Studies on hysteria. In J. Strachey, A. Freud, A. Strachey, & A. Tyson (Eds. & Trans.), *The standard edition of the complete psychological works of Sigmund Freud* (Vol. 2). London: Hogarth Press. (Original work published 1893)

Cohen, S., & Herbert, T. B. (1996). Health psychology: Psychological factors and physical disease from the perspective of human psychoneuroimmunology. *Annual Review of Psychology, 47,* 113–142.

Crews, F. (1994). The verdict on Freud. *Psychological Science, 7,* 63–68.

Crits-Christoph, P., Cooper, A., & Luborsky, L. (1988). The accuracy of therapists' interpretations and the outcome of dynamic psychotherapy. *Journal of Consulting and Clinical Psychology, 56,* 490–495.

Dahl, H., & Teller, V. (1994). The characteristics, identification and applications of FRAMES. *Psychotherapy Research, 4,* 252–274.

Doll, R., & Peto, R. (1981). *The causes of cancer: Quantitative estimates of available risks of cancer in the United States today.* New York: Oxford University Press.

Edelberg, L. (1957). An introduction to the study of the narcissistic mortification. *Psychoanalytic Quarterly, 31,* 657–668.

Efron, A. (1985). The sexual body: An interdisciplinary perspective [Special issue]. *Journal of Mind and Behavior, 6.*

Eissler, K. (1969). Irreverent remarks about the present and the future of psychoanalysis. *International Journal of Psychoanalysis, 50,* 461–471.

Epstein, S. (1994). Integration of the cognitive and psychodynamic unconscious. *American Psychologist, 49,* 709–724.

Felten, S. Y., & Felten, D. L. (1991). Innervation of lymphoid tissue. In R. Ader, D. L. Felten, & N. Cohen (Eds.), *Psychoneuroimmunology* (2nd ed., pp. 27–61). San Diego: Academic Press.

Fenichel, O. (1945). *The psychoanalytic theory of neurosis.* New York: Norton.

Ferenczi, S. (1929). The unwelcome child and his death instinct. *International Journal of Psychoanalysis, 10,* 125–129.

Fisher, S., & Cleveland, S. E. (1968). *Body image and personality* (2nd ed.). New York: Dover.

Fisher, S., & Greenberg, R. P. (Eds.). (1978). *The scientific evaluation of Freud's theories and therapy.* New York: Basic Books.

Fisher, S., & Greenberg, R. P. (1985). *The scientific credibility of Freud's theories and therapy.* New York: Basic Books.

Fisher, S., & Greenberg, R. P. (1996). *Freud scientifically reappraised: Testing the theories and therapy.* New York: Wiley.

Freud, S. (1955). Beyond the pleasure principle. In J. L. Strachey (Ed. & Trans.), *The complete psychological works of Sigmund Freud* (Vol. 18, pp. 3–64). London: Hogarth Press. (Original work published 1920)

Freud, S. (1955). From the history of an infantile neurosis. In J. L. Strachey (Ed. & Trans.), *The complete psychological works of Sigmund Freud* (Vol.

17, pp. 3–122). London: Hogarth Press. (Original work published 1918)

Freud, S. (1957). The psycho-analytic view of psychogenic disturbances of vision. In J. Strachey (Ed. & Trans.), *The complete psychological works of Sigmund Freud* (Vol. 2, pp. 210–218). London: Hogarth Press. (Original work published 1910)

Freud, S. (1957). Thoughts for the times on war and death. In J. Strachey, A. Freud, A. Strachey, & A. Tyson (Eds. & Trans.), *The standard edition of the complete psychological works of Sigmund Freud* (Vol. 14, pp. 273–300). London: Hogarth Press. (Original work published 1915)

Freud, S. (1958). Karl Abraham. In J. L. Strachey (Ed. & Trans.), *The complete psychological works of Sigmund Freud* (Vol. 20, pp. 277–278). London: Hogarth Press. (Original work published 1926)

Freud, S. (1961). The ego and the id. In J. Strachey (Ed. & Trans.), *The complete psychological works of Sigmund Freud* (Vol. 19, pp. 3–66). London: Hogarth Press. (Original work published 1923)

Freud, S. (1962). Sexuality in the aetiology of the neuroses. In J. L. Strachey (Ed. & Trans.), *The complete psychological works of Sigmund Freud* (Vol. 3, pp. 261–285). London: Hogarth Press. (Original work published 1898)

Freud, S. (1965). *The interpretation of dreams* (J. Strachey, Ed. & Trans.). New York: Avon Books. (Original work published 1900)

Friman, P. C., Allen, K. D., Kerwin, M. L. E., & Larzelere, R. (1993). Changes in modern psychology: A citation analysis of the Kuhnian displacement thesis. *American Psychologist, 48,* 658–664.

Gay, P. (1988). *Freud: A life for our time.* New York: Norton.

Greenacre, P. (1958). Early physical determinants in the development of a sense of identity. *Journal of the American Psychoanalytic Association, 6,* 612–627.

Greenfield, J. (1974). *Wilhelm Reich vs. the U.S.A.* New York: Norton.

Grunbaum, A. (1984). *The foundations of psychoanalysis.* Berkeley: University of California.

Hardaway, R. A. (1990). Subliminally activated symbiotic fantasies. *Psychological Bulletin, 107,* 177–195.

Henry, W. P., & Strupp, H. H. (1994). The therapeutic alliance as interpersonal process. In A. O. Horvath & L. S. Greenberg (Eds.), *The working alliance: Theory, research and practice* (pp. 51–84). New York: Wiley.

Holt, R. R. (1984, August). *The current status of psychoanalytic theory.* Paper presented at the 92nd Annual Convention of the American Psychological Association, Toronto, Ontario, Canada.

Jacob, F. (1998). *Of flies, mice, and men* (G. Weiss, Trans.). Cambridge, MA: Harvard University Press.

Jacobson, E. (1964). *The self and the object world.* New York: International Universities Press.

Jelliffe, S. E. (1933). The death instinct in somatic and psycho-pathology. *Psychoanalytic Review, 110,* 121–132.

Jones, E. E., & Windholz, M. (1990). The psychoanalytic case study: Toward a method for systematic inquiry. *Journal of the American Psychoanalytic Association, 38,* 985–1015.

Kagan, J. (with Snidman, N., Arcus, D., & Reznick, J. S.). (1994). *Galen's prophecy: Temperament in human nature.* New York: Basic Books.

Kandel, E. R. (1999). Biology and the future of psychoanalysis: A new intellectual framework for psychiatry revisited. *American Journal of Psychiatry, 156,* 505–524.

Kiecolt-Glaser, J. K., & Glaser, R. (1992). Psychoneuroimmunology: Can psychological interventions modulate immunity? *Journal of Consulting and Clinical Psychology, 60,* 569–575.

Krantz, D. S., Grunberg, N. E., & Baum, A. (1985). Health psychology. *Annual Review of Psychology, 36,* 349–383.

Loftus, E. F. (1993). The reality of repressed memories. *American Psychologist, 48,* 518–537.

Luborsky, L., & Crits-Christoph, P. (1990). *Understanding transference: The core conflictual relationship theme method.* New York: Basic Books.

Masling, J. (1986). Orality, pathology, and the interpersonal behavior. In J. Masling (Ed.), *Empirical studies of psychoanalytical theories* (Vol. 2, pp. 73–106). Hillsdale, NJ: Erlbaum.

Masling, J., & Cohen, I. S. (1987). Psychotherapy, clinical evidence, and the self-fulfilling prophecy. *Psychoanalytic Psychology, 4,* 65–79.

McClelland, D. C. (1989). Motivational factors in health and disease. *American Psychologist, 44,* 675–683.

McGinnis, J. M., & Foege, W. H. (1993). Actual causes of death in the United States. *Journal of the American Medical Association, 270,* 2207–2212.

Meehl, P. E. (1998). Credentialed persons, credentialed knowledge. *Clinical Psychology: Science and Practice, 4,* 91–98.

Menninger, K. (1985). *Man against himself.* New York: Harcourt Brace Jovanovich. (Original work published 1938)

Miller, N. E. (1983). Behavioral medicine: Symbiosis between laboratory and clinic. *Annual Review of Psychology, 34,* 1–31.

Murray, E. J. (1956). A content-analysis method for studying psychotherapy. *Psychological Monographs, 70*(13, Whole No. 420).

Norcross, J. C., Karg, R. S., & Prochaska, J. O. (1997). Clinical psychologists in the 1900s: Part I. *The Clinical Psychologist, 50,* 4–9.

Pyszczynski, T., Greenberg, J., & Solomon, S. (1999). A dual-process model of defense against conscious and unconscious death-related thought: An extension of terror management theory. *Psychological Review, 106,* 835–845.

Reich, W. (1948). *The discovery of the Orgone. Vol. 2: The cancer biopathy* (T. P. Wolfe, Trans.). New York: Orgone Institute Press.

Reich, W. (1973). *Character analysis.* New York: Farrar, Strauss & Giroux.

Rodin, J., & Salovey, P. (1989). Health psychology. *Annual Review of Psychology, 40,* 533–579.

Rogers, M. P., & Reich, P. (1988). On the health consequences of bereavement. *New England Journal of Medicine, 319,* 510–512.

Rosenfeld, P. L. (1992). The potential of transdisciplinary research for sustaining and extending linkages between the health and social sciences. *Social Science and Medicine, 35,* 1343–1357.

Sapolsky, R. M. (1994). *Why zebras don't get ulcers: A guide to stress, stress-related disease, and coping.* New York: Freeman.

Schafer, R. (1976). *A new language of psychoanalysis.* New Haven, CT: Yale University Press.

Scharf, D. E., & Birtles, E. F. (Eds.). (1994). *From instinct to self: Selected papers of W. R. D. Fairbairn.* Northvale, NJ: Aronson.

Shedler, J., Mayman, M., & Manis, M. (1993). The *illusion* of mental health. *American Psychologist, 48,* 1117–1131.

Smyth, J. M., Stone, A. A., Hurewitz, A., & Kaell, A. (1999). Effects of writing about stressful experiences on symptom reduction in patients with asthma or rheumatoid arthritis. *Journal of the American Medical Association, 281,* 1304–1309.

Spence, D. P. (1994). *The rhetorical voice of psychoanalysis.* Cambridge, MA: Harvard University Press.

Stokols, D. (1998, May). *The future of interdisciplinarity in the School of Social Ecology.* Paper presented at the Social Ecology Associates Annual Awards Reception, Irvine, CA. [Available online at http://eee.uci.edu/98f/50990/Readings/stokols.html, retrieved December 15, 1998]

Suedfeld, P., & Bluck, S. (1993). Changes in integrative complexity accompanying significant life events. Historical evidence. *Journal of Personality and Social Psychology, 64,* 124–130.

Summary report of journal operations, 1997. (1998). *American Psychologist, 53,* 983–984.

Tansey, M. J. (1992). Countertransference theory, quantitative research, and the problem of therapist–patient sexual abuse. In J. W. Barron, M. N. Eagle, & D. L. Wolitzky (Eds.), *Interface of psychoanalysis and psychology* (pp. 539–557). Washington, DC: American Psychological Association.

Taylor, S. E., Repetti, R. L., & Seeman, T. (1997). Health psychology: What is an unhealthy environment and how does it get under the skin? *Annual Review of Psychology, 48,* 411–447.

Truax, C. B. (1966). Reinforcement and nonreinforcement in Rogerian psychotherapy. *Journal of Abnormal Psychology, 71,* 1–9.

Weber, M. (1946). Bureaucracy. In H. H. Gerth & C. W. Mills (Eds. & Trans.), *From Max Weber: Essays in sociology* (pp. 196–244). New York: Oxford University Press. (Original work published 1922, posthumously)

Weiner, H. (1999). Praise be to *Psychosomatic Medicine. Psychosomatic Medicine, 61,* 259–262.

Weiss, J., & Sampson, H. (1986). *The psychoanalytic process: Theory, clinical observation and empirical testing.* New York: Guilford Press.

Westen, D. (1998). The scientific legacy of Sigmund Freud: Toward a psychodynamically informed psychological science. *Psychological Bulletin, 124,* 333–371.

Wulsin, L. R., Vaillant, G. E., & Wells, V. E. (1999). A systematic review of the mortality of depression. *Psychosomatic Medicine, 61,* 6–17.

Psychodynamic Perspectives on Sickness and Health

Chapter

1

From Oral Fixation to Object Relations:

Changing Perspectives on the Psychodynamics of Interpersonal Dependency and Illness

Robert F. Bornstein

In 1945, Rene Spitz published the first in a series of classic articles describing the psychological and physical consequences of infants' separation from their primary caregiver. His observations of orphaned children from World War II led Spitz to conclude that without the security and reassurance that comes from a stable, ongoing relationship with a nurturing caregiver, infants experience hopelessness, depression, and despair. Spitz (1945, 1946) found that in a high proportion of such cases—as high as 70% or more in some European orphanages—abrupt and prolonged separation from their caregiver led to early infant death, a consequence of the syndrome he called "hospitalism" (see also Bowlby, 1953, 1960).[1]

---

[1]Spitz's (1945, 1946) data seem dramatic and compelling, but they became controversial when Pinneau (1955a) discovered a number of contra-

Fifty years after Spitz published his groundbreaking studies of hospitalism, a colleague described to me a troubling clinical situation that seemed thematically related to Spitz's earlier observations. The case involved a man in his late 70s who had recently lost his wife to cancer. This man's wife had been his sole companion for several years, helping him manage a serious but stable diabetic condition. Following his wife's death, the man was placed in a nursing home by his daughter, a businesswoman who lived several hours away and could not care for her father on a daily basis. The nursing home was purported to be excellent—one of the finest in the region. By all accounts, the man received superb medical care from the moment he arrived. Nonetheless, after entering the nursing home, he became electively mute and refused to leave his room. He did not eat and became noncompliant with medical treatment. He died within 8 weeks.

What is the link between Spitz's orphaned infant and my colleague's recently widowed patient? In both cases, the person's basic biological needs had been adequately met. Both were well fed and received good medical care. However, in both cases, separation from a valued caregiver resulted in depression, illness, and premature death. These two vignettes tell much about the importance of affiliative ties for physical health and well-being: The disruption of an important relationship is upsetting to almost anyone, but to one who is highly dependent on a caregiver—like Spitz's infant or my colleague's patient—prolonged separation from a valued other can have serious health consequences.[2]

---

dictions in Spitz's clinical findings. Pinneau noted that (among other things), it was impossible to ascertain from Spitz's published results (a) how many children had actually been studied, (b) how frequently they had been tested, and (c) how many times the same children were described in different articles. Following Pinneau's critique, Spitz (1955) defended his methods as intrinsic to the complex clinical problems investigated. However, Pinneau (1955b) reiterated his assertion that Spitz's conclusions could not be accepted uncritically on the basis of the data he described. The controversy continues, although most psychologists today accept the validity of Spitz's general conclusions, while questioning his methodology and reporting of results.

[2]The links between conjugal bereavement and mortality have been confirmed empirically in several large-scale epidemiological studies (see, e.g., Kaprio, Koskenvuo, & Rita, 1987; and Martikainen & Valkonen, 1996).

Oftentimes, dependent relationships arise through life circumstances, as in the case of Spitz's orphaned infants or my colleague's older patient. At other times, dependent relationships are actively sought and cultivated by individuals with strong underlying dependency needs—people who have traditionally been described as having a "dependent personality" (Bornstein, 1993; Millon, 1996). During the past several decades, investigators in myriad studies have explored the link between dependent personality traits and health. Some of these investigations came from a psychodynamic perspective; others did not. Some investigators have assessed the dependency–health status relationship directly; others have focused on the links between dependency and health-related behaviors. Most investigators in this area have conceptualized dependency as a risk factor for illness and disease, but a few have examined the health-promoting features of dependency rather than focusing on its negative aspects.

The purpose of my chapter is to review research on the dependency–illness link and, in doing so, to address two key questions that have long challenged researchers: (a) Are there predictable, meaningful relationships between dependency and health status and between dependency and health-related behaviors? (b) If there are, what pathways link dependency with these health-related variables?

I begin by discussing the psychoanalytic theory of health and illness as this theory has changed over the years. I then trace the evolution of the dependency concept from classical psychoanalysis to contemporary object relations theory and self psychology, placing the ensuing literature review into an appropriate context. Next, I discuss research focusing on the negative health consequences of dependency and studies assessing the ways in which dependent personality traits can promote physical health and well-being. Finally, I integrate extant findings in this area within the context of a contemporary object relations model of dependency and discuss possible avenues for future research on the health-related consequences of dependent personality traits.

Psychoanalytic Health Psychology

Given the breadth and depth of contemporary psychoanalysis, it is somewhat surprising that psychodynamic theorists have had difficulty developing a comprehensive model of health and illness. In part, this gap in the psychoanalytic canon reflects Freud's own ambivalence regarding the mind–body relationship—an ambivalence evident in some of his earliest writings (e.g., Breuer & Freud, 1893/1955). On the one hand, a central aim of Freud's work from the mid-1880s onward was to construct a theoretical framework firmly grounded in physiological principles. On the other hand, the great insight that led Freud to develop his topographic and structural models of the mind—in many ways the *raison d'etre* of psychoanalysis itself—was the idea that many physical symptoms are the product of psychological conflicts rather than organic disease processes (Bowers & Meichenbaum, 1984; Erdelyi, 1985). Freud's early interest in conversion disorders and hysteria set the stage for a psychoanalytic psychology that emphasizes mental—not physical—explanations for changes in health and illness states.

Like many aspects of psychoanalysis, Freud's (Breuer & Freud, 1893/1955) seminal work in this area led to a plethora of refinements and reinterpretations as the theory evolved. By the first decades of the 20th century, the psychosexual stage model occupied a central place in classical psychoanalytic theory; from this framework, there arose a new conceptualization of the psychological factors underlying health and illness. Freud (1905/1955, 1908/1958) assumed that each character type was associated with a set of behaviors that reflected the individual's "fixation" at a particular psychosexual stage. As Freud (1908/1958) described it, "one very often meets with a type of character in which certain traits are very strongly marked while at the same time one's attention is arrested by the behavior of these persons in regard to certain bodily functions" (p. 167). Thus, orally fixated (or *oral dependent*) people were hypothesized to rely on eating, drinking, and other oral activities to cope with stress (Blum & Miller, 1952; Masling, 1986; Sandler & Dare, 1970). Needless to say, these oral behaviors could affect an individual's health status in important ways.

A noteworthy feature of Freud's (1905/1955) psychosexual stage model was that oral-dependent traits are expected to influence health status indirectly through habits and behaviors that increase illness risk (e.g., overeating, excessive alcohol use; see Bornstein, 1996). The same was true of the other psychosexual stages (e.g., anal, Oedipal), although in general the behaviors associated with these stages are less obviously relevant to health and illness than those associated with the oral stage (see Fisher & Greenberg, 1997).

Beginning in the 1920s, the paradigmatic tide began to shift, as Deutsch (1922, 1924) argued that underlying psychodynamic processes not only influence health-related behaviors but also have direct effects on the body's organ systems. The notion that unconscious dynamics (including psychosexual fixation) could influence bodily functioning directly was extended and elaborated by Alexander and others (e.g., Alexander, 1950, 1954; Alexander, French, & Pollock, 1968), who developed a detailed theoretical framework linking specific psychodynamic processes with predictable physiological sequelae and illness states. Where earlier models hypothesized that oral fixation would affect health status indirectly, Alexander's (1950, 1954) "psychosomatic specificity" model contends that unexpressed oral needs affect health directly by altering the functioning of the gastrointestinal tract and placing the oral-dependent person at increased risk for ulcers and other diseases of the stomach. Alexander et al. (1968) summarized the logic of this model, noting that

> the psychological situation in which the patient found himself at the onset of his physical symptoms—which we call the *onset situation*—consisted precisely in the activation of the characteristic psychodynamic conflict pattern that had been present from childhood on. . . . Thus, in ulcer patients it makes physiological sense that frustrated dependent, help-seeking desires should have a specific correlation to stomach activity, the connecting link being the association between the wish to be loved and helped and the wish to be fed. (p. 7, emphasis in original)

Preliminary evidence testing the psychosomatic specificity model seemed promising (e.g., Mirsky, 1958), but over time, contradictory findings began to accumulate, and the specificity hypothesis fell out of favor (Ammon, 1979; Bornstein, 1993; Masling & Schwartz, 1979). By the early 1970s, the emphasis in psychoanalytic theory had shifted away from questions regarding the mind–body relationship, focusing instead on issues related to metapsychology and hermeneutics (Eagle, 1984; Grunbaum, 1984). In part, this shift stemmed from the growth of object relations theory and self psychology, which present viable alternatives to classical psychoanalysis and question many of the fundamental assumptions underlying the drive model (J. R. Greenberg & Mitchell, 1983). This shift also resulted from certain factors external to psychoanalysis (e.g., researchers' increasing interest in the study of consciousness), which raise fundamental questions regarding the physiological underpinnings of affect, cognition, and behavior (see Bowers & Meichenbaum, 1984). Whatever the cause, the psychoanalytic zeitgeist had changed, and attention to the mind–body relationship faded into the background.[3]

Psychoanalytic interest in health-related issues became latent for a brief period, but like all latent contents, it did not disappear completely. By the late 1980s, numerous theoretical frameworks linking mental processes and bodily states had been developed, and whereas most of these frameworks were not explicitly psychoanalytic, several borrowed heavily from psychoanalytic concepts and constructs. Research on health and hardiness (Kobasa, 1979), stress and coping (Pennebaker & O'Heeron, 1984), learned helplessness (Peterson & Seligman, 1987), alexithymia (difficulty with the verbalization of feelings; Sifneos, 1983), emotional disclosure and recovery from illness (Spiegel, Bloom, Kraemer, & Gottheil, 1989), and the characteristics of the "Type C" (cancer-prone) personality (Temoshok, 1987) was rooted in part in earlier psychodynamic concepts regarding personality traits and health-related behaviors.

The Evolution of Dependency: From Oral Fixation to Object Relations

Just as psychoanalytic health psychology evolved over time, the psychoanalytic conceptualization of the etiology and dynamics of dependency has been refined and updated since Freud's (1905/

[3]In recent years, a separate stream of psychoanalytically informed research on personality and health has developed, somewhat independent of object relations theory. This approach—epitomized by the work of Vaillant (1994) and others (e.g., Ihilevich & Gleser, 1986)—focuses on defense style and defense mechanism usage as predictors of health and illness states.

1955) pioneering work on this topic. Broadly speaking, the evolution of dependency in psychoanalytic theory can be divided into three phases: (1) the classical psychoanalytic model, (2) the object relations perspective, and (3) a recently developed object relations/interactionist model, which links the object relations perspective with contemporary empirical research on dependency.

Classical Psychoanalytic Model

In classical psychoanalytic theory, dependency is inextricably linked to events of the infantile, oral stage of development, which lasts for the first 12–18 months of life (Freud, 1905/1955). Frustration or overgratification during the oral stage is hypothesized to result in oral fixation and an inability to resolve the developmental issues that characterize this period (e.g., conflicts regarding dependency and autonomy). Thus, Freud's classical psychoanalytic theory postulates that the orally fixated (or oral dependent) person will (a) remain dependent on others for nurturance, protection, and support; and (b) continue to exhibit behaviors in adulthood that reflect the infantile, oral stage (i.e., preoccupation with activities of the mouth, reliance on food and eating as a means of coping with anxiety).

Following Freud's (1905/1955) speculations regarding the etiology and dynamics of oral dependency, several psychoanalytic writers (e.g., Abraham, 1927; Fenichel, 1945; Glover, 1925) have extended the classical psychoanalytic model, suggesting that two variations in the infant's early feeding experiences could lead to oral fixation and the development of oral-dependent personality traits: (a) frustration during infantile feeding and weaning and (b) overgratification during the feeding and weaning period. Goldman-Eisler (1950) subsequently argued that oral frustration and oral gratification would lead to somewhat different dependent personality styles. Although Goldman-Eisler's (1950, 1951) research has certain methodological flaws (e.g., uncritical reliance on retrospective self-reports), her "frustration–gratification" hypothesis nonetheless had a strong influence on the psychoanalytic conceptualization of oral dependency throughout the 1950s, 1960s, and 1970s (Bornstein, 1993; Masling & Schwartz, 1979).

The classical psychoanalytic model of oral dependency had considerable heuristic value, generating hundreds of empirical studies testing various components of the theory (see Bornstein, 1996; Fisher & Greenberg, 1997; and Masling & Schwartz, 1979, for reviews). However, the classical psychoanalytic oral-dependency model gradually lost influence within the broader psychoanalytic community for two reasons. First, in these empirical studies, researchers generally failed to confirm a link between high levels of dependency and a preoccupation with food, eating, and other oral activities (Bornstein, 1996). Second, the focus of psychoanalytic theory gradually shifted from a drive-based metapsychology to a more object relations-oriented approach, wherein personality dynamics are conceptualized in terms of self–other interactions and internalized mental representations of the self and significant figures (Galatzer-Levy & Cohler, 1993; J. R. Greenberg & Mitchell, 1983). Object relations models of interpersonal dependency replaced drive-based models of oral dependency.

Object Relations Perspective

In most object relations frameworks, dependency is discussed primarily in terms of children's progression from more-or-less complete reliance on their primary caregiver for nurturance and support to a more autonomous state, wherein they are capable of meeting physiological and psychological needs on their own (see Eagle, 1984; Fairbairn, 1952; J. R. Greenberg & Mitchell, 1983; and Mahler, Pine, & Bergman, 1975). The critical importance of the individual's transition from dependency and helplessness to autonomy and mature interdependence is echoed in the attachment theories of Bowlby (1969, 1980), Ainsworth (1969), and others (e.g., Main, Kaplan, & Cassidy, 1985). Self psychologists have also emphasized the importance of early infant–caregiver interactions for the emergence of a cohesive sense of self and the concomitant capacity for autonomy and healthy interconnectedness (e.g., Kohut, 1971, 1977).

In this context, both Jacobson (1964) and Mahler et al. (1975) argued (albeit in somewhat different terms) that infants and young children experience an ongoing tension between their struggle for individuation and their wish to remerge with the omniscient, omnipotent caregiver of infancy. As Galatzer-Levy and Cohler (1993) and Silverman, Lachmann, and Milich (1982) pointed out, a variety of psychological phenomena reflect this ongoing tension between the (a) individual's strivings for separation and independence and (b) the competing desire to regress and remerge with the primary caregiver. These phenomena include (but are not limited to) the experience of romantic love, the use of psychotropic drugs to quell anxiety, and the strong identification that many people develop with members of various religious and social groups.

In recent years, Blatt's (1974, 1991) theoretical framework has been the most influential object relations model of dependency. Integrating concepts from object relations theory and self psychology with ideas and findings from research on cognitive development, Blatt and his colleagues (e.g., Blatt & Shichman, 1983) have argued that dependent personality traits in children and adults result primarily from the internalization of a mental representation of the self as weak and ineffectual. Developmental research on parent–child interactions confirms that parenting styles that help children to view themselves as powerless and weak do in fact lead to high levels of dependency later in life (Blatt & Homann, 1992). As children internalize a mental representation of the self as weak and ineffectual, they (a) look to others to provide protection and support (Bornstein, 1993), (b) become preoccupied with fears of abandonment (Blatt, 1974), (c) behave in a dependent help-seeking manner (Bornstein, 1992), and (d) show increased risk for depression, school phobia, and other dependency-related psychopathologies (Berg & McGuire, 1974; Blatt & Homann, 1992). Moreover, these effects persist through adolescence and adulthood, long after children's age-appropriate dependency behaviors should have waned (Ainsworth, 1969, 1989; Bornstein, 1993, 1996).

Object Relations/Interactionist Model

Blatt's (1974, 1991) contention that the self-representation plays a central role in the etiology and dynamics of dependent personality traits led to the development of the integrative object relations/interactionist model of dependency (Bornstein, 1992, 1993, 1995). The central elements of this model are pictured in Figure 1.1. Because this model explicitly links dependency-related traits with health-related behaviors and makes clear predictions regarding the

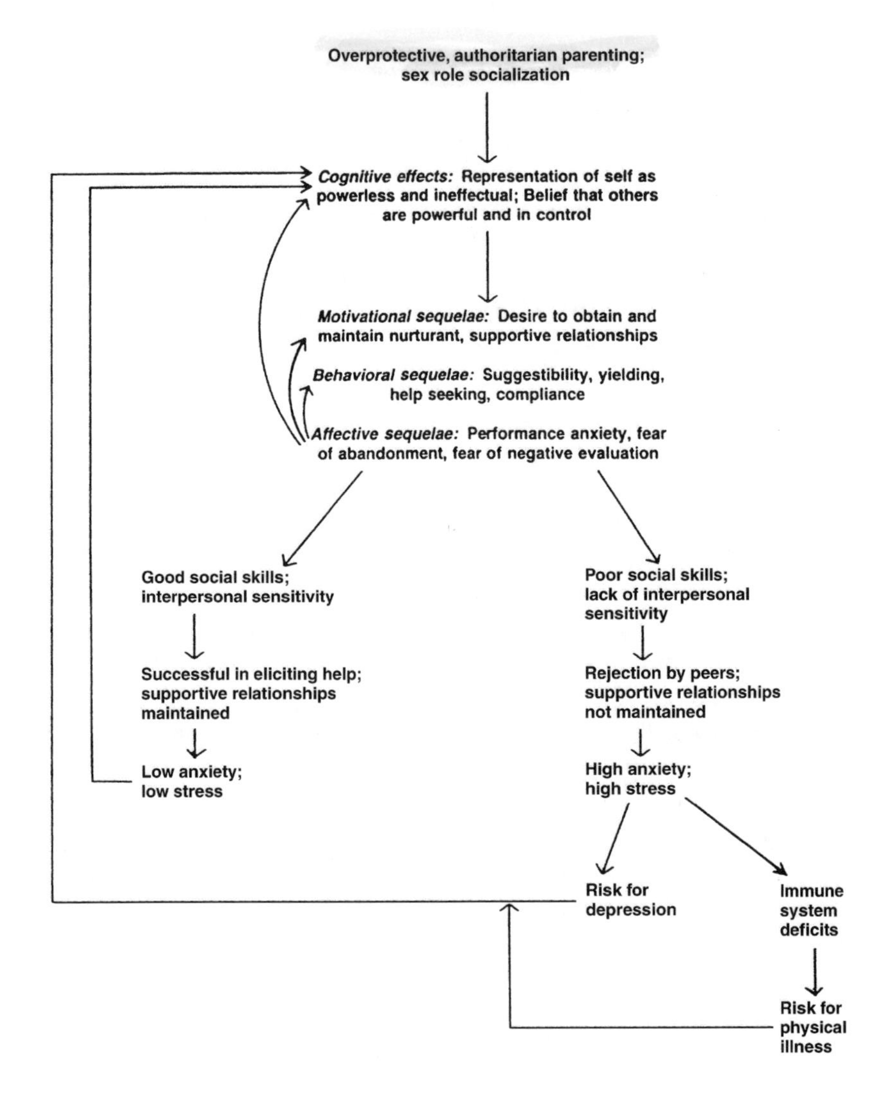

Figure 1.1. The object relations/interactionist model of interpersonal dependency. From *The Dependent Personality* (p. 162), by R. F. Bornstein, 1993, New York: Guilford Press. Copyright 1993 by Guilford Press. Reprinted with permission.

relationship between dependency and health status, it is worth examining its key features in detail.

As Figure 1.1 shows, the etiology of dependency lies primarily in two areas: (a) overprotective, authoritarian parenting and (b) sex role socialization. Overprotective, authoritarian parents foster dependency by preventing their child from developing a sense of mastery and autonomy that follows successful learning experiences (Sroufe, Fox, & Pancake, 1983). Sex role socialization practices may further foster the development of a dependent self-representation in girls, in that traditional socialization practices encourage passivity, acquiescence, and other dependency-related traits in girls more strongly than in boys (Spence & Helmreich, 1978).[4]

In addition to fostering the development of a representation of the self as weak and ineffectual, overprotective, authoritarian parenting encourages children to believe they must rely on others for guidance, protection, and support. Because early experiences with the parents create particular expectations for future interpersonal relationships (Blatt & Homann, 1992; Main et al., 1985), parental overprotectiveness leads children to expect that others will nurture and care for them. Similarly, parental authoritarianism leads children to believe that the way to maintain good relationships with others is to acquiesce to their requests and demands (Ainsworth, 1969; Baumrind, 1971).

The model summarized in Figure 1.1 suggests that cognitive structures (i.e., self- and object representations) formed in response to early experiences within the family influence the motivations, behaviors, and affective responses of the dependent person in predictable ways. A perception of one's self as powerless and ineffectual, first and foremost, has motivational effects. A person with such a self-concept is motivated to seek guidance, protection, and support from others. These self-concept-based motivations in turn produce particular patterns of dependent behavior: The person who is highly motivated to seek the guidance, protection, and support of others behaves in ways that maximize the probability that they will obtain the protection and support they desire. Finally, a

---

[4]These differential socialization experiences may account for the finding that women almost invariably obtain higher scores than men do on self-report measures of dependency that have high face validity (test obviousness), whereas men and women typically obtain comparable scores on projective dependency measures with low face validity (Bornstein, Bowers, & Bonner, 1996; Bornstein, Rossner, Hill, & Stepanian, 1994).

representation of the self as powerless and ineffectual has important affective consequences (e.g., fear of abandonment, fear of negative evaluation).[5]

Although cognitive structures produced in response to early parenting and socialization experiences mediate the motivations, behaviors, and affective responses of a dependent person, affective responses ultimately play a key role in the dynamics of dependency. As Figure 1.1 shows, dependency-related affective responses (e.g., performance anxiety) strengthen and reinforce dependency-related motivations (e.g., need for support). Similarly, when a dependency-related affective response is stimulated, the person is more likely to exhibit dependent behavior. Most important, dependency-related affective responses strengthen the dependent person's belief in his or her own ineffectiveness. Consequently, a feedback loop is formed, wherein affective responses that initially resulted from particular beliefs about the self and other people ultimately come to reinforce those same beliefs. Similar feedback loops characterize the affect–motivation and affect–behavior relationships.

The object relations/interactionist model helps explain why dependency is associated with active, assertive behavior in certain situations. Empirical studies confirm that dependent people behave assertively if they believe that by doing so, they can strengthen ties to potential nurturers and protectors (Bornstein, 1997, 1998b; Bornstein, Riggs, Hill, & Calabrese, 1996). Studies further suggest that one central goal underlies much of the dependent person's interpersonal behavior: obtaining and maintaining nurturant, supportive relationships. This goal has been referred to as the "core motivation" of the dependent person (Bornstein, 1992, 1993), and it represents the link between dependency-related passivity and dependency-related assertiveness. Simply put, dependent individuals exhibit behaviors that maximize their chances of

---

[5]Not surprisingly, dependent people also tend to show an insecure attachment style (Duberstein & Talbot, 1993; Heiss, Berman, & Sperling, 1996), which may reflect a perception of the self as weak and ineffectual (see Figure 1.1). This insecure attachment may also account for the relationship-facilitating behavior frequently associated with high levels of dependency (Bornstein, 1993; Masling, 1986).

obtaining and maintaining supportive relationships. When passive, compliant behavior seems likely to achieve this goal, the dependent person chooses to behave passively. When active, assertive behavior seems more likely to achieve this goal, the dependent person becomes active and assertive.[6]

Because the core motivation of a dependent person is to obtain and maintain nurturant, supportive relationships, the degree to which a dependent individual exhibits good social skills has important implications for the long-term consequences of dependency, including variations in health and illness states. In Figure 1.1, the population of dependent people is divided into those with "good" social skills and those with "poor" social skills, illustrating the effects of this variable on the long-term consequences of dependency. As Figure 1.1 shows, good social skills are associated with success in eliciting social support and with the ability to cultivate nurturant, supportive relationships. To the extent that dependent people are able to obtain and maintain such supportive relationships, anxiety and stress should be minimized; hence, illness rates will be comparatively low. In a sense, this represents the best possible long-term consequence of dependency (Birtchnell, 1988; Millon, 1996).

A dependent person with less effective social skills is not as successful in cultivating nurturant, supportive relationships. As Figure 1.1 shows, the absence of supportive ties leads to increased anxiety and stress, with negative effects on a person's psychological and physical adjustments. With respect to psychological functioning, high levels of stress and anxiety lead to increased risks for depression in a dependent person (Overholser, 1996; Overholser &

[6]The hypothesis that the dependent person's core motivation is to obtain and maintain nurturant, supportive relationships is consistent with the finding that overprotective, authoritarian parenting predicts subsequent dependency levels in children, adolescents, and adults. Figure 1.1 illustrates the connection between early parenting experiences and the core motivation of a dependent person. In a backward path through the model, it is clear that the behaviors exhibited in various contexts and settings reflect the core motivation of a dependent person. This core motivation may be traced to beliefs regarding the self and other people, which in turn may be traced to particular experiences within a dependent person's family.

Freiheit, 1994). With respect to physiological functioning, high levels of anxiety and stress are hypothesized to lead to diminished immunocompetence in the dependent individual, increasing risk for various illnesses mediated by the immune system (Blatt, Cornell, & Eshkol, 1993).

Ironically, the onset of physical or psychological illness can reinforce even further a dependent person's "helpless" self-concept. Numerous studies show that the onset of illness is often followed by increases in dependent, help-seeking behavior (Baltes, 1996; Bornstein, 1993). To the extent that dependent people assume the "sick role" following the onset of physical or psychological illness, their perception of themselves as powerless, ineffectual, and dependent on others for protection and support increases.

Negative Effects of Dependency

The object relations/interactionist model provides an integrative theoretical framework for examining the deleterious effects of dependency on health status and health-related behavior. In the following sections, I review research related to these two issues.

Dependency and Illness Risk

Researchers have examined possible relationships between high levels of interpersonal dependency and a variety of physical disorders, including ulcers, colitis, diabetes, asthma, epilepsy, arthritis, tuberculosis, cancer, heart disease, and chronic pain conditions. Most of these investigators found dependency to be associated with elevated rates of illness (see Bornstein, 1998c; and Masling & Schwartz, 1979, for reviews). Unfortunately, however, most of these investigators used retrospective designs, wherein dependency levels were assessed in individuals already diagnosed with a particular form of illness. Although such individuals generally show higher dependency levels than healthy control participants, it is impossible to tell from these data whether increases in dependency preceded or followed illness onset. This is particularly problematic because research confirms that—as the object relations/interactionist model contends—the onset of physical illness is often followed by an increase in dependent feelings and behaviors, even in individuals who had previously shown no signs of exaggerated dependency needs (Saviola, 1981; Viederman, 1974). Fortunately, two longitudinal studies help resolve some of the methodological ambiguities surrounding retrospective research on the dependency–illness link. These prospective investigations confirm that pre-existing dependency needs constitute a risk factor for a variety of illness and disease states.

In one study of this issue, R. P. Greenberg and Dattore (1981) compared the Minnesota Multiphasic Personality Inventory (MMPI) Dependency (*Dy*) scores (Navran, 1954) of male Veterans Affairs patients who later developed cancer or one of three other physical disorders (i.e., benign tumors, hypertension, or gastrointestinal ulcers) with the *Dy* scores of a control group of men who remained disease free for 10 years following the initial dependency screening. R. P. Greenberg and Dattore found that men who subsequently developed any of the physical disorders assessed in this study had significantly higher initial dependency scores than did men who remained disease free for the duration of the investigation.

As R. P. Greenberg and Dattore (1981) found, Vaillant (1978) also found that dependency was a nonspecific risk factor for subsequent physical illness in nonclinical (i.e., college student) participants. In Vaillant's investigation, projective test and interview measures of dependency obtained during late adolescence predicted the subsequent development of ulcers, hypertension, colitis, allergies, and musculoskeletal problems in a sample of male college students followed over 30 years (Vaillant did not assess cancer rates). Vaillant found that dependency predicted the onset of a variety of physical problems but did not predict the form that illness would take.

The findings of R. P. Greenberg and Dattore (1981) and Vaillant (1978) provide preliminary evidence that dependency constitutes a nonspecific risk factor for a variety of illness states. However, two methodological limitations are relevant in interpreting the results of these investigations. First, none of the researchers statistically controlled for level of depression, thus allowing the possibility that differences in depression levels in dependent and nondependent participants might have accounted, in whole or in part, for the obtained results. Second, none of the researchers controlled for health-related behaviors, such as tobacco, alcohol, or caffeine use, so the pathways linking dependency with subsequent illness onset still remain unknown.

Methodological limitations in these earlier investigations notwithstanding, two studies support the findings of R. P. Greenberg and Dattore (1981) and Vaillant (1978) and extend these findings to women and men (Bornstein, 1995, Study 1; Bornstein, Krukonis, Manning, Mastrosimone, & Rossner, 1993). In both investigations, researchers prescreened mixed-sex samples of healthy college students for level of dependency using the Interpersonal Dependency Inventory (IDI; Hirschfeld et al., 1977), a widely used self-report dependency measure. Self-reports of illness episodes were then obtained periodically throughout a 6-week period. In both studies, high IDI scores at the start of the investigation were associated with a greater number of illness episodes during the 6-week data-collection period.

In a follow-up study involving a new participant sample, Bornstein (1995, Study 2) found that dependent college students undergoing high levels of interpersonal conflict and relationship disruption showed the highest overall illness rates only if they also reported receiving low levels of social support. Those dependent students experiencing high interpersonal stress who had adequate levels of social support showed no elevations in illness rates relative to nondependent control students. Both of these findings are consistent with predictions derived from the object relations/interactionist model, and they confirm that (a) high levels of dependency along with a high level of interpersonal stress place individuals at increased risk for illness and disease and (b) social support ameliorates the negative effects of interpersonal stress on dependent participants' health status.

Additional information regarding the magnitude of the dependency–illness link was obtained in a meta-analytic review of research in this area (Bornstein, 1998c). Using the effect size estimate *r* to quantify the dependency–illness relationship in all published studies of this issue, Bornstein found overall dependency–illness correlations of .31 in retrospective studies (*n* of comparisons = 19) and .27 in prospective studies (*n* of comparisons = 5). Both effect sizes were highly significant, given the large pooled participant samples on which they were based ($p < .000001$ in both analyses). These meta-analytic results indicate that (a) there is a moderate but statistically reliable relationship between dependency levels and illness rates and (b) comparable dependency–illness effect sizes are produced in retrospective and prospective studies.

It is informative to compare the magnitudes of the dependency–disease links obtained by Bornstein (1998c) with the relationships between various personality variables and risk for physical illness reported by Friedman and Booth-Kewley (1987) in their meta-analytic review of research on the "disease-prone personality." Friedman and Booth-Kewley examined studies assessing the relationship of several personality dimensions (i.e., anxiety, depression, anger, hostility, aggression, and introversion) and several physical illnesses (i.e., heart disease, asthma, ulcers, arthritis, and migraine headaches). Correlations between level of a given personality trait and illness status ranged from −.01 (for anger and hostility as predictors of ulcers and headaches) to .32 (for anxiety as a predictor of asthma) in Friedman and Booth-Kewley's meta-analysis.

By using the techniques outlined by Rosenthal (1984), I (Bornstein, 1998c) derived overall personality–disease correlations from the information provided by Friedman and Booth-Kewley (1987, Table 1). The personality dimension that best predicted illness (in general) was trait anxiety, wherein a mean correlation of .18 between level of anxiety and illness status was obtained. Other personality dimensions yielded pooled personality–illness effect sizes of .16 (depression), .11 (anger–hostility), .10 (anger–hostility–aggression), and −.03 (extraversion).

Thus, my (Bornstein, 1998c) meta-analytic dependency–illness effect sizes of .31 and .27 suggest that interpersonal dependency predicts illness at least as well as other theoretically related personality traits. In fact, if future investigations replicate and extend these meta-analytic results, it would appear that dependency actually predicts illness better than any other personality trait examined to date.[7]

Dependency and Health Service Use

High levels of interpersonal dependency not only increase illness risk but also influence patient-related behavior after an individual becomes ill. Several investigators have found that dependent people use health (and mental health) services more frequently than do nondependent people, even when dependent and nondependent participants are matched on salient demographic, diagnostic, and health-related variables (Bornstein et al., 1993; Brown & Rawlinson, 1975; Emery & Lesher, 1982; R. M. O'Neill & Bornstein, in press).

In one recent study, matched samples of dependent and nondependent psychiatric inpatients were constructed on the basis of these patients' MMPI *Dy* scores, along with relevant demographic and diagnostic information (i.e., age, race, gender, and Axis I, II, and III diagnoses). Dependent and nondependent patients were then compared on two dimensions: number of psychotropic medications prescribed during treatment and number of medical consultations ordered by the attending physician. On both dimensions, dependent patients scored significantly higher than nondependent patients (R. M. O'Neill & Bornstein, in press). In fact, dependent patients were prescribed psychotropic medications at nearly a 50% higher rate than were nondependent patients with similar disorders. Moreover, dependent patients received twice as many consultations for medical services than did nondependent patients.

Consistent with these results, other studies' results show that (a)

---

[7]A skeptic might argue that these nonspecific dependency–illness links simply reflect the well-established relationship between neuroticism and illness behavior. To be sure, dependent individuals generally obtain higher scores than do nondependent individuals on self-report measures of neuroticism (Bornstein, 1993; Mongrain, 1993). However, correlations between dependency scores and neuroticism scores are generally modest (see, e.g., Mongrain, 1993; and Trull, 1992). In addition, recent twin study data indicate that family history antecedents and developmental pathways of interpersonal dependency and neuroticism differ substantially (F. A. O'Neill & Kendler, 1998).

dependent college students make a greater number of visits to the college health center than do nondependent college students with similar health profiles (Bornstein et al., 1993) and (b) dependent nursing home residents require a greater number of after-hours emergency consultations than do nondependent nursing home residents with similar disorders (Emery & Lesher, 1982). Dependent psychiatric inpatients also show a "help-seeking response set" (i.e., high Infrequency Scale and low Defensiveness Scale scores) on MMPI protocols administered following admission to a hospital (R. M. O'Neill & Bornstein, 1990). Clearly, the help-seeking tendencies associated with high levels of interpersonal dependency affect a range of patient-related behaviors.

The dependency-related motivations summarized in Figure 1.1 (e.g., fear of abandonment) suggest that dependent psychiatric and medical patients will have difficulty terminating inpatient treatment and relinquishing the protection of an omniscient caregiver. Several researchers have assessed the dependency–treatment duration relationship. In one investigation of this issue, R. P. Greenberg and Bornstein (1989) found that dependent psychiatric inpatients (classified on the basis of their Rorschach Oral Dependency scores; Masling, Rabie, & Blondheim, 1967) remained hospitalized significantly longer than nondependent inpatients with comparable backgrounds and diagnoses. Similar findings have been reported for patients undergoing cardiac surgery (Brown & Rawlinson, 1975). The dependency–treatment duration link is weaker in outpatients than inpatients, but some investigations show that even in outpatient settings, dependent psychiatric and medical patients remain longer in treatment than do matched nondependent patients (Salokangas, Rakkolainen, & Lehtinen, 1980; Snyder, 1963; Stamler & Palmer, 1971).

Positive Effects of Dependency

The findings just reviewed indicate that high levels of interpersonal dependency have two distinct disadvantages with respect to health status and treatment: Not only do dependent individuals show higher illness rates than nondependent individuals, but they also use health services more frequently than nondependent people, even when health status is taken into account. Both of these findings are consistent with the object relations/interactionist model of dependency. Both findings also have important practical implications, insofar as they suggest that high levels of dependency may indirectly increase health care costs by increasing illness rates and health service usage among dependent individuals (see R. P. Greenberg & Bornstein, 1989; and R. M. O'Neill & Bornstein, in press, for discussions of this issue).

One might conclude from the findings discussed thus far that interpersonal dependency has purely negative consequences for health status and health-related behavior, but such a conclusion would be premature. A number of investigations delineate positive effects of dependency on certain forms of health-related behavior. In the following sections, I review research on two adaptive health-related features of dependency.

Dependency and Treatment Delay

Several studies show that dependency predicts treatment delay when physical symptoms appear (Geersten & Gray, 1970; R. P. Greenberg & Fisher, 1977; Hammerschlag, Fisher, DeCosse, & Kaplan, 1964; Stamler & Palmer, 1971). In each of these investigations, high dependency scores were associated with shorter latency in treatment initiation following symptom onset. The dependency–delay relationship has been found for minor illnesses (e.g., colds and flu) as well as more serious illnesses (e.g., heart disease and cancer). Moreover, the dependency–delay relationship is obtained for both objective (i.e., self-report) and projective dependency measures, in children and adults.

R. P. Greenberg and Fisher's (1977) findings illustrate the pattern of results typically obtained in this area. These researchers examined the correlations between self-reports of interpersonal dependency and community participants' estimates of the number of days they would delay before seeking treatment for a variety of physical symptoms. R. P. Greenberg and Fisher found that regardless of symptom type, there was an inverse correlation between dependency score and delay estimate. Dependency–delay correlations ranged from −.30 (for upper body symptoms) to −.56 (for painful symptoms); the mean dependency–delay correlation in R. P. Greenberg and Fisher's investigation was −.40.

What accounts for the inverse relationship between dependency and treatment delay in R. P. Greenberg and Fisher's (1977) study? Perhaps dependent people are more willing than nondependent people to enter into a physician–patient relationship, wherein they may be protected by a powerful caregiver. If this is the case, then dependent people should have different attitudes than nondependent people regarding physicians and medical treatment. Two sets of findings address this issue.

First, R. P. Greenberg and Fisher (1977) found that dependent participants gave more positive descriptions than did nondependent participants of a "typical" physician and a "typical" hospital stay. In R. P. Greenberg and Fisher's investigation, the dependent participants viewed a typical physician as warmer and more pleasant and perceived a typical hospital stay as less stressful and more pleasant than did the nondependent participants. Moreover, the dependent participants in this study reported that their most recent interactions with physicians were generally positive; nondependent participants described these interactions more negatively.

Parker and Lipscombe (1980) suggested that the origin of dependent people's positive attitudes regarding physicians and hospitals may lie in early learning and socialization experiences within the family. These researchers examined the relationship between Depressive Experiences Questionnaire dependency scores (Blatt, D'Afflitti, & Quinlan, 1976) and retrospective reports of parents' reactions to childhood illness in a mixed-sex sample of adult medical patients. Parker and Lipscombe found that the parents of dependent patients were more likely than the parents of nondependent patients to have (a) taken an episode of childhood illness seriously, (b) shown sympathy and concern regarding the illness, and (c) sought the advice of a physician when their child became ill. These results suggest that dependent people's positive attitudes regarding physicians and hospitals may be a product of their parents' own positive attitudes in these areas. Moreover, dependent people's tendency to seek treatment relatively quickly following symptom onset may reflect the parents' inclination to seek a physician's advice when their child becomes ill.

Dependency and Treatment Compliance

The object relations/interactionst model predicts that high levels of dependency are associated with acquiescent, compliant behavior, especially around figures of authority (Bornstein, 1993, 1996). Studies show strong evidence for a dependency–compliance link in social settings (Agrawal & Rai, 1988; Masling, O'Neill, & Jayne, 1981; Weiss, 1969). A number of investigators have assessed the dependency–compliance relationship in medical and psychiatric settings.

Early studies of the dependency–treatment compliance relationship produced highly consistent results, finding that dependent medical patients are viewed by their physicians as more compliant and cooperative than nondependent patients (Davis & Eichorn, 1963; Moran, Fairweather, Fisher, & Morton, 1956). Unfortunately, these investigators relied on subjective reports of patient compliance rather than an objective index of compliance. Moreover, the physicians who provided compliance ratings in these investigations also assessed patients' dependency levels, leaving open the possibility that a "halo" (or carryover) effect could have occurred, so that dependency and compliance ratings were not made independently.

More recent studies in this area are methodologically stronger than earlier ones and yield more conclusive findings. In two studies, investigators assessed the dependency–compliance link in psychiatric outpatients. In the first study, Nacev (1980) used MMPI *Dy* scores to predict psychotherapy attendance in a large, mixed-sex sample of patients and found a small ($r = -.13$), nonsignificant negative correlation between *Dy* scores and number of missed sessions during the study.

Stronger results were obtained by Poldrugo and Forti (1988), who examined dependency and compliance with outpatient treatment for alcoholism. In this investigation, researchers administered structured diagnostic interviews to 717 men undergoing voluntary outpatient alcoholism treatment; 102 of these men (25%) received an Axis II personality disorder diagnosis. Poldrugo and Forti then compared treatment compliance rates (defined as "consistent attendance" in group therapy sessions throughout the 1-year data-collection period) among patients with different personality disorder diagnoses. Patients with dependent personality disorder (DPD) diagnoses showed significantly higher rates of treatment compliance than did patients in any other group. Overall, 75% of DPD patients (vs. 33% of non-DPD patients) completed the 1-year course of treatment and remained abstinent for the duration of the study.

The conflicting results obtained by Nacev (1980) and Poldrugo and Forti (1988) may reflect differences in the participant groups investigated in these two studies (i.e., traditional psychotherapy patients vs. patients undergoing substance abuse follow-up treatment). Alternatively, the conflicting results in these two studies might be due in part to the way that treatment compliance was operationalized in these investigations. It is impossible to say which measure of compliance is more valid, but these findings suggest that dependency may be more strongly related to successful completion of an alcoholism treatment program than to consistent attendance in outpatient psychotherapy sessions. Additional research is needed to delineate more clearly the breadth—and limitations—of the relationship between interpersonal dependency and treatment compliance.[8]

Discussion

Several decades of research converge to confirm that the dependency–illness relationship is more complicated than theoreticians and researchers initially thought: Rather than simply being a flaw or deficit in functioning, dependency has both adaptive and maladaptive consequences with respect to health status and health-related behavior. On the negative side, a dependent personality orientation is associated with an increased risk for a variety of

[8]Although high levels of dependency are associated with treatment compliance in certain psychotherapeutic contexts, studies show no relationship between dependency and compliance with medication treatment for psychological disorders (Fava et al., 1994; Lauer, 1976). It seems that the close, sustained contact between a patient and therapist may be partially responsible for the increased compliance among dependent psychotherapy patients.

illness and disease states and may also be linked with overreliance on certain types of health (and mental health) services. On the positive side, a dependent personality orientation is associated with a minimal delay in the seeking of professional help after symptom onset and with compliance and cooperativeness during medical and psychological treatment.

These findings dovetail with research on other aspects of interpersonal dependency, which also indicates that a dependent personality orientation is linked with an array of positive and negative consequences. For example, in social settings, dependent people tend to be suggestible (Jakubczak & Walters, 1959) and yield to others in interpersonal transactions (Masling, Weiss, & Rothschild, 1968). At the same time, however, dependent people show high levels of interpersonal sensitivity and are particularly skilled at decoding subtle interpersonal cues (Masling, Johnson, & Saturansky, 1974). In elementary school, dependent children often appear insecure and demanding (Sroufe et al., 1983); but by late adolescence, this insecurity and reassurance seeking results in high levels of academic success (Bornstein & Kennedy, 1994).

These findings, taken together, suggest that whether interpersonal dependency is a limitation or a strength depends largely on the circumstances in which it is exhibited and the particular ways in which dependent feelings, attitudes, and behaviors are expressed. Like other personality traits that seem at first glance to represent flaws or deficits in functioning (e.g., narcissism), dependency is neither "all good" nor "all bad." Future research in this area should examine in detail the strengths and weaknesses associated with high levels of interpersonal dependency in children and adults, especially as these strengths and weaknesses are displayed in different contexts and settings. The object relations/interactionist model provides a useful conceptual framework for addressing these issues, and some preliminary research in this area has already appeared (see Bornstein, 1994, 1998a, for reviews).

Although research supports a link between dependency and various dimensions of health and health-related behavior, the pathways linking dependent personality traits with these variables warrant further study. Preliminary evidence confirms that high levels of interpersonal conflict and relationship disruption place dependent people at risk for depression (Overholser, 1996) and various other illness states (Blatt et al., 1993; Bornstein, 1995). However, the pathways linking dependency with adaptive health-related behaviors remain largely unexplored. Research on dependency and help seeking in social settings may provide an empirical framework for examining the dependency–help seeking link in medical settings. Continued scrutiny of the causal links between dependent personality traits and adaptive health-related variables will not only have important practical implications (e.g., in controlling health care costs and treatment expenditures) but may also help test and refine extant theoretical models of interpersonal dependency.

In this context, it is important to note that a key feature of the object relations/interactionist model is the prediction that there is a synergistic relationship between dependency and illness: Not only do dependent attitudes and feelings place an individual at risk for health problems, but also the onset of illness may in turn increase dependency-related feelings, motivations, and behaviors. In fact, researchers have delineated three routes through which illness onset may directly or indirectly increase a person's dependency levels.

First, as noted earlier, the onset of physical illness is sometimes followed by an increase in dependent feelings and behaviors, even in individuals who had previously shown no signs of having exaggerated dependency needs (Saviola, 1981; Viederman, 1974). The experience of physical illness arouses intense feelings of vulnerability and helplessness in many people, which may lead to regression and the re-emergence of long-denied (or repressed) dependent feelings (Galatzer-Levy & Cohler, 1993; Silverman et al., 1982).

Second, intermittent reinforcement of illness-related dependent behavior by friends and relatives can reinforce a "sick role," resulting in a role-related increase in dependent, help-seeking tendencies (Hoare, 1984; Stores & Piran, 1978). In this situation, inadvertently rewarding signs of helplessness and neediness can propagate illness-related dependent behavior.

Third, the experience of being hospitalized and treated for physical or psychological illness may, in and of itself, produce increases in dependent attitudes and behaviors, a phenomenon known as "institutional dependency" (Alsop, 1984; Baltes, 1996). In fact, more recent studies show how unintentional reinforcement of dependent behavior in hospital and nursing home residents can increase feelings of helplessness and vulnerability and even compromise health status among the residents (see Baltes, 1996).

Although physicians have only recently begun to take seriously the proposition that role-related dependency can compromise recovery from physical and psychological illness, psychotherapists have long speculated regarding this issue. Thus, more than 30 years ago, Balint (1964) argued that

> there are many factors . . . which push the patient into a dependent, childish relationship with his doctor. This is inevitable. The only question is . . . how much dependence constitutes a good starting point for psychotherapy, and when does it turn into an obstacle. (pp. 39–40)

Goldfarb (1969) further contended that in many situations, patient dependency can be used to therapeutic advantage if the therapist does not interfere with a dependent transference early in therapy but increasingly discourages the patient from exhibiting dependent, help-seeking behavior as therapy progresses. As several clinicians have noted, the strong transference reactions exhibited by many dependent psychotherapy patients provide numerous opportunities to explore, and eventually challenge, the patients' beliefs regarding their powerlessness and ineffectiveness and regarding the perceived power and potency of others (Cashdan, 1988; Emery & Lesher, 1982; Hopkins, 1986).

Future research on the dependency–illness relationship should assess the generalizability and limitations of extant studies in this area. To date, there have been no long-term prospective cohort studies of dependency and physical illness; such a study would help resolve a number of conceptual and methodological ambiguities that limit the value of extant research in this area. In addition, greater attention to the links between dependency and particular illness states is needed. It may be that dependency is more strongly linked with certain illness states than others but that the methodologies used in initial studies in this area are not sufficiently sensitive to detect these illness-specific links.

The interaction of interpersonal dependency with various types of life events also warrants further study. Several researchers have assessed the interaction of dependency and life events to predict the onset of depression (e.g., Blatt & Homann, 1992; Nietzel & Harris, 1990; Overholser, 1996), but only Bornstein (1995) explored the interaction of dependency and stressful life events in the onset of physical illness. The results of this preliminary investigation suggest that interpersonal stressors might place dependent people at increased risk for minor illnesses (e.g., colds and flu), but continued research on this topic is needed.

Finally, it would be useful to explore the differential relationships of implicit and self-attributed dependency needs to illness onset and health-related behavior. Numerous studies show that implicit dependency strivings (which are assessed through projective tests like Masling et al.'s, 1967, Rorschach Oral Dependency Scale) often produce results different from those obtained when self-attributed dependency strivings (which are assessed through self-report tests like Hirschfeld et al.'s, 1977, IDI) are used (see Bornstein, 1998b, for a review of these investigations). It may be that in general, one type of dependency measure is more strongly related than the other to health and illness variables. Alternatively, it may be that discontinuities between an individual's implicit and self-attributed dependency strivings are the strongest predictors of illness risk.

In this context, researchers should focus on individuals with unacknowledged dependency needs (i.e., people who score high on implicit dependency measures but low on self-attributed dependency tests). It is possible that unacknowledged dependency strivings are a strong predictor of illness onset—a hypothesis that would be consistent in certain respects with Alexander's (1950; Alexander et al., 1968) psychosomatic specificity hypothesis, which contends that frustrated dependency needs are key predictors of certain forms of illness. If that were the case, research on dependency and illness would have come full circle from psychosomatic specificity to object relations and back again.

Conclusion

More than 70 years ago, Freud (1926/1959) helped set the tone for 20th-century psychoanalysis when he warned psychodynamically oriented physicians to "resist the temptation of flirting with endocrinology and the autonomous nervous system . . . [; you] have to detect psychological facts by means of psychological concepts" (p. 198). By making statements such as this, Freud established clear boundaries between traditional medicine and classical psychoanalysis, which he believed could flourish only if it explicitly denied the physical underpinnings of psychosomatic disorders and other stress-related conditions (Ammon, 1979). Freud's strategy was certainly understandable, given the intellectual climate of his time. However, by downplaying the interaction of psychological and physiological processes in the etiology and dynamics of illness states, Freud might have hindered the development of a truly rigorous and innovative psychoanalytic health psychology.

As the world enters the 21st century, it is time to move beyond the traditional Freudian view of health and illness. Although acknowledging the important contributions of Deutsch (1922), Alexander (1950), and others, psychoanalytic health psychologists have an obligation to integrate psychodynamic concepts into empirical research on various aspects of health and illness, including those that come from other theoretical perspectives. Broadening the conceptual and empirical base of psychoanalytic health psychology will not only increase the heuristic value of contemporary psychoanalysis but may also provide opportunities to forge new connections with colleagues in other health-related disciplines.

References

Abraham, K. (1927). The influence of oral erotism on character formation. In C. A. D. Bryan & A. Strachey (Eds.), *Selected papers on psychoanalysis* (pp. 393–406). London: Hogarth.

Agrawal, K., & Rai, S. N. (1988). Post-noise frustration tolerance as a function of controllability of noise and dependence proneness. *Indian Journal of Psychometry and Education, 19,* 85–89.

Ainsworth, M. D. S. (1969). Object relations, dependency, and attachment: A theoretical review of the infant–mother relationship. *Child Development, 40,* 969–1025.

Ainsworth, M. D. S. (1989). Attachments beyond infancy. *American Psychologist, 44,* 709–716.

Alexander, F. (1950). *Psychosomatic medicine.* New York: Norton.
Alexander, F. (1954). *The scope of psychoanalysis.* New York: Basic Books.
Alexander, F., French, T. M., & Pollock, G. H. (1968). *Psychosomatic specificity.* Chicago: University of Chicago Press.
Alsop, A. E. (1984). Purley Day Hospital: An appraisal with special reference to institutionalized behavior and dependence. *Occupational Therapy, 47,* 306–310.
Ammon, G. (1979). *Psychoanalysis and psychosomatics.* New York: Springer.
Balint, M. (1964). *The doctor, his patient, and the illness.* London: Pitman Medical.
Baltes, M. M. (1996). *The many faces of dependency in old age.* Cambridge, UK: Cambridge University Press.
Baumrind, D. (1971). Current patterns of parental authority. *Developmental Psychology Monographs, 4*(1, Pt. 2), 1–103.
Berg, I., & McGuire, R. (1974). Are mothers of school-phobic adolescents overprotective? *British Journal of Psychiatry, 124,* 10–13.
Birtchnell, J. (1988). Defining dependence. *British Journal of Medical Psychology, 61,* 111–123.
Blatt, S. J. (1974). Levels of object representation in anaclitic and introjective depression. *Psychoanalytic Study of the Child, 29,* 107–157.
Blatt, S. J. (1991). A cognitive morphology of psychopathology. *Journal of Nervous and Mental Disease, 179,* 449–458.
Blatt, S. J., Cornell, C. E., & Eshkol, E. (1993). Personality style, differential vulnerability, and clinical course in immunologic and cardiovascular disease. *Clinical Psychology Review, 13,* 421–450.
Blatt, S. J., D'Afflitti, J. P., & Quinlan, D. M. (1976). Experiences of depression in normal young adults. *Journal of Abnormal Psychology, 85,* 383–389.
Blatt, S. J., & Homann, E. (1992). Parent–child interaction in the etiology of dependent and self-critical depression. *Clinical Psychology Review, 12,* 47–91.
Blatt, S. J., & Shichman, S. (1983). Two primary configurations of psychopathology. *Psychoanalysis and Contemporary Thought, 6,* 187–254.
Blum, G. S., & Miller, D. (1952). Exploring the psychoanalytic theory of the "oral character." *Journal of Personality, 20,* 287–304.
Bornstein, R. F. (1992). The dependent personality: Developmental, social, and clinical perspectives. *Psychological Bulletin, 112,* 3–23.
Bornstein, R. F. (1993). *The dependent personality.* New York: Guilford Press.
Bornstein, R. F. (1994). Adaptive and maladaptive aspects of dependency: An integrative review. *American Journal of Orthopsychiatry, 64,* 622–635.
Bornstein, R. F. (1995). Interpersonal dependency and physical illness: The mediating roles of stress and social support. *Journal of Social and Clinical Psychology, 14,* 225–243.
Bornstein, R. F. (1996). Beyond orality: Toward an object relations/interactionist reconceptualization of the etiology and dynamics of dependency. *Psychoanalytic Psychology, 13,* 177–203.

Bornstein, R. F. (1997). Dependent personality disorder in the *DSM-IV* and beyond. *Clinical Psychology: Science and Practice, 4,* 175–187.

Bornstein, R. F. (1998a). Depathologizing dependency. *Journal of Nervous and Mental Disease, 186,* 67–73.

Bornstein, R. F. (1998b). Implicit and self-attributed dependency strivings: Differential relationships to laboratory and field measures of help seeking. *Journal of Personality and Social Psychology, 75,* 778–787.

Bornstein, R. F. (1998c). Interpersonal dependency and physical illness: A meta-analytic review of prospective and retrospective studies. *Journal of Research in Personality, 32,* 480–497.

Bornstein, R. F., Bowers, K. S., & Bonner, S. (1996). Relationships of objective and projective dependency scores to sex role orientation in college student participants. *Journal of Personality Assessment, 66,* 555–568.

Bornstein, R. F., & Kennedy, T. D. (1994). Interpersonal dependency and academic performance. *Journal of Personality Disorders, 8,* 240–248.

Bornstein, R. F., Krukonis, A. B., Manning, K. A., Mastrosimone, C. C., & Rossner, S. C. (1993). Interpersonal dependency and health service utilization in a college student sample. *Journal of Social and Clinical Psychology, 12,* 262–279.

Bornstein, R. F., Riggs, J. M., Hill, E. L., & Calabrese, C. C. (1996). Activity, passivity, self-denigration, and self-promotion: Toward an interactionist model of interpersonal dependency. *Journal of Personality, 64,* 637–673.

Bornstein, R. F., Rossner, S. C., Hill, E. L., & Stepanian, M. L. (1994). Face validity and fakability of objective and projective measures of dependency. *Journal of Personality Assessment, 63,* 363–386.

Bowers, K. S., & Meichenbaum, D. M. (Eds.). (1984). *The unconscious reconsidered.* New York: Wiley.

Bowlby, J. (1953). Some pathological processes set in train by early mother–child separation. *Journal of Mental Science, 99,* 265–272.

Bowlby, J. (1960). Grief and mourning in infancy and early childhood. *Psychoanalytic Study of the Child, 15,* 9–52.

Bowlby, J. (1969). *Attachment and loss. Vol. 1: Attachment.* New York: Basic Books.

Bowlby, J. (1980). *Attachment and loss. Vol. 3: Sadness and depression.* New York: Basic Books.

Breuer, J., & Freud, S. (1955). Studies on hysteria. In J. Strachey, A. Freud, A. Strachey, & A. Tyson (Eds. & Trans.), *The standard edition of the complete psychological works of Sigmund Freud* (Vol. 2). London: Hogarth Press. (Original work published 1893)

Brown, J. S., & Rawlinson, M. (1975). Relinquishing the sick role following open heart surgery. *Journal of Health and Social Behavior, 16,* 12–27.

Cashdan, S. (1988). *Object relations therapy.* New York: Norton.

Davis, M. S., & Eichorn, R. L. (1963). Compliance with medical regimens. *Journal of Health and Human Behavior, 4,* 240–249.

Deutsch, F. (1922). Psychoanalyse und organkrankheiten. *International Journal of Psychoanalysis, 8,* 290–306.

Deutsch, F. (1924). Zur bildung des konversions symptoms. *International Journal of Psychoanalysis, 10,* 380–392.

Duberstein, P. R., & Talbot, N. L. (1993). Rorschach oral imagery, attachment style, and interpersonal relatedness. *Journal of Personality Assessment, 61,* 294–310.

Eagle, M. (1984). *Recent developments in psychoanalysis.* New York: McGraw-Hill.

Emery, G., & Lesher, E. (1982). Treatment of depression in older adults: Personality considerations. *Psychotherapy, 19,* 500–505.

Erdelyi, M. H. (1985). *Psychoanalysis: Freud's cognitive psychology.* New York: Freeman.

Fairbairn, W. R. D. (1952). *An object relations theory of the personality.* New York: Basic Books.

Fava, M., Bouffides, E., Pava, J. A., McCarthy, M. K., Steingard, R. J., & Rosenbaum, J. F. (1994). Personality disorder comorbidity with major depression and response to fluoxetine treatment. *Psychotherapy and Psychosomatics, 62,* 160–167.

Fenichel, O. (1945). *The psychoanalytic theory of neurosis.* New York: Norton.

Fisher, S., & Greenberg, R. P. (1997). *Freud scientifically reappraised: Testing the theories and therapy.* New York: Wiley.

Freud, S. (1955). Three essays on the theory of sexuality. In J. Strachey (Ed. & Trans.), *The standard edition of the complete psychological works of Sigmund Freud* (Vol. 7, pp. 125–245). London: Hogarth Press. (Original work published 1905)

Freud, S. (1958). Character and anal erotism. In J. Strachey (Ed. & Trans.), *The standard edition of the complete psychological works of Sigmund Freud* (Vol. 9, pp. 167–176). London: Hogarth Press. (Original work published 1908)

Freud, S. (1959). The question of lay analysis. In J. Strachey (Ed. & Trans.), *The standard edition of the complete psychological works of Sigmund Freud* (Vol. 20, pp. 177–258). London: Hogarth Press. (Original work published 1926)

Friedman, H. S., & Booth-Kewley, S. (1987). The disease-prone personality: A meta-analytic review of the construct. *American Psychologist, 42,* 539–555.

Galatzer-Levy, R. M., & Cohler, B. J. (1993). *The essential other: A developmental psychology of the self.* New York: Basic Books.

Geersten, H. R., & Gray, R. M. (1970). Familistic orientation and inclination toward adopting the sick role. *Journal of Marriage and the Family, 32,* 638–646.

Glover, E. (1925). Notes on oral character formation. *International Journal of Psychoanalysis, 6,* 131–154.

Goldfarb, A. I. (1969). The psychodynamics of dependency and the search for aid. In R. A. Kalish (Ed.), *The dependencies of old people* (pp. 1–15). Ann Arbor: University of Michigan Press.

Goldman-Eisler, F. (1950). The etiology of the oral character in psychoanalytic theory. *Journal of Personality, 19,* 189–196.

Goldman-Eisler, F. (1951). The problem of "orality" and its origin in early childhood. *Journal of Mental Science, 97,* 765–782.

Greenberg, J. R., & Mitchell, S. J. (1983). *Object relations in psychoanalytic theory.* Cambridge, MA: Harvard University Press.

Greenberg, R. P., & Bornstein, R. F. (1989). Length of psychiatric hospitalization and oral dependency. *Journal of Personality Disorders, 3,* 199–204.

Greenberg, R. P., & Dattore, P. J. (1981). The relationship between dependency and the development of cancer. *Psychosomatic Medicine, 43,* 35–43.

Greenberg, R. P., & Fisher, S. (1977). The relationship between willingness to adopt the sick role and attitudes toward women. *Journal of Chronic Disease, 30,* 29–37.

Grunbaum, A. (1984). *The foundations of psychoanalysis: A philosophical critique.* Berkeley: University of California Press.

Hammerschlag, C. A., Fisher, S., DeCosse, J., & Kaplan, E. (1964). Breast symptoms and patient delay: Psychological variables involved. *Cancer, 17,* 1480–1485.

Heiss, G. E., Berman, W. H., & Sperling, M. B. (1996). Five scales in search of a construct: Exploring continued attachment to parents in college students. *Journal of Personality Assessment, 67,* 102–115.

Hirschfeld, R. M. A., Klerman, G. L., Gough, H. G., Barrett, J., Korchin, S. J., & Chodoff, P. (1977). A measure of interpersonal dependency. *Journal of Personality Assessment, 41,* 610–618.

Hoare, P. (1984). Does illness foster dependency? A study of epileptic and diabetic children. *Developmental Medicine and Child Neurology, 16,* 20–24.

Hopkins, L. B. (1986). Dependency issues and fears in long-term psychotherapy. *Psychotherapy, 23,* 535–539.

Ihilevich, D., & Gleser, D. C. (1986). *Defense mechanisms.* Owosso, MI: DMI Associates.

Jacobson, E. (1964). *The self and object world.* New York: International Universities Press.

Jakubczak, L. F., & Walters, R. H. (1959). Suggestibility as dependency behavior. *Journal of Abnormal and Social Psychology, 59,* 102–107.

Kaprio, J., Koskenvuo, M., & Rita, H. (1987). Mortality after bereavement: A prospective study of 95,647 widowed persons. *American Journal of Public Health, 77,* 283–287.

Kobasa, S. C. (1979). Stressful life events, personality, and health: An inquiry into hardiness. *Journal of Personality and Social Psychology, 37,* 1–11.

Kohut, H. (1971). *The analysis of the self.* New York: International Universities Press.

Kohut, H. (1977). *The restoration of the self.* New York: International Universities Press.

Lauer, J. W. (1976). The effect of tricyclic antidepressant compounds on patients with passive-dependent personality traits. *Current Therapeutic Research, 19,* 495–505.

Mahler, M. S., Pine, F., & Bergman, A. (1975). *The psychological birth of the human infant.* New York: Basic Books.

Main, M., Kaplan, M., & Cassidy, J. (1985). Security in infancy, childhood, and adulthood. *Monographs of the Society for Research in Child Development, 50,* 66–104.

Martikainen, R., & Valkonen, P. J. (1996). Mortality after death of a spouse: Rates and causes of death in a large Finnish cohort. *American Journal of Health, 86,* 1087–1093.

Masling, J. M. (1986). Orality, pathology, and interpersonal behavior. In J. M. Masling (Ed.), *Empirical studies of psychoanalytic theories* (Vol. 2, pp. 73–106). Hillsdale, NJ: Erlbaum.

Masling, J. M., Johnson, C., & Saturansky, C. (1974). Oral imagery, accuracy of perceiving others, and performance in Peace Corps training. *Journal of Personality and Social Psychology, 30,* 414–419.

Masling, J. M., O'Neill, R. M., & Jayne, C. (1981). Orality and latency of volunteering to serve as experimental subjects. *Journal of Personality Assessment, 45,* 20–22.

Masling, J. M., Rabie, L., & Blondheim, S. H. (1967). Obesity, level of aspiration, and Rorschach and TAT measures of oral dependence. *Journal of Consulting Psychology, 31,* 233–239.

Masling, J. M., & Schwartz, M. A. (1979). A critique of research in psychoanalytic theory. *Genetic Psychology Monographs, 100,* 257–307.

Masling, J. M., Weiss, L., & Rothschild, B. (1968). Relationships of oral imagery to yielding behavior and birth order. *Journal of Consulting and Clinical Psychology, 32,* 89–91.

Millon, T. (1996). *Disorders of personality:* DSM-IV *and beyond.* New York: Wiley.

Mirsky, J. A. (1958). Physiologic, psychologic, and social determinants in the etiology of gastrointestinal ulcer. *American Journal of Digestive Diseases, 3,* 285.

Mongrain, M. (1993). Dependency and self-criticism located within the five-factor model of personality. *Personality and Individual Differences, 15,* 455–462.

Moran, L. J., Fairweather, G. W., Fisher, S., & Morton, R. B. (1956). Psychological concomitants of recovery from tuberculosis. *Journal of Consulting Psychology, 20,* 199–203.

Nacev, V. (1980). Dependency and ego strength as indicators of patients' attendance in psychotherapy. *Journal of Clinical Psychology, 36,* 691–695.

Navran, L. (1954). A rationally derived MMPI scale to measure dependence. *Journal of Consulting Psychology, 18,* 192.

Nietzel, M. T., & Harris, M. J. (1990). Relationship of dependency and achievement–autonomy to depression. *Clinical Psychology Review, 10,* 279–297.

O'Neill, F. A., & Kendler, K. S. (1998). Longitudinal study of interpersonal dependency in female twins. *British Journal of Psychiatry, 172,* 154–158.

O'Neill, R. M., & Bornstein, R. F. (1990). Oral dependence and gender: Factors in help-seeking response set and self-reported psychopathology in psychiatric inpatients. *Journal of Personality Assessment, 55,* 28–40.

O'Neill, R. M., & Bornstein, R. F. (in press). The dependent patient in a psychiatric inpatient setting: Relationship of interpersonal dependency to consultation and medication frequencies. *Journal of Clinical Psychology.*

Overholser, J. C. (1996). The dependent personality and interpersonal problems. *Journal of Nervous and Mental Disease, 184,* 8–16.

Overholser, J. C., & Freiheit, S. R. (1994). Assessment of interpersonal dependency using the MCMI-II and the Depressive Experiences Questionnaire. *Personality and Individual Differences, 17,* 71–78.

Parker, G., & Lipscombe, P. (1980). The relevance of early parental experiences to adult dependency, hypochondriasis, and utilization of primary care physicians. *British Journal of Medical Psychology, 53,* 355–363.

Pennebaker, J. W., & O'Heeron, R. C. (1984). Confiding in others and illness rate among spouses of suicide and accidental death victims. *Journal of Abnormal Psychology, 93,* 473–476.

Peterson, C., & Seligman, M. E. P. (1987). Explanatory style and illness. *Journal of Personality, 55,* 237–265.

Pinneau, S. R. (1955a). The infantile disorders of hospitalism and anaclitic depression. *Psychological Bulletin, 52,* 429–452.

Pinneau, S. R. (1955b). Reply to Dr. Spitz. *Psychological Bulletin, 52,* 459–462.

Poldrugo, F., & Forti, B. (1988). Personality disorders and alcoholism treatment outcome. *Drug and Alcohol Dependence, 21,* 171–176.

Rosenthal, R. (1984). *Meta-analytic procedures for social research.* Beverly Hills, CA: Sage.

Salokangas, R. K. R., Rakkolainen, V., & Lehtinen, P. (1980). The psychiatric treatment system as an adaptational treatment structure: A study of dependency in the treatment behavior of schizophrenic patients. *Psychiatrica Fennica, 7,* 99–109.

Sandler, J., & Dare, C. (1970). The psychoanalytic concept of orality. *Journal of Psychosomatic Research, 14,* 211–222.

Saviola, M. E. (1981). Personal reflections on physically disabled women and dependency. *Professional Psychology, 12,* 112–117.

Sifneos, P. E. (1983). Psychotherapies for psychosomatic and alexithymic patients. *Psychotherapy and Psychosomatics, 40,* 66–73.

Silverman, L. H., Lachmann, F. M., & Milich, R. L. (1982). *The search for oneness.* New York: International Universities Press.

Snyder, W. U. (1963). *Dependency in psychotherapy.* New York: Macmillan.

Spence, J. T., & Helmreich, R. L. (1978). *Masculinity and femininity: Their psychological dimensions, correlates, and antecedents.* Austin: University of Texas Press.

Spiegel, D., Bloom, J. R., Kraemer, H. C., & Gottheil, E. (1989, October 14). Effect of psychosocial treatment on survival of patients with metastatic breast cancer. *The Lancet,* pp. 888–891.

Spitz, R. A. (1945). Hospitalism. *Psychoanalytic Study of the Child, 1,* 53–74.

Spitz, R. A. (1946). Hospitalism: A follow-up report on investigation described in Volume 1, 1945. *Psychoanalytic Study of the Child, 2,* 113–117.

Spitz, R. A. (1955). Reply to Dr. Pinneau. *Psychological Bulletin, 52,* 453–459.

Sroufe, L. A., Fox, N. E., & Pancake, V. R. (1983). Attachment and dependency in developmental perspective. *Child Development, 54,* 1615–1627.

Stamler, C., & Palmer, J. O. (1971). Dependency and repetitive visits to the nurse's office in elementary school children. *Nursing Research, 20,* 254–255.

Stores, G., & Piran, N. (1978). Dependency of different types of schoolchildren with epilepsy. *Psychological Medicine, 8,* 441–445.

Temoshok, L. (1987). Personality, coping style, emotion, and cancer: Toward an integrative model. *Cancer Surveys, 6,* 545–567.

Trull, T. J. (1992). *DSM-III-R* personality disorders and the five-factor model of personality: An empirical comparison. *Journal of Abnormal Psychology, 101,* 553–560.

Vaillant, G. E. (1978). Natural history of male psychological health. IV: What kinds of men do not get psychosomatic illness? *Psychosomatic Medicine, 40,* 420–431.

Vaillant, G. E. (1994). Ego mechanisms of defense and personality pathology. *Journal of Abnormal Psychology, 103,* 44–50.

Viederman, M. (1974). Adaptive and maladaptive regression in hemodialysis. *Psychiatry, 37,* 68–77.

Weiss, L. R. (1969). Effects of subject, experimenter, and task variables on compliance with the experimenter's expectation. *Journal of Projective Techniques and Personality Assessment, 33,* 247–256.

I Dependency
II Hostility

Chapter

2

Heart and Unconscious Mind: A Psychoanalytic Examination of Cardiovascular Psychology

Richard M. O'Neill

Cardiovascular psychology has been called one of the "most promising" (Allan & Scheidt, 1998) specialties in health psychology and focuses on psychosocial and behavioral factors contributing to the development and outcome of coronary heart disease. Scientists have long speculated on the connections between these factors and coronary heart disease (CHD; e.g., see Dusch, 1868; and Osler, 1892, cited in Rosenman & Chesney, 1980). Related empirical work began in earnest in the 1950s after the delineation of the Type A coronary-prone behavior pattern (Friedman & Rosenman, 1959). That and subsequent work has been almost totally uniformed by psychoanalytic theory. Even though cardiovascular psychology researchers have made impressive, exciting strides in discovering various psychological factors that predict CHD, these findings and the cardiovascular psychology field in general suffer from a lack of a strong theoretical framework to integrate these findings. Essentially, it is a field of research data in search of an explanation. Consider the following question and related research as an example of how psychoanalytic theory can illuminate an ongoing debate in the field.

Is virtually all CHD in middle-aged people partly a result of psychological and behavioral factors? Although many experts would say *no*, cardiologist Meyer Friedman, an originator of the Type A coronary-prone behavior pattern (TABP) concept,[1] and a colleague (Friedman & Ghandour, 1993) suggested that the answer is more complex. In their study, 99 men and women in the prime of their lives (ages 44–65) had suffered a myocardial infarction (MI), the death of heart muscle commonly known as a "heart attack," following the decades-long buildup of atherosclerotic plaque on the walls of their coronary arteries. Using a specially redesigned protocol, the Videotaped Clinical Examination (VCE), a clinician asked each patient after recovery to report on two key dimensions of experience and behavior, free-floating hostility and time urgency, while covertly monitoring psychomotor signs of impatience and hostility exhibited during the interview itself. When only the self-report component of hostility was scored, 55 of the 99 patients were classified as showing Type A coronary-prone behavior (TAB). When the observed psychomotor signs of hostility were also included in the score, 81 CHD patients were identified as having TAB. Ignoring the self-reported and observed signs of hostility and scoring only the self-report component of time urgency classified 82 patients as showing TAB, whereas adding the observed physical signs of time urgency categorized 90 patients as exhibiting TAB. Combining all four self-report and observed components of hostility and time urgency classified 97 of these 99 successive post-MI patients as demonstrating TAB (Friedman & Ghandour, 1993).

As part of this same study, 23 healthy men with no clinical evidence of CHD and normal electrocardiograms were also inter-

---

[1]Friedman recently changed the original term Type A behavior pattern (TABP) to Type A behavior (TAB), reflecting refinements in the classification criteria.

viewed (by clinicians unaware of CHD status). Using the same cutoff score as for the 99 post-MI patients, only 1 of these 23 men was classified as having TAB. Friedman and Ghandour (1993) noted that contrary to the beliefs of many researchers, the time urgency component alone was a better predictor of MI status than the hostility component. They also stressed that the added sensitivity obtained by including the observed psychomotor signs indicates the necessity of monitoring them in such research and in designing CHD risk-reduction interventions. Furthermore, they hypothesized that people who exhibit Type A behavior must be either reluctant to admit to or are partially unaware of their free-floating hostility and impatience. They attributed the failure of numerous cardiovascular psychology research projects to find a TABP–CHD link to a lack of consideration of these socially undesirable and perhaps unconscious psychomotor signs. Referring to this study and others in the TABP literature, Friedman, Fleischmann, and Price (1996) concluded that

> once a clinician learns how to diagnose the presence of TAB, he or she will find almost without exception that a patient (under 60 years of age) who suffers from CHD also exhibits TABP. Conversely, any person who exhibits Type B behavior (*the relative absence of TABP*) is relatively immune to clinical CHD before the age of 60. (p. 193, emphasis added)

This bold and astonishing statement appeared in the book *Heart & Mind: The Practice of Cardiac Psychology* (Allan & Scheidt, 1996b) and followed nearly 40 years of TABP research begun by Friedman and Rosenman (1959). However, in the same volume, the editors called TABP and CHD research results "variable" and concluded their review of research into the link between hostility, the suspected "pathological core" of TABP, and CHD with this comment: "As with the Type A literature, initially promising results have been followed by mixed findings. It seems highly likely that the main culprit for this state of confusion is the lack of a standardized assessment methodology" (Allan & Scheidt, 1996a, p. 80).

What accounts for this controversy? I agree with Allan and Scheidt (1996a) that the problem lies, at least partly, in the assessment process because researchers have failed to adequately consider unconscious impulse, anxiety, and defense. Specifically, researchers have frequently relied on self-report, objective questionnaires in assessing the relations between psychological factors and CHD, the responses to which are open to biases of unconscious defense and social desirability (which I argue later is a type of defense). Furthermore, however, researchers have largely neglected to use the ideas of unconscious impulse and defense in hypothesizing and conceptualizing results or in connecting findings from seemingly "independent" areas of research. Take for example, the impressive results linking CHD and depression. Depressed people who are otherwise healthy are more likely to develop CHD than healthy, nondepressed people (Anda et al., 1992; Barefoot & Schroll, 1996; Carney, Freedland, Rich, Smith, & Jaffe, 1993). Approximately 20–40% of CHD patients are depressed (Cay, Vetter, Philip, & Dugard, 1972; Lloyd & Cawley, 1978). MI patients who are also diagnosed with major depression are over five times more likely to die in the next 6 months than MI patients who are not depressed (Frasure-Smith, Lesperance, & Talajic, 1993). Even a level of depression that does not warrant clinical diagnosis puts someone with MI at greater risk of death over the next 18 months (Frasure-Smith et al., 1995).

Although Tabrizi, Littman, Williams, and Scheidt (1996) noted that "there is a striking overlap" (p. 399) between patterns of sympathetic and parasympathetic response in depressed people and those in hostile people, they do not mention the theoretical relationship Freud (1917/1957) proposed between hostility and depression nor any empirical research supporting the theoretical connection. In their scientific reappraisal of Freud's theory, Fisher and Greenberg (1996) summarized part of Freud's theory of depression as follows: "The depressed person 'constructs' within the self an internal authority that can incite depression because of its hostile onslaughts against the ego (parts of which are equated with negative aspects of the last object)" (p. 23). This key psychodynamic notion, that anger at another can be unconsciously turned against the self resulting in depression, is the psychoanalytic concept linking the empirical findings relating hostility, depression, and heart disease.

In the remainder of this chapter, I provide further evidence of why I believe psychoanalytic theory to be one of the most useful ways of conceptualizing current data about CHD and of generating new hypotheses. First, I review basic information regarding CHD incidence, prevalence, development, clinical manifestations, and risk factors. I then selectively review the psychoanalytic theory that laid the groundwork for the field prior to Friedman and Rosenman's 1959 study; summarize contemporary research on TABP and CHD, and illustrate how empirical psychoanalytic research can be applied to cardiovascular psychology. These latter findings help provide a theoretical context for cardiovascular psychology, thus allowing a future integration of seemingly disparate results and the generation of new hypotheses and research.

Overview of Coronary Heart Disease

CHD is arguably the epidemic of the century in Western industrialized nations (Zevallos, Chiriboga, & Hebert, 1992). After the end of World War I, the number of CHD deaths rose dramatically in the United States, increasing 23% for middle-aged White men from 1940 to 1950 (Borhani, 1966). CHD has declined approximately 50% since the 1960s. Much of this decline is attributed to a shift in cultural norms in the 1960s marked by President Kennedy's establishing the President's Council on Physical Fitness and the Surgeon General of the United States declaring smoking a health hazard. This normative shift brought about lifestyle changes of increased exercise and smoking cessation related to key CHD risk factors. Despite this decline, CHD remains the leading cause of death in the United States today (American Heart Association, 1997). Currently about 13.5 million people in the United States alone are experiencing CHD, with millions of those seriously disabled.

The four major clinical manifestations of CHD are angina pectoris, MI, sudden cardiac death (SCD), and congestive heart failure. Atherosclerosis, the disease process underlying nearly all CHD, involves the development of atheromatous plaque, a combination of smooth muscle cells, blood platelets, cholesterol, and lipids (fat) in the lining of the coronary arteries (Allan & Scheidt, 1996a). As the plaque grows, the ability of the affected coronary artery to transport blood is progressively limited. If the atherosclerosis progresses to the point that the blood supply needs of the heart muscle (myocardium) itself are not met, chest pain and possible death of myocardial tissue result. If the chest pain occurs without tissue death, the disease is termed angina pectoris. MI is the death of a portion of the heart muscle due to a total blockage of a coronary artery. Congestive heart failure can be brought on by an MI and is diagnosed when the damaged heart is unable to pump sufficient blood to supply the body adequately. This results in fluid buildup throughout the body, most dramatically in the lungs. SCD may be precipitated by an MI that affects the heart's electrical regulatory system resulting in cardiac arrhythmia or ventricular fibrillation (Scheidt, 1996). Abnormal autonomic tone, as seen in reduced heart rate variability, is related to CHD mortality and may be a biological factor precipitating MI. Every year about 1.5 million American men and women experience an MI, with a third dying as a result (American Heart Association, 1997).

Gender (being male), age, and family history of CHD have been identified as "unmodifiable risk factors" for atherosclerosis and CHD (Allan, 1996). However, a number of other empirically demonstrated CHD risk factors (see Allan & Scheidt, 1996a, for review) can potentially be modified. These include diabetes, hypertension, cigarette smoking, obesity, elevated serum cholesterol level, elevated ratio of low density lipoprotein to high density lipoprotein, low social support, psychological stress, sedentary lifestyle, cardiovascular denial (of CHD symptoms), vital exhaustion, job strain, anxiety, TABP including time urgency and free-floating hostility, and depression (Allan, 1996).

Relatively little is known about what connects psychological and behavioral risk factors to CHD. Most prominent among the proposed explanatory models (see Allan & Scheidt, 1996a; and Miller, Smith, Turner, Guijarro, & Hallet, 1993, for a review) is the cardiovascular reactivity hypothesis (see Manuck, 1994, for a review). This suggests that the atherosclerotic process and life-threatening cardiac events such as cardiac spasm or arrhythmias are increased due to altered sympathetic or parasympathetic nervous system activity related to psychological stress. The stress may result from uncontrollable life events or be brought about through a spiraling interaction of characteristic behaviors (e.g., Type A time urgency and hostility, depressive withdrawal) and environmental response (e.g., reduced social support). Another explanatory model involves an indirect exacerbation of traditional CHD-development risk factors by adopting an unhealthy lifestyle. These unhealthy behaviors may be the result of intrapersonal psychological variables; for example, depressed, anxious, or hostile people are more likely to eat a high-fat diet, exercise infrequently, or smoke cigarettes (Leiker & Hailey, 1988). Behavioral factors may also indirectly influence CHD outcome; for example, a prescribed medical regimen is not followed (Lee et al., 1992) or a CHD patient is unaware of physical experience or denies its importance and fails to obtain treatment when necessary. Most likely, components of all these models have validity and it is the goal of cardiovascular psychologists to develop and test theories, methods, and techniques to identify, understand, and modify those CHD risk factors that have a psychosocial and behavioral component.

Psychoanalytic Theory

As mentioned, clinical observations relating CHD, personality, and behavior predated Freud's development of psychoanalytic theory. In 1868, Dusch noted that people who spoke forcefully and were overly involved in their work were prone to coronary disease (also see Rosenman & Chesney, 1980). In 1892, Osler suggested that stress and "the habit of working the machine to its maximum capacity" (cited in Rosenman & Chesney, 1980, p. 3) were responsible for the development of CHD. Osler described the typical CHD patient in his practice as follows:

> It is not the delicate neurotic person who is prone to angina, but the robust, the vigorous in mind and body, and the keen and ambitious man, the indicator of whose engine is always at full speed ahead! (p. 3)

Neither Dusch nor Osler developed psychological theories on what drove CHD patients to behave in these unhealthy ways, on how they developed these "habits," or on whether they were consciously aware of doing so.

At the same time, Freud (1896/1953) was exploring the relationship of the psychological and the physical. Freud rooted psycho-

analytic theory in evolutionary biology. He conceptualized human beings as basically animals propelled by sexual and aggressive drives. To gain the survival and development benefits of group membership, individuals have to compromise their personal drive for instinctual gratification into cooperative actions toward common goals (Freud, 1930/1961). Because parents and other adult models teach societal values, children in their developing years learn to link instinctual energy, emotion, and related behavior to anxiety, which then signals danger if expression were to follow. The knowledge of these links is both conscious and unconscious.

The notion that unconscious events play a central, indeed paramount, role in psychic life is one of two hypotheses distinguishing psychoanalytic theory from other theories of mental functioning—the other being that mental events, experiences, and behavior are not random but determined by a complex interplay of unconscious and conscious forces (Brenner, 1974). Freud's concept of the unconscious refers to an active psychic agency churning with instinct and emotion and engaged in a dynamic interplay with the conscious. He metaphorically described the unconscious as a

> large entrance hall, in which the mental impulses jostle one another like separate individuals. Adjoining this entrance hall is a second, narrower, room—a kind of drawing-room—in which consciousness too resides. But on the threshold between these two rooms a watchman performs his function: he examines the different mental impulses, acts as a censor, and will not admit them into the drawing-room if they displease him. (Freud, 1917/1963, p. 295)

Thus, some excitations experienced as dangerous are kept from conscious awareness through repression, with the person's physiological experience and often outward behavior changing as a result.

Repressed instinctual energy is actively barred from consciousness but seeks and partially finds expression and physical gratification in several ways. Some instinctive energy is allowed limited expression in repetitive behavior patterns called "character traits," which endure into adulthood. Some gains partial expression through physical symptoms, such as elevated heart rate or blood pressure, or psychological symptoms, such as rationalized hostile acting out or depression. Successful development is marked by relatively anxiety-free conscious access to instinctual energy and the ability to obtain impulse gratification in a socially acceptable fashion. Much of Freud's early clinical work was with patients who displayed physical symptomatology that defied explanation by medical science. He went on to assert that for at least some of these patients, the etiology of the disturbance was unconscious, psychological, and not primarily organic (Breuer & Freud, 1893/1955; Freud, 1896/1953). The psychoanalytic theory he developed states that personality, behavior, and some physical symptoms result from the influence of constitution and childhood experience (primarily with caregivers representing society's rules) on the developing body's natural libidinal and aggressive drive energy. These drives give rise to physical experiences and subsequently to actions designed to change these physiological states.

Clearly, Freud's (1974) is a body-based theory; his 23 volumes of psychological writings refer often to skin on skin; the lips, teeth, and tongue sucking and biting breasts for food and comfort; and buttocks and anal regions being cleansed, stroked, tightened, and disciplined in a raging struggle for power and control. He focused on young girls' yearning for their fathers, boys' desiring an older woman also known as mother, both sexes' resting and playing for several years, later both shifting their attention to each other as potential mates, and then boys' engaging in genital stimulation and inserting the penis into the ready vagina to ensure species survival. Curiously, the index to *The Standard Edition of the Complete Psychological Works of Sigmund Freud* (Freud, 1974) lists only two specific references to the heart and those appear in a dream.

Freud's (1927/1961) later words, "the ego is first and foremost a body ego" (p. 31), re-emphasize the inseparable union of mind and body, psychological and physical for the analytic theorist and clinician. The German word translated into the English *ego* can also be translated as "I" or "self." So for Freud, one's primary sense of self is first and foremost linked to one's body and experiences related to one's body. Thus, one's conscious sense of self and related actions are determined by one's body and how one's developing self and body are treated by others, who generate experiences for and respond to one's self. If treated in such a way that one comes to fear a portion of one's own impulses, the experience of that portion of impulse and its associated energy can be blocked from one's consciousness. Blocking these impulses from consciousness leaves an altered sense of self, an altered perception of the world, an altered set of assumptions about how to act physically in the world as one sees it, and an altered physiology and physical experience, based partly on which defense(s) one uses against the impulse (e.g., with physical tension, turning against the self, acting out, projection, rationalization) and partly on altered behavior and consequently an altered response from others.

Some of Freud's followers extended his theory of impulse, defense, and unconscious literally and figuratively into the heart of the mind–body arena. In his classic book, Fenichel (1945) chronicled these clinical observations and theoretical speculations about "somatic changes of a psychogenic nature" under the chapter title "Organ Neuroses." Fenichel (1945) cited the work of Dunbar (1938, 1944) and Weiss (1940, 1943) and stated that

> a chronic irritability of heart and circulatory system is more typically due to unconscious aggressiveness and retaliation fear of aggressiveness. Characteristically, such patients suffer from an inhibited hate toward the parent of the same sex, and simultaneously from a fear of losing his or her love or affection, if this hate were openly expressed. (p. 252)

Citing Alexander (1939a, 1939b) and Hill (1935, 1938) as well, Fenichel continued, saying that "the increase in essential hypertension in modern man is probably connected with the mental situation in individuals who, having learned that aggressiveness is bad, have to live in a world where an enormous amount of aggressiveness is asked for" (p. 254).[2]

In his seminal work linking psychoanalytic theory and somatic disturbances, Alexander (1950) credited Freud with discovering "that when emotion cannot be expressed and relieved through normal channels by voluntary activity it may become the source of chronic psychic and physical disorder" (p. 40). Thus, an emotion when repressed because of psychic conflict and as a result allowed

---

[2]Remember that these words were written during the second of two world wars in a span of 30 years.

little conscious voluntary discharge may fuel physiological symptoms such as the hysterical "conversion symptoms" that Freud recognized. Alexander (1950) differentiated "vegetative organ neuroses" from hysterical conversion symptoms. He explained that hysterical symptoms affect only voluntary muscle and sensory organs and are a symbolic expression and relief of emotional tension.

In contrast, Alexander (1950) defined *vegetative neurosis* as a functional disturbance of visceral organs controlled by the autonomic nervous system. He saw the psychogenic disturbance of a visceral organ as the simple result of the organ's functioning being affected by overly prolonged or intense emotional activation. Like Fenichel (1945), Alexander (1950) stressed the role of aggressive energy in functional cardiovascular disturbances: "Elevation of blood pressure, for example, under the influence of rage does not relieve the rage but is a physiological component of the total phenomenon of rage" (p. 42). Following Cannon (1920), he suggested that the physiological rage reaction is part of the body's natural fight or flight autonomic reaction to a perceived threat to survival. He focused primarily on essential hypertension and said little about CHD itself, except to add that "organic lesions" (Alexander, 1950, p. 143) may develop as a result of "continued functional disturbance" (p. 142) related to "free-floating anxiety and repressed hostile impulses" (p. 143), as is characteristic of "intimidated, inhibited personalities" (p. 143).

Around the same time, numerous other psychiatric clinicians had observed CHD patients as unusually aggressive, hard driving, and ambitious (Dunbar, 1944; Gildea, 1949; Kemple, 1945; K. A. Menninger & Menninger, 1936). However, of the first five retrospective empirical studies of the "CHD personality" (Arlow, 1945; Gertler & White, 1954; Miles, Waldfogel, Barrabee, & Cobb, 1954; Storment, 1951; Weiss, Dlin, Rollin, Fischer, & Bepler, 1957), only Arlow (1945) found reliable differences between CHD patients and controls on these dimensions. Despite this discouraging history, cardiologists Friedman, Rosenman, and Carrol (1958) persevered to find that cyclical periods of work overload for male tax accountants were followed by a rise in serum cholesterol level. Although the experimental design did not allow conclusions regarding causality, this was the first relatively strong empirical evidence providing some construct validity for the notion that excessive work involvement could be implicated in heart disease. As a result, Friedman and Rosenman (1959) began investigating the relationship between behavior patterns and CHD. The initial results were encouraging. When given an earlier version of the VCE, called the Structured Interview (SI), men reporting a pattern of behaviors, including excessive drive, job involvement, competitiveness, hostility, time urgency, and impatience and being observed to exhibit hyperalertness, tense facial musculature, restless motor mannerisms, impatience, and explosive speech characteristics, were more than twice as likely than control participants to have concurrent CHD (Friedman & Rosenman, 1959). Shortly thereafter, they demonstrated the same relationship for women (Rosenman & Friedman, 1961).

Curiously, however, and perhaps as a result of the ascendance of behaviorism to prominence in academic and clinical psychology arenas at that time—as well as his training as a cardiologist rather than psychoanalytic psychiatrist—Friedman did not relate his 1958 findings to the psychoanalytic theory supporting the prior related research cited earlier. Instead, Friedman, Rosenman, and Byers (1964) coined the term Type A behavior pattern to describe the behaviors they found to be characteristic of individuals prone to CHD. TABP heavily emphasizes observable behavior and "environmental challenge," specifically differentiates the TABP from a "complex," and does not explicitly mention unconscious processes. This launched 40 years of research involving hundreds of studies emphasizing observable behavior and self-report factors related to CHD.

Almost all of this research was in complete isolation from psychoanalytic theory until 1984, when Friedman and Ulmer attempted a basic psychodynamic explanation of TABP. They proposed that insufficient self-esteem drives the person exhibiting TABP to compensate with an intense emphasis on achievement; they hypothesized that time urgency is a frantic attempt to bolster accomplishment-based self-esteem in people who received approval from their parents primarily following a significant accomplishment. Type A hostility is the adult perpetuation of the child's angry protest over insufficient love and affection (Blatt, D'Afflitti, & Quinlan, 1976), whereas the concept *inadequate self-esteem* is analogous to the notion of introjective depression (Blatt et al., 1976).

Whereas anaclitic depression is "characterized by feelings of helplessness and weakness, by fears of being abandoned, and by wishes to be cared for, loved, and protected" (Blatt et al., 1976, p. 383), introjective depression is "characterized by intense feelings of inferiority, guilt, and worthlessness and by a sense that one has failed to live up to expectations and standards" (p. 384). These latter are analogous to obsessive characteristics (see Exhibit 2.1 for a comparison of Type A and obsessive characteristics). Van Heijningen and Treurniet (1966) suggested that the obsessive characteristics of CHD patients served the defensive purpose of keeping oral-dependent longings for passive gratification out of awareness. Whereas Friedman and Ulmer (1984) similarly recognized the defensive nature of TABP, this possibility has rarely been examined in the TABP literature.

Type A Behavior Pattern

> Type A behavior pattern is an action–emotion complex that can be observed in any person who is aggressively involved in a chronic, incessant struggle to achieve more and more in less and less time, and, if required to do so, against the opposing efforts of other things or other persons. It is not psychosis or a complex of worries or fears or phobias or obsessions, but a socially acceptable—indeed often praised—form of conflict. Persons possessing this pattern also are quite prone to exhibit a free-floating but extraordinarily well-rationalized hostility. For Type A behavior pattern to explode into being, the environmental challenge must always serve as the fuse for this explosion. (Friedman & Rosenman, 1974, p. 67)

Friedman and Rosenman's (1959) initial work in this area generated numerous studies in which researchers examined the relationship of this TABP action–emotion complex and CHD. In the Western Collaborative Group Study (WCGS; Rosenman et al., 1975), 3,524 men, age 39–59, mostly White middle managers, were classified as either Type A, B, or X (indeterminate) by way of the SI, which was specifically designed to elicit impatient, hostile behavior and related psychomotor manifestations of TABP. They

Exhibit 2.1

A Comparison of Character Descriptions and Traits

Obsessive

1. "Overconcern with time" (Dooley, 1941, p. 21)
2. "Exceedingly systematic, methodical, and thorough" (Sandler & Hazari, 1960, p. 115)
3. "Obstinacy, defiance, irascibility, vindictiveness" (Freud, 1908/1948, p. 169)
4. "Annoyed by interruptions" (Gottheil, 1965, p. 156)
5. "Excessive devotion to duty" (W. C. Menninger, 1943, p. 189)
6. "Power of self-control" (W. C. Menninger, 1943, p. 189)
7. "Intense application" (Brooks, 1969, p. 398)
8. "Restriction of attention" (Shapiro, 1965, p. 25)
9. "Desire to domineer" (Beloff, 1957, p. 158)
10. "The emphasis on production, the value of time, the importance of material possessions, the striving for wealth and its implied power are all paramount goals" (W. C. Menninger, 1943, p. 161)

Type A

1. "A chronic sense of time and urgency" (Rosenman & Chesney, 1980, p. 5)
2. "Orderly and well-planned" (Barry, 1967, p. 848)
3. "Hostility" (Rosenman, 1978, p. 55)
4. "Irritated when his activities are slowed down" (Glass et al., 1974, p. 135)
5. "Deeply committed to their vocation" (Rosenman & Chesney, 1980, p. 5)
6. "Self-controlled" (Russek, 1967, p. 1)
7. "Worked . . . at near maximum capacity" (Burnam et al., 1975, p. 76)
8. "Hyperalert" (focused in their attention; Matthews & Brunson, 1979, p. 2081)
9. "Engaged in a struggle for control" (Glass, 1977, p. 181)
10. "Individuals . . . engaged in a relatively chronic struggle to obtain an unlimited number of poorly defined things from their environment in the shortest period of time, and, if necessary, against the opposing effects of other things or persons" (Friedman, 1969, p. 84)

were thoroughly screened for heart disease and followed prospectively for $8^1/_2$ years. The researchers found that SI-determined TABP predicted CHD that was independent of all other risk factors. Specifically, men exhibiting Type A behavior were about twice as likely to develop CHD as those exhibiting Type B behavior. These findings generated considerable excitement in the CHD research community.

To facilitate TABP research by reducing the amount of time an expert needs to classify participants as Type A, Jenkins, Rosenman, and Friedman (1967) developed a TABP self-report questionnaire, the Jenkins Activity Survey (JAS). This questionnaire quickly became very popular and was widely used in TABP research. Other questionnaires were developed as well, for example, the Framingham Type A Scale (Haynes, Levine, Scotch, Feinleib, & Kannel, 1978). In the subsequent Framingham Heart Study (Haynes & Feinleib, 1982; Haynes, Feinleib, & Kannel, 1980), 725 men and 949 women, age 45–77, were classified according to TABP criteria using a 10-item self-report, objective questionnaire on time urgency and competitiveness, were screened for CHD, and were followed prospectively. Other researchers have demonstrated a positive relationship between the questionnaire scores and CHD (including MI, SCD, and angina pectoris) for both men and women. More recent results (Eaker, Abbott, & Kannel, 1989) demonstrate a positive relationship only between the self-reported TABP and angina pectoris.

In other studies published around the same time, researchers however had failed to demonstrate positive relationships among TABP, the predicted characteristic behavior, and various indices of CHD (e.g., Case, Heller, Case, & Moss, 1985; Ragland & Brand, 1988a, 1988b; Ruberman, Weinblatt, Goldberg, & Chaudhary, 1984; Shekelle et al., 1985; also see Allan & Scheidt, 1996a; and Friedman et al., 1996, for a review). Researchers began to question the reliability and validity of the overall TABP, including the three central components of hostility, competitive achievement striving, and time urgency (Rosenman, Swan, & Carmelli, 1988) for predicting CHD. Booth-Kewley and Friedman (1987) conducted a meta-analysis of 87 studies examining the relations between psychological factors and CHD, including 55 TABP studies almost equally divided between those using the SI and those using the JAS (Jenkins, Zyzanski, & Rosenman, 1971), the most popular objective questionnaire method to assess TABP. A central conclusion was that the overall TABP is a risk factor for CHD of roughly the same magnitude as other CHD risk factors, specifically that the TABP anger and hostility component predicts CHD. A second was that the SI is clearly superior to the JAS questionnaire assessment in predicting CHD, and "the Structured Interview and the Jenkins Activity Survey classify individuals on different aspects of Type A behavior and that it is those aspects tapped by the SI that are most predictive of cardiovascular disease" (Booth-Kewley & Friedman, 1987, p. 355).

Hostility: Does the Hating Mind Kill the Heart?

Many researchers have focused on hostility as a key dimension in the development of CHD. Matthews, Glass, Rosenman, and Bortner's (1977) reanalysis of data from WCGS suggests that hostility (as rated from the SI) may indeed have been the primary factor causing the observed CHD–TABP link. Following Booth-Kewley and Friedman's (1987) meta-analysis, considerable subsequent research with other samples also supports this finding of a hostility–CHD connection (see Helmers, Posluszny, & Krantz, 1994; and Smith, 1992, for reviews).

In numerous hostility and CHD studies, researchers have used self-report hostility measures, frequently the Cook–Medley Hostility Scale (Cook & Medley, 1954). One was a 25-year follow-up study of 255 physicians (Barefoot, Dahlstrom, & Williams, 1983) in which the researchers found high Cook–Medley Hostility scores predicted subsequent CHD. When Barefoot et al. included all causes of death, they found the dramatic result that five to seven times more physicians who reported conscious suspicion of others while in their 20s died before age 50 compared with those who were not as mistrusting in their youth. However, although in the majority of studies using the Cook–Medley and other self-report hostility measures, researchers have found a positive relationship between hostility and CHD, once again as with the TABP research, results were inconsistent. This left researchers wondering what unknown factors accounted for the discrepancies (see Siegman, 1994a, 1994b).

In response, Miller et al. (1993) conducted a meta-analysis of research on hostility and physical health, with a specific focus on CHD and SI versus self-report methods of assessing hostility, such as the Cook–Medley Hostility Scale. Their results parallel and reinforce Friedman and Ghandour's (1993) findings, reviewed earlier. Specifically, their meta-analysis reveals that SI assessment of hostility was predictive of CHD, independent of other CHD risk factors (weighted mean r = .18), and that the Cook–Medley Hostility Scale (and similar self-report hostility measures) predicted CHD with less accuracy (weighted mean r = .08).

Empirical Psychoanalytic Research

In summarizing the findings of their meta-analysis of psychological factors predicting CHD, Booth-Kewley and Friedman (1987) stated "information about the interrelationship of personality predictors of CHD is sorely needed" (p. 343). As mentioned earlier, psychoanalytic theory and research provide the information and conceptual frame necessary to advance the field beyond its current boundaries. In the past decade or so, a virtual revolution has occurred regarding unconscious processes, an area of psychology formerly frequently filled with acrimonious debate and controversy. As convincing experimental evidence has mounted, the existence of unconscious processes has not only been acknowledged but also integrated into the leading-edge theories and empirical work of researchers from across previously divided ideological camps. In their book on this topic, Bornstein and Masling (1998) suggested that "the study of the unconscious has the potential to become a unifying force in psychology, linking cognition and emotion, infancy and old age, normal and pathological development, brain and psyche" (p. xxi). I would add mind and body to the list and, in the case at hand, unconscious mind and the cardiovascular system.

In a review of experimental evidence about unconscious processes, Westen (1998) pointed out that conclusive evidence is now present, not only for a general unconscious but for the operation of unconscious processes in many areas of psychological functioning: perception, cognition, affect, emotion, motivation, and defense. In addition, Westen (1998) neatly delineated a basic psychoanalytic hypothesis regarding psychosomatic disease: "Blocking conscious emotional experience also carries a cost, because people who chronically keep themselves unaware of their feelings are more likely to suffer physical disorders such as heart disease" (p. 29). Bornstein and Masling (1998) pointed out that this transformation from debate about the existence of unconscious processes to an integration of the concept and related data has been so complete that articles questioning the existence of such processes disappeared from the literature in the 10-year period prior to the publication of their book.

Articles now demonstrate the influence of unconscious processes, not only in the areas mentioned earlier but also in the development and outcome of physical disease. The basic psychoanalytic premise that unconscious defense against anxiety-arousing, unconscious impulse exacts a physiological toll on the cardiovascular system leads to a number of testable hypotheses. They include that (a) some defended people would be unaware of their defensive processes but exhibit predictable differences on measures of defensiveness from those who are less defended, (b) there would be functional cardiovascular differences between those who are more defended and less defended, (c) cardiovascular differences would be reduced with the reduction of defense and vice versa, (d) greater incidence and prevalence of CHD would be found in characterologically more-defended people than less-defended people, (e) a reduction in symptoms of CHD would be found in people who undergo psychotherapy that reduces defense, and (f) different defenses lead to different cardiovascular states and to different disease outcomes within a single CHD category (e.g., MI, SCD, angina).

I now examine some representative studies. Shedler, Mayman, and Manis (1993) published a landmark article in this area with results bearing on the first three hypotheses. In addition, their article has specific relevance to the discrepancy between the results of TABP and hostility–CHD studies using objective, self-report measures and those using indirect measures such as SI, VCE, or projectives that assess unacknowledged and unconscious factors.

Shedler et al. (1993) first tested the idea that a portion of the people who score in the psychologically healthy range on objective, self-report measures are actually psychologically distressed but are unaware of their distress because of unconscious defense; that is, they have the "illusion of mental health created by psychological defenses" (p. 1117). Second, they asked if psychological defense has physiological consequences in the cardiovascular system. Their participants completed the Eysenck Neuroticism Scale (Eysenck & Eysenck, 1975), an objective, self-report measure of psychological health or distress. They also completed the Early Memory Test (Mayman, 1968), a projective measure of psychological health or distress scored by clinical judges.

Shedler et al. (1993) defined three subgroups of interest for comparison. The first subgroup consisted of people who were "genuinely psychologically healthy"; that is, both their self-report and clinician's judgment of the projective Early Memory Test indicated health. The second was composed of participants demonstrating "illusory mental health"; that is, their self-report indicated health, but clinician scoring of the Early Memory Test indicated psychological disturbance. The third consisted of those who were "manifestly distressed"; that is, both the self-report Eysenck Neuroticism Scale and projective Early Memory Test indicated distress. (A fourth subgroup, distressed on self-report but judged healthy on the Early Memory Test, contained too few participants [3] to allow meaningful analysis.)

Results show that of those participants who reported distress, most (11 out of 14) were also rated as distressed by the clinician. However, of those participants who self-reported psychological health, more than half were judged distressed and categorized as having illusory mental health. Once categorized, participants were put through a series of psychologically stressful tasks while their heart rate (HR) and blood pressure were automatically monitored. The dependent measure was an index of cardiovascular reactivity termed the "rate–pressure product" (RPP). RPP is defined as HR $\times$ systolic blood pressure (SBP)/100. While HR and SBP were monitored, participants rested during baseline physiological measurement periods and then performed three separate psychologically stressful tasks: (1) mental arithmetic with demands for good, quick performance; (2) production of Thematic Apperception Test stories

(Murray, 1943); and (3) phrase association to neutral phrases and phrases with aggressive, dependent, and sexual themes. Changes in the RPP from baseline to that obtained during these tasks were compared across the three subgroups.

As predicted, results show that participants in the illusory mental health category, that is, those who manifested the most psychological defensiveness, had significantly greater coronary reactivity when compared with manifestly distressed participants and with the participants reporting and judged to be mentally healthy—who showed the least changed in RPP overall. Shedler et al. (1993) pointed out that the increases in RPP shown by the illusory mental health participants were large enough to be medically significant. In addition, they found that for participants who were judged on the projective Early Memory Test as distressed, the less they self-reported distress on the Eysenck scale, the greater their physiological reactivity. That is, the more defended the participants were regarding their physiological distress, the greater their coronary reactivity. As Shedler et al. (1993) concluded, "the findings suggest that mental health scales may be measuring different things in different people. For some they may be assessing mental health, but for a sizeable group of others, they may instead be assessing degree of psychological defense" (p. 1123).

Weinberger, Schwartz, and Davidson (1979) explored the impact of repression on autonomic nervous system activity as indexed by HR, galvanic skin response, and electromyogram score. Participants completed the Bendig (1962) Manifest Anxiety Scale and the Marlowe–Crowne Social Desirability Scale (Crowne & Marlowe, 1964). Participants were categorized as "high anxious" when they acknowledged high anxiety on the Manifest Anxiety Scale and scoring low on the Social Desirability Scale, as "low anxious" when scoring low on both the Manifest Anxiety Scale and Social Desirability Scale, and as "repressors" when scoring low on the Manifest Anxiety Scale but high on the Social Desirability Scale. Participants completed a stressor task involving sentence completions to stems with neutral, aggressive, and sexual themes, while their physiological responses were automatically monitored. Galvanic skin response and electromyogram scores were most elevated for repressors, whereas HR was significantly greater for repressor participants than nonanxious participants.

Building on Kniep et al.'s (1993) work, Ketterer and his colleagues (Ketterer et al., 1996, 1998) examined CHD patients and controls to explore the link between (a) denial of depression and severity of angiographically documented CHD and (b) denial of emotional distress and subsequent "cardiac events (deaths, new MI's, and/or revascularization)" (Ketterer et al., 1998, p. 241). In the first study to operationalize denial, Ketterer et al. (1996) asked patients to rate themselves on the Ketterer Stress Symptom Frequency Checklist. They also had each patient ask a significant other—close friend or family member—to rate the patient as well. Significant other minus self-rating yielded the index of denial. The Ketterer Stress Symptom Frequency Checklist assesses three dimensions of experience in subscales: (a) conscious experiences of aggravation, irritation, anger, and impatience; (b) depression; and (c) anxiety/worry. In addition, the participants completed the Framingham Type A Scale, the Cook–Medley Hostility Scale, and SI. In the first study, multiple regression analyses show that none of the psychosocial variables except denial of depression and frequency of unprovoked nocturnal awakening predicted CHD severity. (The data on nocturnal awakening were collected as a correlate of depression with which there was no emotional or social desirability valence.)

In the second study, Ketterer et al. (1998) followed the CHD patients an average of 59.7 months after they completed the initial assessment. Multiple regression analyses again show that none of the psychosocial variables significantly predicted later negative cardiac events (deaths, subsequent MIs, and revascularization), except denial of aggravation, irritation, anger, and impatience. Hours of exercise per week and frequency of unprovoked nocturnal awakenings also significantly predicted negative CHD events. It is interesting that these two studies' results (Ketterer et al., 1996, 1998) do not support those of numerous other studies and meta-analyses of psychosocial factors and CHD. Many explanations are possible: sampling differences, failure to use a large enough sample to detect relatively small effects, prediction to different heart disease endpoints, interviewer unreliability in using SI to create valid Type A and Type B groups, selective participant dropout over the course of the longitudinal study, just to name a few. Furthermore, it is interesting that in the first study, denial of depression predicted CHD, whereas denial of anger predicted CHD in the second. But what is most interesting is that defense against emotional experience is powerfully predictive of CHD and, as in Shedler et al.'s (1993) report, more powerful than other widely used measures typically seen as accurate assessments for aspects of psychological process central to physical health.

Another study (Forrest & Hokanson, 1975) testing the anger-in depression hypotheses demonstrates the potential value of psychoanalytic theory for CHD, TABP, hostility and depression research to discover the mechanism(s) responsible for the CHD and impulse–defense connection. This study's college student participants were split into depressed and not depressed groups on the basis of the Beck (1967) Depression Inventory and Minnesota Multiphasic Personality Inventory Depression scale scores (Dahlstrom & Welsh, 1960). In addition, the participants' level of autonomic nervous system arousal was indirectly monitored using a plethysmograph to record vasodilation and constriction. In this complex experiment, participants interacted with a confederate who chose from giving the participant a painful electric shock, rewarding the participant, or apparently self-administering a shock. The participant then had to choose a response from the same three options.

Results show that depressed participants shocked themselves significantly more often than nondepressed participants after they had been shocked by the confederate. Furthermore, the vasodilation and constriction pattern in response to self-shock or shocking the confederate was different for depressed and nondepressed participants. Depressed participants showed a greater drop in autonomic nervous system arousal after shocking themselves, whereas nondepressed participants showed the greater drop in autonomic arousal after they had administered a shock. This finding is especially compelling because one of the leading explanations for the link between depression and CHD is altered autonomic tone, which is seen, in decreased HR variability, as related to increased CHD mortality (Carney et al., 1995). Thus, this study demonstrates that not only do depressed people use the defense of turning anger against themselves in the context of experiencing a stressful event with no social support but also the defense itself results in changes in autonomic tone, which, speculatively, could be related to the development and outcome of CHD. It is intriguing to speculate what possible effect taking unconscious defense and social desirability into consideration would have on these results. Research in this area may be especially fruitful.

A Psychodynamic Context

It seems highly likely that similar defensive processes, as seen in the studies cited, may be operating in responses to self-report measures of TABP, time urgency, competitiveness, and free-floating hostility, such as JAS or the Framingham Type A Scale, as well as on self-report measures of hostility, such as the Cook–Medley Hostility Scale and Buss–Durkee Hostility Inventory, or of depression, such as the Beck Depression Inventory. Indeed, it also seems very probable that the same processes operate in the self-report portion of the TABP SI and VCE. The clinician's judgment involved in the SI and VCE interviews and the significant other minus self-rating methodology (Ketterer et al., 1996, 1998; Kneip et al., 1993) overrides these defensive processes, thus allowing for greater validity in predicting the presence or absence of CHD.

These findings make sense from a psychoanalytic viewpoint of unconscious impulse, defense, and altered conscious awareness. If the psychologically coronary-prone person's unhealthy behavior is part of, and also partly a result of, the defensive processes that keep unconscious impulse and related emotional states out of awareness and if the defensive process is itself unconscious, then such coronary-prone people would not be aware of the totality of their CHD-promoting behavior nor of their unconscious impulses and emotions beneath. For example, psychoanalytic theory predicts a difference between clinician-observed TABP and self-reported TABP because the defenses keep the person from being aware and able to report it. Even if people who exhibit Type A behavior are simply attempting to produce "socially desirable" responses, I would argue that this too is an example of defense because it is a failure to take one's specific environmental context accurately into account.

Psychoanalytic theory defines the ego's defensive function as mediating between the impulse–gratification demands of the id and the requirements of the environment. In the context of a cardiovascular psychology experiment in which participants are guaranteed protection from social censure by confidentiality and in which the goal of advancing science requires accurate information about participants, if a participant consciously or unconsciously chooses to bias self-report toward what is viewed as socially desirable outside of the experimental context, then the choice probably results from a distortion of perception brought about by defense. For example, a participant not accurately reporting because of a distrust of the experimenter regarding confidentiality would indicate the kind of pervasive distrust and cynicism apparently tapped by the Cook–Medley Hostility Scale and taken as an indicator of a defensively skewed perceptual–cognitive style, similar to paranoid thinking. Given the U.S. work ethic culture with its high value on quick, efficient production, it is no surprise that the TABP is, as Friedman and Rosenman (1974) suggested, "a socially acceptable—indeed often praised—form of conflict" (p. 67). However, from a psychoanalytic viewpoint, although the Type A time-urgent, hostile behavior may be socially desirable, it is not necessarily evidence of successful sublimation of aggressive energy. Instead, it may be syntonic with a culturewide defense while still exacting a physiological toll.

What defenses might play a part in the psychosocial factors–CHD link? Here the broader framework of psychoanalytic theory, not just the notion of unconscious defense, may be useful. For example, the constellation of defensive character traits and behaviors defined as part of the TABP is strikingly similar to the obsessive (anal) character (see Exhibit 2.1). Although there is little empirical evidence supporting the hypotheses of human developmental progression through Freud's (1920/1956) psychosexual oral, anal, Oedipal, latency, and genital stages, there is considerable empirical support for the clustering of character traits and behaviors consistent with Freud's notion of dependent (oral) and obsessive (anal) characters (see Fisher & Greenberg, 1996, for a review of these empirical studies). Here again the vast body of psychoanalytic literature is useful. As seen in Exhibit 2.1, a central interpersonal conflict for people who are obsessive (as well as those who exhibit Type A behavior) is often said to be around issues of power, control, dominance, and submission to authority, with the intrapersonal issue of underlying aggressive impulses defended against by obsessive defenses, such as ruminating, intellectualizing, and rationalizing. People who are obsessive are said to be especially concerned with time, dirt, and money. Time urgency issues are conceptualized as a defense against unconscious aggressive impulses. Viewing the time-urgency of people who exhibit Type A behavior in this way with Friedman and Rosenman's (1974) psychodynamic TABP exploration and the Shedler et al. (1993) results in mind makes it possible to hypothesize about the "interrelationships of personality predictors of CHD" (Booth-Kewley & Friedman, 1987, p. 343).

Psychoanalytic theory has an additional strength and potential integrative advantage here as well in that it posits a developmental hierarchy of defense. This may help clinicians and researchers understand why behavioral expression of anger (e.g., assessed in SI or as seen by friends and family of Ketterer's deniers of hostility) is associated with increases in HR and blood pressure, whereas fully consciously experiencing anger without being defensively compelled to act on it is not (Siegman, 1994a). Freud (1930/1961) did not view pure discharge of aggressive energy without regard to environmental context as psychologically healthy. This is a popular misconception. Indeed, psychoanalytic theory defines indiscriminately acting on impulses as the defense of acting out, that is, acting on impulse out of context. The mark of psychological health and maturity is to be able to fully, consciously experience the impulse and have a choice to act in an appropriate fashion, taking the environment and goal into account, that is, sublimating the aggressive energy. In this theoretical frame, the repetitive, compulsively hostile behavior linked to CHD is seen as the defensive behavior of outrage rather than the healthy experience of aggressive energy that can potentially be used to reach an appropriate goal (see Agazarian, 1997, for a compelling integration of psychodynamic and systems theories that reinvigorates the concept of psychic energy and presents a related therapeutic strategy).

In fact, the hostile action may shortcircuit the aggressive energy before a full consciousness of it is attained and the discharge is then rationalized. Furthermore, the obsessive tendency to perceive the actions of others with a cynical, suspicious bias can also be seen as a characterological manifestation of defense against aggressive energy, one that predisposes the cynic to a repetitive cycle of hostile exchanges with others in the environment (often with fellow cynics similarly primed for discharge).

From an evolutionary biological perspective, this makes sense as well. Having full access to one's aggressive energy with a choice about whether to act or not certainly would have been advantageous for human beings' ancestors in actually dangerous flight or fight situations. In this sense, I do not believe the currently popular view that CHD results simply from a too frequent activation of the cardiovascular system, similar to that proposed by Cannon (1920) in his fight or flight scenario, is correct. The psychological–behavioral contribution to CHD seems to result from, among other factors (Miller et al., 1993), the defensive misperception of danger along with a defense-induced alteration of the cardiovascular system.

Faced with a hungry saber-toothed tiger, the Neanderthal in a blind, emotionally unintelligent (i.e., defensive) rage reaction would be at a life-threatening disadvantage to the Neanderthal in a consciously aggressive stance with all aggressive energy available and none being wasted in defensive processes, such as becoming depressed, acting out aimlessly, hurrying to finish his or her work, loudly outraging to his or her fellow Neanderthals about the injustice of the threat, or otherwise ruminating and intellectualizing while precious seconds slipped away. Attacking one's self-worth, killing oneself, having a temper tantrum, lecturing the tiger, or obsessing about the options endlessly would not be as effective in keeping one's genes available for future dissemination as would thrusting a sharp spear smoothly, skillfully, and forcefully into the advancing predator's heart.

References

Agazarian, Y. (1997). *Systems-centered therapy for groups.* New York: Guilford Press.

Alexander, F. (1939a). Emotional factors in essential hypertension. *Psychosomatic Medicine, 1,* 173–179.

Alexander, F. (1939b). Psychoanalytic study of a case of essential hypertension. *Psychosomatic Medicine, 1,* 139–152.

Alexander, F. (1950). *Psychosomatic medicine: Its principles and applications.* New York: Norton.

Allan, R. (1996). Introduction: The emergence of cardiac psychology. In R. Allan & S. Scheidt (Eds.), *Heart & mind: The practice of cardiac psychology* (pp. 3–13). Washington, DC: American Psychological Association.

Allan, R., & Scheidt, S. (1996a). Empirical basis for cardiac psychology. In R. Allan & S. Scheidt (Eds.), *Heart & mind: The practice of cardiac psychology* (pp. 63–123). Washington, DC: American Psychological Association.

Allan, R., & Scheidt, S. (Eds.). (1996b). *Heart & mind: The practice of cardiac psychology*. Washington, DC: American Psychological Association.

Allan, R., & Scheidt, S. (1998). Group psychotherapy for patients with coronary heart disease. *International Journal of Group Psychotherapy, 48,* 187–214.

American Heart Association. (1997). *Heart and stroke facts: 1996 statistical supplement*. Dallas, TX: Author.

Anda, R., Williamson, D., James, D., Macera, C., Eaker, E., Glassman, A., & Marks, J. (1992). Depressed affect, hopelessness, and the risk of ischemic heart disease in a cohort of U.S. adults. *Epidemiology, 4,* 285–294.

Arlow, J. A. (1945). Identification mechanisms in coronary occlusion. *Psychosomatic Medicine, 7,* 195–209.

Barefoot, J. C., Dahlstrom, W. G., & Williams, R. B. (1983). Hostility, CHD incidence and total mortality: A 25-year follow-up study of 255 physicians. *Psychosomatic Medicine, 45,* 59–63.

Barefoot, J. C., & Schroll, M. (1996). Symptoms of depression, acute myocardial infarction, and total mortality in a community sample. *Circulation, 93,* 1976–1980.

Barry, A. J. (1967). Physical activity and psychic stress/strain. *Canadian Medical Association Journal, 96,* 848–885.

Beck, A. (1967). *Depression: Clinical, experimental, and theoretical aspects.* New York: Harper & Row.

Beloff, H. (1957). The structure and origin of the anal character. *Genetic Psychology Monograph, 55,* 141–172.

Bendig, A. W. (1962). The development of a short form of the Manifest Anxiety Scale. *Journal of Consulting Psychology, 20,* 384.

Blatt, S. J., D'Afflitti, P., & Quinlan, D. M. (1976). Experiences of depression in normal young adults. *Journal of Abnormal Psychology, 85,* 383–389.

Booth-Kewley, S., & Friedman, H. S. (1987). Psychological predictors of heart disease: A quantitative review. *Psychological Bulletin, 101,* 343–362.

Borhani, N. O. (1966). Magnitude of the problem of the cardiovascular–renal disease. In A. M. Lilienfeld & A. J. Gifford (Eds.), *Chronic disease and public health* (pp. 492–526). Baltimore: Johns Hopkins Press.

Bornstein, R. F., & Masling, J. M. (1988). Introduction: The psychoanalytic unconscious. In R. F. Bornstein & J. M. Masling (Eds.), *Empirical per-*

spectives on the psychoanalytic unconscious (pp. xiii–xxviii). Washington, DC: American Psychological Association.

Brenner, C. (1974). *An elementary textbook of psychoanalysis*. New York: Anchor/Doubleday.

Breuer, J., & Freud, S. (1955). Studies on hysteria. In J. Strachey, A. Freud, A. Strachey, & A. Tyson (Eds. & Trans.), *The standard edition of the complete psychological works of Sigmund Freud* (Vol. 2). London: Hogarth Press. (Original work published 1893)

Brooks, J. (1969). The insecure personality: A factor analytic study. *British Journal of Medical Psychology, 42*, 395–403.

Burnam, M. A., Pennebaker, J. W., & Glass, D. C. (1975). Time consciousness, achievement striving, and the Type A coronary-prone behavior pattern. *Journal of Abnormal Psychology, 84*, 76–79.

Cannon, W. B. (1920). *Bodily changes in pain, hunger, fear and rage* (2nd ed.). New York: Appleton.

Carney, R. M., Freedland, R. E., Rich, M. W., Smith, L. J., & Jaffe, A. S. (1993). Ventricular tachycardia and psychiatric depression in patients with coronary artery disease. *American Journal of Medicine, 95*, 23–28.

Carney, R. M., Saunders, R. D., Freedland, K. E., Stein, P., Rich, M. W., & Jaffe, A. S. (1995). Association of depression with reduced heart rate variability in coronary artery disease. *American Journal of Cardiology, 76*, 562–564.

Case, R. B., Heller, S. S., Case, N. B., & Moss, A. J. (1985). Type A behavior and survival after acute myocardial infarction. *New England Journal of Medicine, 313*, 737–741.

Cay, E. L., Vetter, N., Philip, A. E., & Dugard, P. (1972). Psychological status during recovery from an acute heart attack. *Journal of Psychosomatic Research, 16*, 425–435.

Cook, W. W., & Medley, D. M. (1954). Proposed Hostility and Pharisaic–Virtue Scales for the MMPI. *Journal of Applied Psychology, 38*, 414–418.

Crowne, D. P., & Marlowe, D. (1964). *The approval motive: Studies in evaluative dependence*. New York: Wiley.

Dahlstrom, W. G., & Welsh, G. S. (1960). *An MMPI handbook: A guide to use in clinical practice and research*. Minneapolis: University of Minnesota Press.

Dooley, L. (1941). The concept of time in defence of ego integrity. *Psychiatry, 4*, 13–23.

Dunbar, F. (1938). *Emotions and bodily changes*. New York: Columbia University Press.

Dunbar, F. (1944). *Psychosomatic diagnosis*. New York: Hoeber.

Dusch, T. von (1868). *Lehrbuch der herzkrankheiten* [Textbook of heart diseases]. Leipzig, Germany: Verlag Von Wilhelm Engelman.

Eaker, E. D., Abbott, R. D., & Kannel, W. B. (1989). Frequency of uncomplicated angina pectoris in Type A compared with Type B persons (the Framingham Study). *American Journal of Cardiology, 63*, 1042–1045.

Eysenck, H. J., & Eysenck, S. B. G. (1975). *Eysenck Personality Questionnaire manual*. San Diego: Educational & Industrial Testing Service.

Fenichel, O. (1945). *The psychoanalytic theory of neurosis*. New York: Norton.

Fisher, S., & Greenberg, R. P. (1996). *Freud scientifically reappraised*. New York: Wiley.

Forrest, M. S., & Hokanson, J. E. (1975). Depression and autonomic arousal reduction accompanying self-punitive behavior. *Journal of Abnormal Psychology, 84*, 346–357.

Frasure-Smith, N., Lesperance, F., & Talajic, M. (1993). Depression following myocardial infarction: Impact on 6-month survival. *Journal of the American Medical Association, 270*, 1819–1825.

Freud, S. (1948). Character and anal erotism. In J. Strachey (Ed. & Trans.), *The standard edition of the complete psychological works of Sigmund Freud* (Vol. 9, pp. 169–180). London: Hogarth Press. (Original work published 1908)

Freud, S. (1953). The aetiology of hysteria. In J. Strachey (Ed. & Trans.), *The standard edition of the complete psychological works of Sigmund Freud* (Vol. 3, pp. 187–221). London: Hogarth Press. (Original work published 1896)

Freud, S. (1957). Mourning and melancholia. In J. Strachey (Ed. & Trans.), *The standard edition of the complete psychological works of Sigmund Freud* (Vol. 14, pp. 243–258). London: Hogarth Press. (Original work published 1917)

Freud, S. (1961). The future of an illusion. In J. Strachey (Ed. & Trans.), *The standard edition of the complete psychological works of Sigmund Freud* (Vol. 21, pp. 3–56). London: Hogarth Press. (Original work published 1927)

Freud, S. (1961). Civilization and its discontents. In J. Strachey (Ed. & Trans.), *The standard edition of the complete psychological works of Sigmund Freud* (Vol. 21, pp. 21–134). London: Hogarth Press. (Original work published 1930)

Freud, S. (1963). Introductory lectures on psychoanalysis. Part 3. General theory of the neuroses. Lecture 19. Resistence and repression. In J. Strachey (Ed. & Trans.), *The standard edition of the complete psychological works of Sigmund Freud* (Vol. 16, pp. 286–302). London: Hogarth Press. (Original work published 1917)

Freud, S. (1974). Indexes and bibliographies. In J. Strachey (Ed. & Trans.), *The standard edition of the complete psychological works of Sigmund Freud* (Vol. 24). London: Hogarth Press.

Friedman, M. (1969). *Pathogenesis of coronary artery disease*. New York: McGraw-Hill.

Friedman, M., Fleischmann, N., & Price, V. A. (1996). Diagnosis of Type A behavior pattern. In R. Allan & S. Scheidt (Eds.), *Heart & mind: The practice of cardiac psychology* (pp. 179–195). Washington, DC: American Psychological Association.

Friedman, M., & Ghandour, G. (1993). Medical diagnosis of Type A behavior. *American Heart Journal, 126*, 607–618.

Friedman, M., & Rosenman, R. H. (1959). Association of specific overt behavior pattern with blood and cardiovascular findings. *Journal of the American Medical Association, 169*, 1284–1296.

Friedman, M., & Rosenman, R. H. (1974). *Type A behavior and your heart.* New York: Knopf.

Friedman, M., Rosenman, R. H., & Byers, S. O. (1964). Serum lipids and conjunctival circulation after fat ingestion in men exhibiting Type A behavior pattern. *Circulation, 29*, 874–886.

Friedman, M., Rosenman, R. H., & Carrol, V. (1958). Changes in the serum cholesterol and blood clotting time in men subjected to cyclic variation of occupational stress. *Circulation, 17*, 852–860.

Friedman, M., & Ulmer, D. (1984). *Treating Type A behavior and your heart.* New York: Knopf.

Gertler, M. M., & White, P. D. (1954). *Coronary heart disease in young adults.* Cambridge, MA: Harvard University Press.

Gildea, F. (1949). Special features of personality which are common to certain psychosomatic disorders. *Psychosomatic Medicine, 11*, 273–277.

Glass, D. C. (1977). Stress, behavior patterns, and coronary disease. *American Scientist, 65*, 177–187.

Glass, D. C., Snyder, M. L., & Hollis, J. F. (1974). Time urgency and the Type A coronary-prone behavior pattern. *Journal of Applied Social Psychology, 4*, 125–140.

Gottheil, E. (1965). Conceptions of orality and anality. *Journal of Nervous and Mental Disease, 141*, 155–160.

Haynes, S. G., & Feinleib, M. (1982). Type A behavior and the incidence of coronary heart disease in the Framingham Heart Study. *Advances of Cardiology, 29*, 85–95.

Haynes, S. G., Feinleib, M., & Kannel, W. B. (1980). The relationship of psychosocial factors to coronary heart disease in the Framingham Study III: Eight-year incidence of coronary heart disease. *American Journal of Epidemiology, 111*, 37–58.

Haynes, S. G., Levine, S., Scotch, N., Feinleib, M., & Kannel, W. B. (1978). The relationship of psychosocial factors to coronary heart disease in the Framingham Study I: Methods and risk factors. *American Journal of Epidemiology, 107*, 362–383.

Helmers, K. F., Posluszny, D. M., & Krantz, D. S. (1994). Associations of hostility and coronary artery disease: A review of studies. In A. W. Siegman & T. W. Smith (Eds.), *Anger, hostility and the heart* (pp. 215–237). Hillsdale, NJ: Erlbaum.

Hill, L. (1935). A psychoanalytic observation on essential hypertension. *Psychoanalytic Review, 22*, 60–64.

Hill, L. (1938). The use of hostility as a defense. *Psychoanalytic Quarterly, 7*, 254–264.

Jenkins, C. D., Rosenman, R. H., & Friedman, M. (1967). Development of an objective psychological test for the determination of the coronary-prone behavior pattern in employed men. *Journal of Chronic Disease, 20,* 371–379.

Jenkins, C. D., Zyzanski, S. J., & Rosenman, R. H. (1971). Progress toward validation of a computer-scored test for the Type A coronary-prone behavior pattern. *Psychosomatic Medicine, 33,* 193–202.

Kemple, C. (1945). Rorschach method and psychosomatic diagnosis. *Psychosomatic Medicine, 7,* 85–89.

Ketterer, M. W., Huffman, J., Lumley, M. A., Wassef, S., Gray, L., Kenyon, L., Kraft, P., Brymer, J., Rhoads, K., Lovallo, W. R., & Goldberg, A. D. (1998). Five-year follow-up for adverse outcomes in males with at least minimally positive angiograms: Importance of "denial" in assessing psychosocial risk factors. *Journal of Psychosomatic Research, 44,* 241–250.

Ketterer, M. W., Kenyon, L., Foley, B. A., Brymer, J., Rhoads, K., Kraft, P., & Lovallo, W. R. (1996). Denial of depression as an independent correlate of coronary artery disease. *Journal of Health Psychology, 1,* 93–105.

Kneip, R. C., Delamater, A. M., Ismond, T., Milford, C., Salvia, L., & Schwartz, D. (1993). Self- and spouse ratings of anger and hostility as predictors of coronary heart disease. *Health Psychology, 12,* 301–307.

Lee, D. J., Mendes de Leon, C. F., Jenkins, C. D., Croog, S. H., Levine, S., & Sudilovsky, A. (1992). Relation of hostility to medications adherence, symptoms complaints, and blood pressure reduction in a clinical trial of antihypertensive medication. *Journal of Psychosomatic Research, 36,* 181–190.

Leiker, M., & Hailey, B. J. (1988). A link between hostility and disease: Poor health habits? *Behavioral Medicine, 3,* 129–133.

Lloyd, G. G., & Cawley, R. H. (1978). Psychiatric morbidity in men one week after first acute myocardial infarction. *British Medical Journal, 2,* 1453–1454.

Manuck, S. B. (1994). Cardiovascular reactivity in cardiovascular disease: Once more unto the breach. *International Journal of Behavior Medicine, 1,* 4–31.

Matthews, K. A., & Brunson, B. I. (1979). Allocation of attention and the coronary-prone behavior pattern. *Journal of Personality and Social Psychology, 37,* 2081–2090.

Matthews, K. A., Glass, D. C., Rosenman, R. H., & Bortner, R. W. (1977). Competitive drive, Pattern A, and coronary heart disease: A further analysis of some data from the Western Collaborative Group Study. *Journal of Chronic Diseases, 30,* 489–498.

Mayman, M. (1968). Early memories and character structure. *Journal of Projective Techniques and Personality Assessment, 32,* 303–316.

Menninger, K. A., & Menninger, W. C. (1936). Psychoanalytic observations in cardiac disorders. *American Heart Journal, 11,* 10–26.

Menninger, W. C. (1943). Characterologic and symptomatic expressions related to anal phase of psychosexual development. *Psychoanalytic Quarterly, 12,* 161–193.

Miles, H. H., Waldfogel, S., Barrabee, E. L., & Cobb, S. (1954). Psychosomatic study of 46 young men with coronary artery disease. *Psychosomatic Medicine, 16,* 456–477.

Miller, T. Q., Smith, T. W., Turner, C. W., Guijarro, M. L., & Hallet, A. J. (1993). A meta-analytic review of research on hostility and physical health. *Psychological Bulletin, 119,* 322–348.

Murray, M. H. (1943). *Thematic Apperception Test.* Cambridge, MA: Harvard University Press.

Ragland, D. R., & Brand, R. J. (1988a). Coronary heart disease mortality in the Western Collaborative Group Study. *American Journal of Epidemiology, 127,* 462–475.

Ragland, D. R., & Brand, R. J. (1988b). Type A behavior and mortality from coronary heart disease. *New England Journal of Medicine, 318,* 65–69.

Rosenman, R. H. (1978). The interview method of assessment of the coronary-prone behavior pattern. In T. M. Debroski, S. M. Weiss, J. L. Shields, S. G. Haynes, & M. Feinleib (Eds.), *Coronary-prone behavior* (pp. 55–69). New York: Springer-Verlag.

Rosenman, R. H., Brand, R. J., Jenkins, C. D., Friedman, M., Straus, R., & Wurm, M. (1975). Coronary heart disease in the Western Collaborative Group Study: Final follow-up of eight and one half years. *Journal of the American Medical Association, 223,* 872–877.

Rosenman, R. H., & Chesney, M. A. (1980). The relationship of Type A behavior pattern to coronary heart disease. *Activitas Nervosa Superior, 22,* 1–45.

Rosenman, R. H., & Friedman, M. (1961). Association of specific behavior pattern in women with blood and cardiovascular findings. *Circulation, 24,* 1173–1184.

Rosenman, R. H., Swan, G. E., & Carmelli, D. (1988). Definition, assessment, and evolution of the Type A behavior pattern. In B. K. Houston & C. R. Snyder (Eds.), *Type A behavior pattern: Research, theory, and intervention* (pp. 8–31). New York: Wiley.

Ruberman, W., Weinblatt, E., Goldberg, J. D., & Chaudhary, B. S. (1984). Psychosocial influences on mortality after myocardial infarction. *New England Journal of Medicine, 311,* 552–559.

Russek, H. I. (1967). Role of emotional stress in the etiology of clinical coronary heart disease. *Diseases of the Chest, 52,* 1–9.

Sandler, J., & Hazari, A. (1960). The "obsessional": On the psychological classification of obsessional character traits and symptoms. *British Journal of Medical Psychology, 33,* 113–122.

Scheidt, S. (1996). A whirlwind tour of cardiology for the mental health professional. In R. Allan & S. Scheidt (Eds.), *Heart & mind: The practice of cardiac psychology* (pp. 15–62). Washington, DC: American Psychological Association.

Shapiro, D. (1965). *Neurotic styles*. New York: Basic Books.
Shedler, J., Mayman, M., & Manis, M. (1993). The illusion of mental health. *American Psychologist, 48*, 1117–1131.
Shekelle, R. B., Hulley, S. B., Neaton, J. D., Billings, J. H., Borhani, N. O., Gerace, T. A., Jacobs, D. R., Lasser, N. L., Mittlemark, H. B., & Stamler, J. (1985). The MRFIT behavior pattern study: II. Type A behavior and incidence of coronary heart disease. *American Journal of Epidemiology, 122*, 559–570.
Siegman, A. W. (1994a). Cardiovascular consequences of expressing and repressing anger. In A. W. Siegman & T. W. Smith (Eds.), *Anger, hostility, and the heart* (pp. 173–197). Hillsdale, NJ: Erlbaum.
Siegman, A. W. (1994b). From Type A to hostility and anger: Reflections on the history of coronary-prone behavior. In A. W. Siegman & T. W. Smith (Eds.), *Anger, hostility, and the heart* (pp. 1–21). Hillsdale, NJ: Erlbaum.
Smith, T. W. (1992). Hostility and health: Current status of a psychosomatic hypothesis. *Health Psychology, 11*, 139–150.
Storment, C. T. (1951). Personality and heart disease. *Psychosomatic Medicine, 13*, 304.
Tabrizi, K., Littman, A., Williams, R. B., Jr., & Scheidt, S. (1996). Psychopharmacology and cardiac disease. In R. Allan & S. Scheidt (Eds.), *Heart & mind: The practice of cardiac psychology* (pp. 397–419). Washington, DC: American Psychological Association.
Van Heijningen, H. K., & Treurniet, N. (1966). Psychodynamic factors in acute myocardial infarction. *International Journal of Psychoanalysis, 47*, 370–374.
Weinberger, D., Schwartz, G., & Davidson, R. (1979). Low-anxious, high-anxious, and repressive coping styles: Psychometric patterns and behavioral and physiological responses to stress. *Journal of Abnormal Psychology, 88*, 4.
Weiss, E. (1940). Cardiovascular lesions of probable psychosomatic origin in arterial hypertension. *Psychosomatic Medicine, 2*, 249–264.
Weiss, E. (1943). Neurocirculatory asthenia. *Psychosomatic Medicine, 5*, 93–96.
Weiss, E., Dlin, B., Rollin, H. R., Fischer, H. K., & Bepler, C. C. (1957). Emotional factors in coronary occlusion. *Archives of International Medicine, 99*, 628.
Westen, D. (1998). Unconscious thought, feeling, and motivation: The end of a century-long debate. In R. F. Bornstein & J. M. Masling (Eds.), *Empirical perspectives on the psychoanalytic unconscious* (pp. 1–43). Washington, DC: American Psychological Association.
Zevallos, J. C., Chiriboga, D., & Hebert, J. R. (1992). An international perspective on coronary heart disease and related risk factors. In I. S. Ockene & J. K. Ockene (Eds.), *Prevention of coronary heart disease* (pp. 147–170). Boston: Little, Brown.

Chapter

3

Dreaming and Illness

Milton Kramer

A close connection between sleep and health has been accepted as a central maxim in health education (Hauri & Linde, 1990). The complete absence of sleep, an alteration in the amount of sleep, or a disturbance of the sleep process each can negatively affect the quality and quantity of life (Kripke, Simmons, Garfinkel, & Hammond, 1979; Rechtshaffen, Bergman, Everson, Kushida, & Gilland, 1989).

A connection between dreaming and increases in morbidity and mortality is not as well recognized as the connection between disturbed sleep and illness. My intent in this chapter is to review the relationship between dreaming and illness. This essay touches on the historically recognized connection between dreaming and illness, the relationship of dreaming and the mind–body problem, a psychodynamic (Freudian) review of dreaming and the dream initiation process, an experimentally based theory of dream function, the biology of dreaming, the alterations in dreaming found in major mental illnesses, dream reports of physically ill patients, and dream disturbances related to intrinsic alterations in the sleep process.

History

The intimate relationship between dreaming and disease, both mental and physical (Schiller, 1985), found early merit in ancient Greece. Hippocrates (460–400 BC) believed that dreams enable people to uncover hidden disease. Aristotle (384–322 BC) pointed out the predictive value of dreams, as they may indicate the early symptoms of disease. Galen (129–199 BC) noted that dreams can elaborate actual pathogenic stimuli.

The priests in the Aesculapian temples of ancient Greece (circa 600 BC) used the dream experience to treat disease (Meier, 1967). In the earliest period of this healing cult, the patient came to the temple and was prepared by the priest for sleep in the temple after undergoing a series of purifying rites. The dream the patient had was in itself the "curative" experience. Later on, this direct experience of cure was replaced by the god Aesculapius appearing in the dream of patients and telling them what steps they were to take to effect a cure. The god provided the prescription for the patient in the dream. In the late phases of the work of the Aesculapian cult, the dream the patient reported after awakening from sleeping in the temple required an interpretation by the priest to extract the prescription for healing.

In the immediately pre-Freudian era, Schiller (1985) recognized that the positive effects of sleep could be altered by dreaming and that studying dreams could offer access to inner states, both physical and mental. Albrecht von Holler, a 19th-century physiologist, wrote "that sleep refreshes most in which there are no dreams, or at least that in which we have no remembrance of any" (cited in Schiller, 1985, p. 904). Even though Ernst von Feuchterleben in 1847 observed that "dreaming, as the precursor and accompaniment of diseases, deserves continued investigation [because it is] the unconscious language of coenesthesias (sensations originating within our body)," there is, he believed, "a delicate affinity of dreams with pathological states of the mind" (p. 905).

The Mind–Body Problem

Dreams have been seen as the point of intersection between the mind and the body (brain; Antrobus, 1993). An examination of dreaming from neurophysiological and psychological points of view holds open the possibility that a resolution of the mind–body problem might be possible. However, the promise in the discovery that rapid eye movement (REM) sleep might be the biological basis for dreaming was not fulfilled. Dreaming can be recovered from non-REM stages of sleep and REM stages of sleep. Dreaming appears to be the mental concomitant of some arousals during sleep. REM sleep is a frequent and regular cause of arousals during sleep, which accounts for the high recovery rate of dreaming from REM sleep. REM sleep is not a necessary condition for dreaming to occur.

A Psychodynamic (Freudian) View of Dreaming and the Dream Initiation Process

The dream for Freud (1900/1955) was the attempted, disguised fulfillment of a repressed, infantile, usually sexual wish. The universal wish, which also contributes to every dream, is the wish to remain asleep, and every successful dream is a fulfillment of that wish. Stimuli, whether external or internal to the dreamer, must be "misinterpreted" in a dream to prevent awakening and thereby protect sleep. All dreams are, in a sense, dreams of convenience because they prolong sleep. Dreams are the guardians, not the disturbers, of sleep.

Freud (1900/1955) noted that there are four sources of potentially disturbing stimuli that may disrupt the continuity of sleep: mental, external, internal subjective sensory, and somatic. The two major sources of potentially sleep disturbing stimuli of concern in the exploration of dreams and illness are mental in the case of psychiatric illness and somatic in the case of physical illness. During sleep, potentially disturbing stimuli can be responded to by ignoring them, being aware of them without responding, waking up, or elaborating a dream. It is the last possibility that is important, namely, the formation of a dream in response to mental or somatic stimuli to prolong the sleeping state.

How does the dream control the disturbing stimuli and accomplish its sleep-protecting function (Freud 1900/1955)? This occurs when individuals withdraw interest from themselves and from the world around them and lose awareness. Motor discharge or activity is blocked as a concomitant of this withdrawal. In this state of altered awareness and motor blockade, the automatic control over troublesome inner feelings is relaxed and inner states (wishes) press toward active release, active satisfaction. These stimuli, mental and somatic, press toward discharge. To move toward satisfaction and to reach the motor apparatus, these disturbances, whether mental or somatic, link up with concerns left over from the previous day. These concerns are left over in the sense of being incomplete. This combination of troublesome inner feelings and leftover concerns from the previous day are reworked into a wish that if satisfied would resolve the tension they create.

The search for satisfaction through the motor system is unavailable because it is blocked. A regressive process then occurs in the systemic, formal, temporal, and libidinal aspects of the stimulus wish, during which the wish is subjected to a series of transformations (i.e., condensation, displacement, considerations for representability, and symbolic activity). The wish moves toward the perceptual system, toward a representation as fulfilled, albeit in a disguised manner, in the hallucination experienced as the manifest dream.

One's dream is preoccupied with the same issues with which one was concerned during the day. In every dream, it is possible to find a point of contact with the experiences of the previous day. To disguise the impact of the waking concerns so that sleep can be maintained, the dream uses an indifferent but related event or thought of the prior day to be represented in the dream. The dream can also include impressions from childhood, which are usually only alluded to in the dream rather than directly represented. The dream can have more than one meaning, have more than one wish fulfilled, and be side by side or layered, with a childhood wish at the bottom.

The dream is a reaction to all currently active stimuli both mental and somatic. All currently active material is combined into the dream if associative bridges, even if remote, among them can be found. If somatic sensations become active during sleep, they are added to the other currently active material for construction of a dream and worked up into a wish.

The model for dream formation that Freud (1900/1955) offered provides a way to understand how sleep-disturbing stimuli, mental or somatic, are processed to maintain the continuity of sleep. The Freudian dream formation scheme is the mind's response to disturbing stimuli. Freud's dream interpretive method offers one approach to establish the connection between the sleep disturbing stimulus and the consequent dream. The connection between the mental or somatic stimulus and the dream provides the basis for studying the connection between dreams and illness.

Experimental and Clinical Studies

Evidence from sleep laboratory and neuropsychological studies supports Freud's hypothesis about dreaming. The selective mood regulatory function of dreaming (Kramer, 1993) offers observations consistent with Freud's view that troubling presleep concerns are processed across the night during dreaming. Solms (1997) used the neuropsychological study of brain-damaged patients to describe the anatomical areas of the brain involved in dream formation. This neuropsychologically derived model of normal dream production is consistent with Freud's hypothesis about dream formation and function.

An Experimentally Based Theory of Dream Function

In examining the data that may suggest a particular function for dreaming (Kramer, 1993), I need first to explore a problem inherent in the concept of dream function. The role of mental processes in a causal behavioral chain is central to the notion of dream function (Sternberg & Smith, 1988). The cognitive sciences deal very little with non-goal-directed, emotionally related thinking (E. Smith, 1988), but the issue of a mental cause needs to be considered in the exploration of any theory of dream function.

There are two senses in which the idea of cause can be applied to psychological dreaming (Kramer, 1982). First, it can be used to describe what the dream accomplishes or how the dream is constructed. In studies of the dream function, the dream is the independent variable and the consequent of the dream is the dependent variable. In the case of how the dream functions, the focus is on the construction and organization of the dream. By what rules are the contents selected, and how are they melded together? Researchers who have examined which presleep elements are selected (Piccione, Jacobs, Kramer, & Roth, 1977) and entered directly or by transformation into the dream (Witkin & Lewis, 1967), have described the interconnection of the parts of the dream (Klinger, 1971) and have delineated the sequential development of the dream across the REM period (Kramer, Roth, & Czaya, 1975) and across the night (Kramer, McQuarrie, & Bonnet, 1980; Kramer, Whitman, Baldridge, & Lansky, 1964) all study the how function of dreaming. The dream is the dependent variable in an examination of the dream construction.

Freud (1900/1955) clearly related the what and how of dream function. The dream for Freud was constructed in response to a disturbing infantile wish to provide disguised gratification of the wish and to protect the continuity of sleep. The infantile wish is the independent variable, the disguised gratification the dependent variable, the dream work the mechanism for constructing the dream, and the continuity of sleep the dependent variable when the disguised gratification is the independent variable.

Theories that specify a consequence for dreaming are adaptive. The theory may be assimilative (Piaget, 1962), in which the process functions automatically outside of awareness, achieves a corrective (Kramer & Roth, 1973a) or reductive goal (French, 1952, 1953, 1958), and accounts for most dreaming. In accommodative theories of dream function, the dream enters the dreamer's awareness and the dreamer may be altered as a result of the dream (Jung, 1974). Dreams probably subserve both functions (Kramer, 1981).

A complete theory of psychological dreaming would place the dream in a wake–dream–wake paradigm and explain the how of dream construction and the what of dream consequence. Manipulating the presleep (Breger, 1967) and the dream experience (Tart, 1979) is necessary to show an effect on dreaming and subsequent wakefulness. Presleep suggestion (Meier, 1967), posthypnotic suggestion (Schrotter, 1912/1951), stimuli introduced during REM sleep (Castaldo & Holzman, 1969), and prior REM deprivation (Firth, 1974) are ways of affecting dream content. The variables that influence dream content and that dream content may affect are more likely to be affective than cognitive (Ekstrand, Barrett, West, & Maier, 1977; Kramer, Roth, & Palmer, 1976; Piccione et al., 1977).

The Core Observation

Starting from the dream's function, Freud (1900/1955) suggested that dreaming protects sleep by containing the emotional disruption that unconscious wishes create as they press for satisfaction. Several observations derived from REM physiology, a paradigm for dreaming, support this view. REM sleep—in this case, dreaming—increases across the night as the likelihood of waking increases. The end of REM (dream) periods are associated with arousals. Dreams usually have no accompanying feeling; however, if they do, the feeling is more likely to be negative than positive (Hall & Van de Castle, 1966). The disturbing dream, the nightmare, that disrupts the continuity of sleep has the most intense feeling associated with it (Taub, Kramer, Arand, & Jacobs, 1978).

The intensity of the dream experience shows a systematic development across the REM period, which is primarily linear (Kramer et al., 1975). Aserinsky (1971) and B. Johnson, Kramer, Bonnet, Roth, and Jansen (1980) woke participants at 0.5, 2.5, 5.0, 10.0, 20.0, and 30.0 minutes into their REM periods; the researchers also scored for content and intensity reports of the last 10 seconds of their dream experiences. The pattern of content–intensity, which had a plateau at 20–30 minutes, fit the eye movement pattern (density). The increase in variability and to a lesser degree the magnitude of alternations in autonomic functions associated with the REM period also point to the affective nature of the REM experience (Freemon, 1972). If the integrative, sleep-maintaining function of the dream is successful and controls the affective surge that accompanies REM sleep, the dream does not enter awareness; instead, it is encompassed in the amnesia of sleep, and the dream displays an assimilative function.

In a study comparing participants who experienced twice-weekly nightmares with those who experienced vivid dreams, Kramer, Schoen, and Kinney (1984a) examined a series of factors that might affect the control of the affective surge that accompanies REM sleep. Although the dream-content categories did not distinguish the groups, the vivid dreamers had higher recall rates than the nightmare sufferers. The nightmare sufferers had higher psychopathology scores on the Minnesota Multiphasic Personality Inventory (MMPI) and Cornell Medical Index, were more likely to have seen a psychiatrist, and saw their disturbing dreams as related to current disturbing feelings. All of this suggests that an emotional predispositional factor influences the integrative capacity of every dreamer. Nightmare sufferers are described by observers as more responsive and frightened during sleep.

The integrative failure of dreaming in patients with more emotional troubles, for example, patients with chronic posttraumatic stress disorder (PTSD), is reflected in their greater responsiveness to disturbances in sleep to above threshold tones (Kinney & Kramer, 1985). The elevated awakening threshold found in PTSD patients (Schoen, Kramer, & Kinney, 1984), using an ascending auditory stimuli method, and their lack of awareness of the source of the disruption (Kinney & Kramer, 1985) support the concept that these patients are more internally focused (i.e., on dreaming rather than on an external threat).

The dream process attempts to contain a fluctuating emotional surge across the REM period. If successful, sleep continues; if not successful, an arousal occurs. The disturbed emotional state of participants predisposes them to be hyperresponsive to disturbances during their sleep. An examination of the affective and mental state of participants should clarify the function of dreaming.

Mood Before and After Sleep

By containing the emotional surge during REM sleep, the dream maintains the continuity of sleep. Sleep is responsive to the experiences of the prior day, to feelings of depression and anxiety (Rimon, Fujita, & Takahata, 1986; Rosa, Bonnet, & Kramer, 1983), to the more intense emotional experiences of the day (Piccione et al., 1977), and to the thoughts one has before falling asleep (Kramer, Moshiri, & Scharf, 1982). Sleep is also related to the activities of the next day. The loss of even 1 hour of sleep affects performance (Wilkinson, 1968). How one feels in the morning influences performance (L. C. Johnson, Spinweber, Gomez, & Matteson, 1990). Prior sleep is linked to mental activity the next day (Kramer et al., 1982). Sleep may serve to alter subjective state and mood; hence, an exploration of the sleep–mood relationship seems appropriate.

The mood measurement device used in the mood–sleep studies reported below is the Clyde Mood Scale (CMS; Clyde, 1963), a 48-item adjective checklist that yields six factors: Friendly, Aggressive, Clear Thinking, Sleepy, Unhappy, and Dizzy (anxious). In a study of 8 male participants who slept 15 consecutive nights in the laboratory and completed CMS before and after sleeping (Kramer & Roth, 1973a), the six mood factors were independent, similar in magnitude to published norms, and the mean and standard deviation did not show evidence and adaptation over time. The intensity and variability of mood decreased from night to morning (Kramer, 1992; Kramer & Roth, 1973a; Roth, Kramer, & Roehrs, 1976) and was not altered by where the participants slept (Kramer & Roth, 1973a; Lysaght, Kramer, & Roth, 1979; Roehrs, Kramer, Lefton, Lutz, & Roth, 1973), their age (Roth et al., 1976), gender (Lysaght et al., 1979), hypnotic drug use (Schwartz, Kramer, & Roth, 1974), or awakenings for dream collection (Kramer, 1993). Generally, the researchers found that the Friendly, Unhappy, and Sleepy factors decreased from night to morning across these studies.

The mood of a person is stable in general and to a degree from day to day, as is dreaming, which is unique to the individual but varies from day to day (Kramer, Hlasny, Jacobs, & Roth, 1976). Kramer (1993) studied the night and morning mood scores of 52 participants (normal volunteers) from four groups made up of 40 women and 12 men who slept for 15–21 nights. He calculated two correlations for each group. The first was a between-subject Pearson correlation from the mean night and morning score on each

CMS factor. The correlations were then averaged, after a Z transform, across the four studies. The second was a within-subject Pearson correlation, averaged across participants in each group and then across the four groups. The trait aspect of mood showed, on average, a high correlation (.87), with relatively low correlations being Sleepy (.26) and anxious (.62), whereas the five factors of Friendly, Aggressive, Unhappy, Clear Thinking, and average (the average is the mean of the six factor scores) showed high correlations (.87–.95). The state aspect of mood overall was not significant. However, 88 of 364 correlations (7 factors × 52 participants) of the within-subject correlations were statistically significant. Forty-two of the fifty-two participants showed at least one significant correlation. The largest number of significant correlations was with the Unhappy factor, whereas the smallest was with the Sleepy factor (Kramer, 1993). There were 999 individual night–morning scores, of which 63% showed a decrease from night to morning.

The linkage of mood change from night to morning was the focus of two sleep deprivation studies. In one, the participants were sleep deprived but slept at home before and after the deprivation (Roth, Kramer, & Lutz, 1976). Scores on the Sleepy and Aggressive factors were higher after deprivation than at baseline or recovery. The sleep deprivation study was repeated in the laboratory over 2 consecutive nights (Vaccarino, Rosa, Bonnet, & Kramer, 1981). With increasing sleep deprivation, scores on the Sleepy and anxious factors increased and those on the Clear Thinking factor decreased. These results show that mood is sensitive to even 1 night of sleep deprivation.

In the sleep-through studies, the decrease in scores on the Friendly factor may be related to the social isolation of sleep. The decrease of scores on the Unhappy factor remains to be explained. Mood change across the day shows a different but related pattern (Lysaght, Roth, Kramer, & Salis, 1978) to that found across the night. The activation scales were maximal at 12 noon and minimal at presleep, whereas the deactivation scales showed a reverse pattern. The activation–deactivation scales peak 4 hours before the temperature curve peaks and are not epiphenomenal to the diurnal temperature curve.

The real-life significance of mood and performance was examined in three studies. In the first study, Lutz, Kramer, and Roth

(1975) tested participants who had been given a short-acting hypnotic medication on cognitive and psychomotor skills over 22.5 hours. They found significant performance correlations with factors of CMS. In the second study, Rosa, Bonnet, Warm, and Kramer (1981) found clear-cut decrements in mood and performance over 2 nights of sleep deprivation. In the third study, L. C. Johnson et al. (1990) showed a relationship between morning mood and performance.

Mental Content Before, During, and After Sleep

Kramer, Winget, and Whitman (1971) examined dreams in conditions that were psychologically significant to see if they vary analogously to mood. In a population study, they found that demographic variables that have cognitive and affective covariates, such as gender, age, race, marital status, and social class, have associated dream-content differences. The largest number of differences were associated with gender. Women have more characters and emotions in their dreams, whereas men have more aggression and achievement striving with success. There is more guilt anxiety in those under 35 years old, more characters in the dreams of lower class people, more covert hostility in Whites, and more death concerns in divorced individuals. Kramer, Kinney, and Scharf (1983b) confirmed gender differences in a laboratory study as well. They noted differences in the content of dreams of various psychiatric patient groups. This was true for schizophrenia, depressed (Kramer, Baldridge, Whitman, Ornstein, & Smith, 1969; Kramer & Roth, 1973a), and PTSD patients (Kramer, Schoen, & Kinney, 1984b).

Dream reports are nonrandom events that reflect the subjective state of the dreamer. Dreaming has the specificity and variability to be potentially relatable to mood. There is clinical interest to determine if dreams permit discrimination at the individual level and among nights within an individual. Judges were able to sort the dreams of normal participants from each other at a significant level and those of schizophrenia patients (Kramer, Hlasny, et al., 1976). The judges were also able to sort the multiple laboratory-collected dreams from different nights of the same individuals, both for normal participants and those with schizophrenia, at a statistically significant level. Dreams are different among individuals, and they are different by nights within an individual.

Dreams show a systematic content change across the night. Kramer, McQuarrie, and Bonnet (1981) collected the dreams of 22 participants from the first four REM periods of the night over 20 consecutive nights. The word count of each dream report showed an increase across the night, and 8 of 22 content categories showed a content change across the night, with word count held constant.

Dreaming is related to waking thought. Twenty-four participants slept for 3 nonconsecutive nights in the laboratory. Kramer, Roth, et al. (1976) collected dreams from the first four REM periods of the night. The participants also gave responses to 10 Thematic Apperception Test cards. The dreams and cards were scored for intensity with a 6-point scale on 10 of the 20 Murray need–press variables. The rank order intensity scores were significantly correlated (.72, p = .05). Hence, the intensity levels of dreams and waking fantasy are similar.

In a different study, 40 participants gave 5-minute verbal samples before and after sleeping in a laboratory and having dreams collected from each of the first four REM periods of the night (Kramer, Roth, Arand, & Bonnet, 1981). The verbal samples and dreams were scored with 18 scales of the Hall–Van de Castle system (1966), 9 of which showed a significant correlation between the participants' verbal samples and their dreams.

Kramer et al. (1982) showed thematic similarity across verbal samples and dreams for 20 participants who slept 3 nonconsecutive nights in a laboratory and had dreams collected from the first four REM periods. Night verbal samples are more likely to be connected to subsequent dreaming than dreaming is to the morning verbal samples. So dreams may be more reactive than proactive.

Dreams vary with mood. Dreams reflect psychological differences in demographically and psychopathologically different groups. Dreams are different among individuals and among nights within an individual, as are moods. Dreams change linearly across the night, as does mood. Mood change across the day is related to mood change across the night, as are dreams, and both are related.

Dream Responsiveness to the Emotional State of the Dreamer

Emotionally significant waking experiences influence dreams. Seven participants slept for 10 consecutive nights in a laboratory and had their dreams collected from each REM period. During the day, they gave hourly activity and emotional tone reports. Judges selected the activity report that appeared to be incorporated into the dreams. Those selected were from experiences that were more intense (i.e., had higher emotional tone ratings; Piccione et al., 1977). When presented with paired dream reports from the beginning and ending of a series of consecutive nights of laboratory dream collection, an emotionally challenging experience, judges were able to distinguish Night 1 from Night 20 and Night 3 from Night 18 but not the intermediate nights (Kramer, Roth, & Cisco, 1977). Whitman, Pierce, Mass, and Baldridge (1962) showed that male experimental participants in a sleep laboratory dreamed of exploitation, whereas female participants dreamed of rape. Piccione, Thomas, Roth, and Kramer (1976) looked at 20 consecutive nights of dream collection from 14 participants and had judges rate their dreams for direct and indirect laboratory references. On average, 34% of dreams have a laboratory reference, which remains essentially the same over the 20-day period.

In a series of studies, researchers have demonstrated that emotionally charged interpersonal situations affect dreaming. A male and female participant were awakened from each REM period; they were asked to report their dreams to a technician and again the next morning to a psychiatrist (Whitman, Kramer, & Baldridge, 1963b). Some dreams reported at night were not recalled in the morning and vice versa. For the female participant, dreams criticizing the psychiatrist were not reported to him, but they were to the male dream collector at night (e.g., a dream of a patient questioning a doctor's competence). The male participant did not report those dreams that showed him in a less assertive manner. Dreams expressing negative feelings about the dream collector were reported by both participants only to the psychiatrist.

A study of patient–therapist dyads, each sleeping in a separate laboratory on the same night (Whitman, Kramer, & Baldridge, 1963a), reveals that patients dreamt about the therapist (41% of the time), the therapist dreamt about the next day's supervisory conference (42% of the time), and from informal reports the therapists' supervisors dreamt about the research team. Fox, Kramer, Baldridge, Whitman, and Orstein (1968) looked at varying the gender of the experimenter on dream content; they found that in the heterosexual situation, more groups of people appeared in the dreams. Hence, emotional preoccupations influence the focus of a dream.

In another study, researchers examined the effect on dream content of altering the emotional state of the dreamer with medication. Researchers collected the dreams of 10 depressed patients in a sleep laboratory before and after successful treatment with an antidepressant (Kramer, Whitman, Baldridge, & Ornstein, 1968). They found that depression, hostility, anxiety, and intimacy decreased in the patients' dreams, whereas heterosexuality and motility increased as the patients improved.

During REM sleep, Kinney, Kramer, and Bonnet (1981) found that playing familiar and unfamiliar names recorded in the participant's voice led to a greater incorporation of known names than unknown names (see also Kramer, Kinney, & Scharf, 1983a). Participants incorporated high meaning names 49% of the time, low meaning names 8%, but recall of hearing the names played the same in both experiments about 18%. Therefore, the dream is related to emotionally meaningful experiences because of what is incorporated into the dream and how the dream responds to meaningful interpersonal situations.

Relationship Between Mood and Dreams

In two studies, Kramer and Roth (1973a, 1980) were able to show a relationship between mood, as measured by CMS, and dream content, as measured by the Hall–Van de Castle dream-content scoring system. In the first study, 2 male volunteers slept for 20 consecutive nights and had dreams collected from each of the first four REM periods. In the second study, 12 men were studied in a similar manner. The Unhappy factor and the character scale in both studies had the largest number of significant correlations, although five of six mood factors and all categories of the content scales had a larger number of significant correlations expected by chance. The Unhappy factor was one of the three factors that showed a significant change in scores from night to morning in the sleep-through studies. The other factors were Friendly and Sleepy.

Observations about dream-content change in depressive illness support the view that affective state covaries with and may influence dream content. Kramer, Trinder, Whitman, and Baldridge (1969) confirmed Beck's (Beck & Hurvich, 1959) observation in the laboratory that masochistic content is found in depression. In a laboratory and nonlaboratory study of depressed people, Kramer, Baldridge, et al. (1969; see also Kramer, Trinder, & Roth, 1972) found the typical dream character to be a family member, whereas in patients with schizophrenia, it was a stranger (Kramer & Roth, 1973b). Dream content changed with improvement in hospitalized depressed patients treated with antidepressant medications (Kramer et al., 1968). In a single case report of a patient who had a manic-depressive illness, dream content was different in each phase of the illness (Kramer, Brunner, & Trinder, 1971). A review of dream content in depressive illness underscores many changes in the dreams of depressed people (Kramer, in press).

Relationship Between Mood and Physiology of Sleep

Total sleep deprivation results in alterations in mood (Roth, Kramer, et al., 1976; Vaccarino et al., 1981), in which scores on the Sleepy and anxious factors increase and Clear Thinking decreases. In a study of 6 participants who had their sleep recorded for 15 consecutive undisturbed nights and had their mood change scores (night–morning) correlated with five aspects of sleep (total sleep time, total REM time, Stage 2 time, Stage 3–4 time, and number of awakenings), Kramer and Roth (1973b) found that the largest number of significant correlations were between Sleepy and total sleep time.

In a second study involving 11 male volunteers who slept for 15 consecutive undisturbed nights and had their sleep monitored, Kramer, Roehrs, and Roth (1972a) found that Stage 2 time, Stage 3–4 time, and sleep latency significantly predicted the Sleepy and Friendly factor score changes. Unhappy, the factor most related to dreaming, was not predicted by the sleep physiology parameters. For 11 male participants who slept for 15 consecutive nondisturbed nights and who completed an MMPI and CMS before and after each night in the laboratory, neither the *D* scale of the MMPI nor the presleep Unhappy score on the CMS correlated significantly with the participant's REM time (Kramer, Roehrs, & Roth, 1972b). Dream content and sleep physiology are related to different aspects of mood change across the night (Kramer & Roth, 1973b), dream content primarily to Unhappy factor scores and sleep physiology to Sleepy and anxious factor scores.

Dream Mechanism for Mood Change: Problem Solving

Two principal patterns of dream development across the night are discernible (Kramer et al., 1964). One is a progressive–sequential type, in which emotional problems are stated, worked on figuratively, and resolved. The other is a repetitive–traumatic type, in which the problem is simply restated in figurative terms. It could be through this mechanism of "problem solving" that the affective alteration described takes place (French & Fromm, 1964). Problem solving may be concomitant with the change in the Unhappiness factor score across the night and is associated with the appearance of appropriate character types in a dream. Participants showed both patterns, with "successful" dreaming occurring about 50% of the time (Kramer et al., 1964), approximating the frequency (63%) with which successful mood change occurs (Kramer, 1993).

A Progressive–Sequential Dream Pattern of a Female Participant During Dream Night 6:

(6-1) "This little girl was asleep. She was being real cute, prolonging things for money in order to stay in the hospital longer."

(6-2) "I passed Frank's wife in a car. She saw me come . . . . She pulled away. I got kind of mad. I decided it didn't make any difference. . . ."

(6-3) "I was playing tennis. I hit it back real hard. We won the game."

(6-4) "A patient didn't need a doctor after all. She started out thinking she needed a doctor but she didn't. She had a big bandage on her stomach."

(6-5) "The doctor was not able to treat patient because he was

> not properly licensed. The patient is planning to use surgery against the doctor." (p. 430)[1]

The sequential pattern in this series expressed a dependent-sexual longing toward the experimenter–doctor, which led to a feared rejection by the wife–mother in the second dream. The conflict was mastered in the third dream by an aggressive victory with her own partner. The fourth dream revealed the rejection of the previous need, although a recognition was present that the need still existed. In the last dream of the night, a more intense rejection in the form of an attack on the doctor served further to deny the need.

> The Repetitive Traumatic Pattern of a Female Participant During Dream Night 3:
>
> (3-1) "Somebody was lost, it was a dog and they were trying to find out where it lived. A little kid or something. He couldn't tell where he lived. It wasn't my dog, though. I wasn't lost. The person was lost. He was always fumbling around leading everybody else around because he didn't know what he was doing. Some boy I think. Somehow we had telephone numbers trying to find the right one. It was supposed to be the little boy that was lost."
>
> (3-2) "They filled up the car. There wasn't enough room, unless I went back with people we went back with before. I could go back with someone else. The place we were going was an orphanage some place, some house, a place like that."
>
> (3-3) "I was dreaming about visiting. I think it was some EEG laboratory or something like that where the mothers could leave their children, and they could go shopping. I doubt whether they could. There wouldn't be enough room for all these people." (p. 433)[2]

In all the dreams of the night, the participant dealt with her fear of being abandoned and her method of recontacting her family: calling on the phone, riding in a car, or being picked up.

---

[1] From "Patterns of Dreaming: The Interrelationship of the Dreams of a Night," by M. Kramer, R. Whitman, B. Baldridge, & L. Lansky, 1964, *Journal of Nervous and Mental Disease, 139,* Copyright 1964 by Lippincott Williams & Wilkins. Reprinted with permission.

[2] *Ibid.*

Summary

Theories of dream function need to address the dreaming that goes on outside of awareness, which is assimilative and reductive, and the dreaming that enters awareness and is potentially accommodative and transformative. The selective mood regulatory theory of dreaming (Kramer, 1993) is an assimilative theory that supports a psychodynamic view of dream function. The dream serves to contain the affective surge of REM sleep and maintain the continuity of sleep. Mood changes systematically across the night, as do dreams. A successful night's dreaming is the result of a progressive–sequential problem-solving sequence across the night. As a consequence, it shows an increase in the person's happiness in the morning, accompanied by the proper type and number of characters appearing in the dream. The experience of the recalled dream permits the extension of this assimilative, reductive aspect of dreaming to encompass a degree of transformation of accommodation as well.

Alterations in mood states, which are common accompaniments of emotional and physical illness, may reflect failures in dream function. Dreams may not be able to contain the affective surge of REM sleep because of alterations in the dreamer and a decrease in the capacity for finding figurative emotional solutions for immediate emotional problems. This should lead to an increase in dream recall and in traumatic repetitive dream patterns across the night.

A Biology for Dreaming

Based on the neuropsychological examination of 332 patients with localized brain damage, confirmed by computerized tomography and magnetic resonance imaging techniques, Solms (1997) hypothesized the anatomical locations of processes that contribute to dream formation. He placed the site of dream formation in the cerebral hemispheres. The specific initiating role for dreaming attributed to the pons (the subcortical part of the brain) is rejected as patients with lesions in the brain stem core reported no alteration in dreaming.

If an arousing stimulus occurs during sleep, no matter what its source (i.e., external noise, pontine activation of REM sleep, pain, or disturbing thoughts from the day), one possible response that could maintain sleep is to elaborate a dream. With the route to motor function blocked (i.e., no activation of the dorsilateral frontal area where thought is translated into action), the arousing impulse is registered in the medial bifrontal area. This area involves affective regulation and impulse control and is associated with appetitive circuits involving curiosity, interest, and expectancy. The dream process begins from this point. Activation of the inferior parietal lobules contributes the symbolic (left inferior parietal) and concrete spatial (right inferior parietal) aspects of the dream experience. The final step is the activation of the medial occipitotemporal area, which provides the visual aspects of dreaming. Dreaming, as a response to arousing stimuli, may serve the function of protecting sleep. Solms (1997) found that brain-injured patients who reported the loss of dreaming were more likely to report disturbed sleep.

Major Mental Illness

Freud (1900/1955) observed a significant relationship between dreams and mental disorders. Statements such as "the madman is the waking dreamer" (Jung, 1974) and that if one could "find out about dreams, [one could] find out about insanity" (Jackson, 1911/1958, p. 45) illustrate the belief that mental illness and dreams are related. When Freud (1900/1955)

> speaks of the relationship of dreams to mental disorders [, he says that he] has three things in mind: 1) the etiological and clinical connections as when a dream represents a psychotic state, or introduces it, or is left over from it; 2) modifications to which dream life is subject in cases of mental disease; and 3) intrinsic connections between dreams and psychosis, analogies pointing to their being essentially akin. (p. 120)

Most of the literature on dreams and psychopathologic states is devoted to the "modifications to which dream life is subject in cases of mental disease" (Kramer, in press).

Frosch's (1976) evaluative review of "The Psychoanalytic Contributions to the Relationship Between Dreams and Psychosis" provides some partial answers to Freud's (1900/1955) questions about the relationship. Frosch concluded that (a) dreams and psychosis, although similar in some ways, differ in basic respects, especially in factors concerned with their production; (b) there is no agreement on whether there are aspects of the manifest dream indicating psychosis; and (c) there is suggestive evidence that some dreams herald the onset of psychosis.

Kramer and Roth (1979) reviewed in detail the literature dealing with the relationship between dreaming and mental illness; their review was extended in 1993 (Mellen, Duffey, & Craig, 1993) and recently extensively updated (Kramer, in press). The scientific adequacy of the literature covered in these reviews is problematic. The review of dreaming in several major mental illnesses (e.g., schizophrenia, depression, and PTSD) does suggest an alteration in dreaming with mental illness in general and with specific illnesses in particular.

Schizophrenia

People with schizophrenia are less interested in their dreams, and their dreams are more primitive (i.e., less complex, more direct, more sexual, anxious, and hostile). Their dreams show evidence of their thought disorder being more bizarre and implausible than those of people without schizophrenia. Hallucinations and dream content are relatable, and the degree of paranoia awake and during dreaming are similar, contrary to Freud's view that in paranoia, waking and dreaming thought were compensatory. The most frequent dream character type of patients with schizophrenia is a stranger (Kramer, in press). Increasing anxiety either decreased or increased dream reporting. Increasing anxiety increased motion and affect in these patients' dreams, whereas a decrease in anxiety in their dreams was the first change noticed when they received antipsychotic medication. Dream recall was lower in lobotomized than nonlobotomized patients with schizophrenia.

Dreams of hospitalized male patients with schizophrenia showed more social alienation and more difficulties in adopting a conventional male role, whereas the dreams of hospitalized female patients with schizophrenia showed more self-consciousness, envy of the activities of others, and hostility to those who tried to restrict them (Kramer, in press). Some female patients with schizophrenia reported the feeling that they were forced to dream. A patient blinded at age 3 reported visual dreaming after being hospitalized. The visual experience was explained as part of the regression that accompanied being hospitalized. In the parents of patients with schizophrenia, there was an inverse relationship between markers of a thought disorder in waking and dreaming. In psychotherapy, the wish fulfilling motives of the dreams of a schizophrenia patient may be shown. Discussing their dreams in a group decreased the insomnia of schizophrenia patients and increased their self-understanding.

Depression

There is a more extensive literature exploring the dreams of depressed patients than is the case for schizophrenia patients. It is not clear whether depressed patients dream as often or less than normal participants. Dreams of depressed patients are shorter and overall have commonplace themes, with a paucity of traumatic or depressive content, even after the depression had lifted. There were some content characteristics of interest, such as the increase in death themes in depressed suicidal patients and in patients with bipolar depression before they became manic. Family members were more frequent in their dreams. A focus on the past in the dreams of depressed patients was neither universal nor unique (Kramer, in press).

Masochism in the dreams of depressed patients was more common in women than men and appeared as more of a trait than state characteristic. Affects such as anxiety and hostility were more prominent in the dreams of depressed patients. Hostility when present could be directed at or away from the dreamer, whereas in patients with schizophrenia, it was directed at the dreamer. Depressed patients had more friendly and fewer aggressive interactions and more failure and misfortune than did patients with schizophrenia. With the improvement in depression, hostility decreases, whereas intimacy, motility, and heterosexuality increase.

Dream content may have a prognostic significance for the response of the depressed patient to treatment (Kramer, in press).

A most striking implication of the results of the studies of dreaming in depressed patients was that the affective state of the dreamer covaried with dream content. Changes in dreams across the night may contribute to a dreamer's coping capacity, as was proposed in the selective mood regulatory function of dreaming (Kramer, 1993). Changes in dream content across the night alter the affective condition of a dreamer and contribute to the adaptive state of the dreamer the next day.

Posttraumatic Stress Disorder

PTSD, a condition in which disturbing dreams are recognized as a key part of the illness, occurs in 1% of the general population and 20% of those wounded in the Vietnam War. The symptom triad of chronic PTSD patients includes nightmares, insomnia, and jumpiness. For patients with acute PTSD precipitated by civilian traumas, waking recollection of the trauma was a more frequent symptom than dreaming about the trauma (Kramer, in press). Relying on the dream-content difference between REM and non-REM sleep, Ross, Ball, Sullivan, and Caroff (1989) suggested that a sleep disturbance, particularly in REM sleep mechanisms, is the hallmark of PTSD. The dream in PTSD, in this view, is seen as vivid, affect laden, disturbing, outside of the realm of current waking experience, stereotyped, and easy to recall. Kramer et al. (1984a) suggested earlier that disturbed dreaming was at the core of PTSD. Nightmares can occur during non-REM sleep as well, so that nightmares are not sleep stage bound and not all nightmares in PTSD are stereotyped. Nightmares of PTSD patients tend to occur early in the night, when less REM sleep occurs. Symptoms associated with nightmares, such as increased awakenings, motor activity, and sweating, also occur earlier in the night in PTSD patients. Elevated arousal thresholds and more intense startle response are found earlier in the night in these patients as well.

The assumption that the affective tone of the dreams in PTSD patients is highly disturbing is not well supported. The dreams of PTSD patients are not inevitably stereotyped when systematically examined and various dream types have been described. A focus on the past in the dreams of PTSD patients is neither universal nor unique because it also occurs in depressed patients. The trauma that precipitated the patient to develop PTSD can be linked to childhood traumas, and the continuation or reactivation of disturbing dreams can occur 3–4 decades after the traumatic event. There have been very limited attempts to describe the long-term transformations, if any, of traumatic dreaming.

An adequate characterization of the disturbing dream in PTSD patients remains to be described. It can be confirmed that such a dream is disturbing and that the dream events may be outside the realm of current waking experience. The dreams of PTSD patients are not affect laden nor easy to recall. It is not known if their dreams are more vivid than others. Decreased dream recall in PTSD patients may be a way to deal with memories of the trauma. Those who have most effectively coped with a trauma have the lowest dream-recall rates. Avoidance of dream recall may be an adaptational strategy in PTSD patients.

The hallmark of PTSD patients is a disturbance in the psychological aspects of dreaming and possibly of non-REM sleep earlier in the night but not particularly of REM sleep. Vietnam veterans' combat experience covaries with dream disturbance to a much greater degree than do their difficulties in sleep. Dream disturbances in veterans occur only in those who have PTSD.

Unlocking the secrets of psychosis has not come about from the study of dreaming of patients with disturbed states. Despite the paucity of studies and lack of scientific rigor, researchers do know more about dreaming in such mental illnesses as schizophrenia, depression, and PTSD. These dream studies suggest the intriguing possibility that what one does or does not dream about may contribute to one's waking adaptational ability.

Physical Illness

Freud (1900/1955) attempted to trace the view of the relationship between somatic stimuli and dreaming. As the symbolic elaboration of somatic sensations during sleep, the dream was the dominant medical view of dreaming in Freud's era. Freud (1917/1957) believed physical illness often could be detected earlier in dreams than in waking life.

Krauss, Freud (1917/1957) noted, described in 1851 that organic sensations from bodily systems, namely, muscular, respiratory, gastric, sexual, and peripheral, are one of the two sources, the other being general mood, elaborated in dreams. These somatic stimuli evoke a cognate image, chosen on the basis of associations, which incorporates stimuli into an image. Consciousness reacts to the image in an altered fashion, focusing on the image and not the sensation. It is not possible to trace back from the image to the sensation in this view.

Freud (1900/1955) acknowledged Scherner (1861), as explicated by his student Volkvelt (1875), to be the true discoverer of dream symbolism in his exploration of the relationship between somatic stimuli and dream image. Scherner saw the mental activity of imagination, free of reason, as dominant during sleep. Imagination has productive and reproductive powers and preferred immediate experiences, immoderately expressed. The imagination turns the inner life into pictures, presenting them in outline form, selecting extraneous images that emphasize just the point at issue, which is incorporated into an event rather than left as an image. When not distracted by external stimuli, the mind is more attentive to internal somatic stimuli and represents them in magnified and dramatic images. The dream is the mind's imaginative response to a somatic stimulus. The dream has no function and serves no purpose. The dream is the mind playing with the stimuli that impinge on it, according to Scherner.

Scherner (1861, cited in Freud, 1900/1955) believed that a dream symbolically represented the organism as a whole, the form and function of the body organism, and the somatic state of the organism. He proposed that a house in a dream was a representation of a body and that rooms in a house represented the various organs of the body. For example, breathing lungs might appear as a blazing furnace, a heart as a hollow box, a bladder as bag-shaped objects, a penis as a clarinet or pipe, and a vagina as a slippery, narrow foot path. The dream imagination may represent the substance in an organ. For example, intestinal stimuli may appear in a dream as a muddy street, whereas a urinary stimulus may be represented by a foamy stream. The state of the organism can be symbolically represented as well. A painful stimulus may appear as biting dogs, nakedness as a smooth loaf of bread, and a sexual feeling in a woman as a pursuit by a man.

The confirmation of the connection between the stimuli and the dream symbol was established by the source of the somatic stimulus' being revealed at the end of the dream. A dream symbol based on a dental stimulus such as entering a high vaulted room may end with the dreamer extracting a tooth. Freud (1900/1955) suggested that Scherner (1861) made the most serious effort to explore the relationship between somatic stimuli and dreams. Scherner drew on the productive role of the imagination. He identified symbolic representation in dreams. In these areas, he was an effective precursor of Freud's and laid the groundwork for the connection of dreams to somatic stimuli, whether one accepts his particular symbol system or not.

Was there more direct corroborative evidence that what one thought and, more particularly, how one felt, especially in bodily feelings, were expressed, transformed, or represented in dreams? The connection of physical illness and dreams, if it exists, may be seen by a representation of the illness in dreams. That body sensations can be represented in dreams is essential for connecting dreams and physical illness. The work of Herbert Silberer (1909/1951) early in this century illustrates the transformation of thought and feelings into visual symbols during hypnagogic dreamlike states.

Silberer (1909/1951) observed, in himself, that in the transition from wake to sleep during a drowsy state while he was trying to focus his thoughts on an idea, his thoughts and feelings could be represented by visual images, such as brief action scenes. He labeled this phenomenon "autosymbolic" and thought it was worthy of study because it demonstrated Freud's (1900/1955) third factor of the dream work, the "regard for representability." These phenomena can be classified into three groups on the basis of the content symbolized in them: material or content, functional or effort, and somatic phenomena.

To illustrate the material autosymbolic category, Silberer (1909/1951) described an experience in which he was thinking he had to improve a halting passage in an essay and then he saw himself planing (smoothing) a piece of wood. In describing a functional autosymbolic experience, Silberer reported that he had lost the thread of his thought, made an effort to pick it up, but had to admit that he had lost the connecting link. He then saw, in his mind's eye, a piece of typesetting with the last few lines gone. The somatic autosymbolic transformation reported by him is one in which he takes a deep breath, his chest expands, and he sees himself lifting a tablet high with someone's help. The illustrations provided by Silberer (1909/1951), for how ideas and feeling states can be visually represented in hallucinations, provide the connection between dreaming and physical illness. They show how an awareness of the illness or response to a feeling state can be automatically represented in an hallucination.

In describing the mental life of children by comparing play, dreams, and imitation, Piaget (1962) stated that by age 3, children begin representing feeling states in dreams. A child reported "I dreamt I was pouring water out of a watering can in the garden, and I wetted my bed." Piaget described the dream of a 6-year-old in which the child told of a bean growing larger and larger, which Piaget attributed to the young boy having an erection that frightened him. Piaget reported the dream of a man that was a response to his dentist's having left a small pad of cotton between the man's two molars. The man had a dream where he saw wet moss in between two rocks just when in his half-sleeping state, he was feeling the pad of cotton with his tongue. The attribution of images to stimuli from various parts of the body hinges on the physical and spatial equivalence between the body part and the image. This does not preclude the possibility that there are psychodynamic factors involved in an image, which occur in response to a particular stimulus (Shafton, 1995).

Somatic Sensations

Somatic sensations are reported as being magnified and dramatized when transformed into an image in dreams. Breger, Hunter, and Lane (1971) reported dreams from awakenings in the sleep laboratory of patients before and after surgery. One of their participants, a 64-year-old retired veteran, who had worked on the railroad, was currently hospitalized for vascular surgery on his legs. His major symptoms were coldness in his legs and feet, some cramping in his legs, and reduced mobility. He was scheduled for an operation to remove a portion of a blood vessel in his leg, which would open the vascular blockage in his leg. He had had a similar procedure 8 months before to remove an aortic aneurysm. He dreamt on the night before surgery of a railroad switch.

> We lined the switch, it seemed like a switch . . . it was a funny thing . . . them switches weren't standard switches, we had to dig some rocks out of the ground . . . and throw this switch over . . . they were flopped over, the ends of the two pipes together and there was a piece of this crooked zigzag piece of iron that was run first in one pipe and then the other so you couldn't lift the one out. But anyway, it was a complicated thing and so we got down there and was digging them things out of them pipes so we could throw the switch for them guys (on the train) so they wouldn't have to stop . . . it took a little time and they hadn't used that switch it seemed like for years and naturally the sand and dust had blown into these pipes and it was all rusty. It took quite a little while . . . then when I raised up and told them to come on, the switch was open. (p. 214)

This sort of dramatic presentation, which was only a portion of one of this patient's preoperative dreams, did not typify all his dreams. The patient was aware that he was to have his blocked blood vessel repaired and blood flow restored. This dream could also be attributed to a mental stimulus rather than a somatic stimulus.

Body Image

In a study by Breger et al. (1971), only one of the five surgical participants was unable to recall any dreams preoperatively at all. Because of advanced colon cancer, he was to receive a colostomy. On his second night postoperatively in the laboratory, he reported a dream of a spring box: "It had a pipe going in and a pipe out and the pipes had a plug . . . possibly it had been some line for a supply of water." Breger et al. speculated that the plugged pipes might have referred to his bowels, which had been "shut off by the colostomy." It is certainly a magnified and dramatic representation, but this plugging dream came after his surgery. The question is then raised whether dreams are determined by a somatic stimulus, as his colostomy apparently was working or his mental concern about his bowels working.

Whitmont and Perera (1989) in discussing body imagery in dreams reported a dream of a woman the day before she had a stroke. In the dream, she saw her house roof pierced by the branches of a tree torn loose in a wind storm. No further information about the dreamer is reported. This anecdote is a very thin reed on which to build a concept of somatic stimuli contributing in a premonitory way to a symbolic awareness in dreams of an impending biological catastrophe, such as a stroke.

In exploring the possible relationship between recurrent dreams and temporal lobe epilepsy, Epstein (1964) reported about a patient who had developed a recurrent dream, which then became incorporated into his seizures. At age 17 the patient developed a stereotypic, repetitive dream of falling and twisting, preceded by thoughts of fighting and in which he always felt very frightened. He had the dream nightly, but it gradually disappeared, only to return at age 33 as an intermittent waking experience. When the dream returned again at age 38, it was always immediately followed by a generalized seizure. Epstein's literature review cited five additional cases in which terrifying recurrent dreams preceded the onset of seizures, later appeared during the day, and finally became incorporated into the seizure at least as a prodrome (an experience prior to a seizure). The question then arises if the dream is linked to the sense of fear rather than to the altered biological state.

Specific Physical Illnesses

Patients with various physical illnesses have reported their dreams, but the validity of the observations are open to serious question. The reports are almost all anecdotal, and if they were from a group of patients, their dreams are often unsystematically collected, inadequately quantified, or inappropriately controlled. The physical illnesses included heart disease, neoplasms, gastrointestinal illness, respiratory disorders, immunological conditions, nervous system derangements, and sleep alterations.

Heart Disease

In a most interesting report of patients with heart disease, R. Smith (1987) investigated whether dreams reflect biological states. His specific hypothesis was that the number of dream references to death for men and to separation for women would correlate with the severity of cardiac disease. R. Smith asked 214 consecutive patients admitted to the nonacute cardiology service to participate, but 119 (56%) did not meet the criteria for inclusion because they were too ill, denied dreaming, or refused to participate. The remaining 95 (44%) were interviewed, and 48 were included in the study because they were able to recall a dream of at least 100 words that was less than 10 months old. Of the 29 men in the study group, 19 had had a coronary angiography and 17 had had a cardiac ejection fraction determination. For the 19 women, 12 had had an angiography and 13 had had an ejection fraction determination. A fellow on the cardiac service used the highest percentage occlusion in any of the coronary vessels to classify the anatomical severity of the heart disease on a 6-point scale. He did the same for the left ventricular ejection fraction. He established these categorizations on the basis of test results from the patient's chart.

Study participants reported their dreams within 48 hours of admission. An interviewer unfamiliar with the hypothesis of the study asked each participant to "tell me your (any) dream [Stage 1], please run through the dream again from the beginning [Stage 2], and last what else comes to mind when thinking about the dream [Stage 3]" (R. Smith, 1987). All three stages yielded both manifest content and associations. Only dreams that occurred within the past 12 months (the average was 54 days prior to admission) and were 100 words or more were used. Two raters used the Gottschalk–Gleser definitions of death and separation to score the dream content and associations from each stage. These raters were unfamiliar with the study hypotheses; their reliability on rating death and separation themes had been determined as acceptable: .89 agreement for death themes and .84 agreement for separation themes. R. Smith corrected the number of content references scored for word length, yielding a "density" score. He reported the death and separation mean and standard deviation scores for manifest content and associations for Stage 1 and for all three stages combined.

R. Smith (1987) found that for men density scores for death references from all three stages showed a significant negative correlation with the ejection fraction ($r = -.50$, $p = .02$) but not with death references in Stage 1 alone. For women, density scores of separation references from interview Stage 1 showed a significant correlation with the ejection fraction ($r = -.50$, $p = .05$) but not with separation references from all three stages. There was no statistically significant correlation for men's scores on death references or women's scores on separation to the degree of those on coronary artery stenosis. R. Smith concluded that the data support the hypothesis that dreams reflect a (functional) biological state.

R. Smith (1987) made a serious attempt to explore dreaming in a physical illness. The care with which he collected and scored the dream report and associations is admirable. His use of clearly defined cardiac illness markers, both anatomic and physiologic, further allows for the possibility of replication. But there are problems about the study and the validity of the inferences drawn. The relationship proposed was between the biological state of the patients and their dreams. No information was provided on how aware the patients were of the severity of their illness. Given the distribution of diagnoses and outcomes such that two-thirds were improved or unchanged at discharge, patients may have known or been told of their relative health status. An inquiry of how ill the patients believed they were would have been appropriate.

The use of the spontaneously recalled dream presents a problem. This dream was selected from a larger pool of dreams the patients experienced, not all of which contained the target topic of death or separation (R. Smith, 1987). In a laboratory-collected dream series from 4 nights of a male patient awaiting surgery on a leg for an aneurysm, only 1 of 14 dreams contained a death reference (Breger et al., 1971). Is the degree of concern about the illness rather than the illness per se the determiner of what dream is recalled and reported?

The statistical analyses of the data are problematic. The means reported were smaller than the standard deviations (R. Smith, 1987), suggesting a highly skewed distribution that probably should have had a log transformation. It is not stated if the correlations were to the percentage occlusion, the ejection fraction, or the categories in which they were grouped. If it were to the categories, then the Pearson statistic is not appropriate because it requires an equal interval between scale points and a normal data distribution, which assesses the potentially linear relationship between the variables.

Some concern exists over the number of correlations calculated and the setting of a significance level at .05. An adjusted level might have been appropriate because a minimum of 15 correlations per gender was recorded. Finally, referring to the dream data as the independent variable and the anatomical and physiological data as the dependent variables is incorrect. The study was correlative, not experimental, neither variable was manipulated, and no causality could be inferred. This content dream study exemplifies the problems that emerge in what may be considered one of the better illness–dream studies. Careful attention to experimental design and statistical application are necessary if valid inferences are to be drawn.

Gastrointestinal Illness

While in psychological treatment, one of my colleagues started to report dreams of savage rectal assault by a wild animal. He then developed a change in bowel habits and was found to have a malignant tumor of the colon, with metastases to the liver. He died within 18 months. This anecdotal report calls attention to the possibility of somatic stimuli, in this case from the bowel, registering cortically and being elaborated as a rectal assault. There has been no systematic examination of dream content in gastrointestinal illnesses that explore the question of what people with gastrointestinal disease dream about and whether there is representation of the illness that might be attributed to either somatic or mental stimulus.

Breger et al. (1971) reported on the laboratory-collected dreams of a 34-year-old man who was in the hospital awaiting surgery for peptic ulcer. He was to undergo a vagotomy and a possible gastric resection. The patient slept for 4 nights preoperatively and 4 nights postoperatively in a sleep laboratory and had dreams collected from awakenings during each of his REM periods of the night. The patient's preoperative dreams contained elements and themes related to surgery and to symbolic representations of his thought and fears. "There were frequent references to surgery, hospitals, patients, doctors and medical instruments" (Breger et al., 1971, p. 214). The dream characters including the patient tended to be "physically handicapped, hurt or inadequate" (p. 214). The preoperative dreams in 53% of the cases referred directly to surgery, whereas the postoperative dreams did in only 8% of the dreams. Bodily deficits appeared in 53% of preoperative dreams, compared with in 30% of the postoperative dreams. The patient believed that the surgery was successful. He dreamt in 39% of the postoperative dreams of a dream character changing or preparing to alter his life but in only 7% of dreams preoperatively. This more detailed but still anecdotal study illustrates that patients dream about an upcoming experience, but the content is related to the patient's conception of the experience and does not suggest that the source of the dream experience was from somatic stimuli.

Respiratory Disorders

The respiratory system is significantly altered during sleep, as reflected in the high rate of disturbances during the sleep of patients with respiratory illness. Klink and Quan (1987) reported on the rate of sleep complaints in patients with respiratory illness as compared with those from a general population. Their data were obtained from participants in the Tucson Epidemiological Study of Obstructive Airway Disease, a prospective longitudinal study of the natural history of obstructive lung disease, which began in 1972. The study was based on a random-stratified sample of the White population of Tucson, Arizona. The sleep data were self-reports obtained from eight questions in the 1985 survey; the illness categorization was self-reported data from the 1984 and 1985 survey. The results were based on data obtained from 2,187 participants, 82.9% of the potential participants. The patients with respiratory disorders (e.g., chronic bronchitis, asthma with chronic bronchitis, and emphysema) showed an increased prevalence of complaints. Of particular interest is the elevated prevalence of nightmares in those with obstructive airway disease (asthma, chronic bronchitis, and emphysema) from 9.9% to 26.3%, compared with 7.1% in those without respiratory disease.

The increased prevalence of nightmares in patients with asthma alone as compared with normal participants (13.1% vs. 7.1% in control participants) in the Klink and Quan (1987) study is perplexing in view of asthma being considered a part of the alexithymic syndrome (Hirsch, Kramer, & Kinney, 1981). People with this syndrome include individuals with psychosomatic or somatoform disorder such as asthma. "They are said to dream only rarely, and they describe what little dream material they produce in bland, literal and concrete form" (Miller, 1986–1987, p. 199). They were perhaps considered to have a functional brain syndrome, analogous to the split-brain patients who have a marked alexithymic cognitive style.

Monday, Montplaisir, and Malo (1987) studied dream recall in asthmatic patients in their sleep laboratory. They compared 12 patients having asthma (4 men and 8 women) with 12 healthy controls, matched for age and gender but without a history of respiratory disease or any other psychosomatic illness. Participants slept for 3 consecutive nights in the sleep laboratory. The first 2 nights the patients slept through the night and were asked to recall their dreams in the morning. On the third night, the patients were awakened from the end of each REM period and asked to report their dreams. Monday et al. found that 10 asthma patients and 10 control participants reported that they had dreamt following Nights 1 and 2. However, only 2 asthma patients compared with 8 control participants reported any dream content (p = .01). However, asthma patients reported more dream experience (81%) than did control participants (61%) after REM sleep on Night 3 and had more vivid dream impressions but could not recall any content (9 asthma patients and 2 control participants, p = .05). There were no dream-content differences between the groups, but the asthma patients' dream-content self-reports had shorter (p = .0001) and fewer sentences (p = .05).

Nielsen, Quelle, Warnes, Malo, and Montplaisir (1997) studied the self-reports of dream and nightmare recall frequency in 33 male and 43 female patients with asthma, as related to scores on alexithymic and neuroticism scales. Dream recall was significantly correlated with alexithymic scores for men (r = −.45, p = .01) but not for women. Nightmare recall was predicted by the neuroticism score in women ($r = .40$, $p = .01$) but not in men. Shapiro, Borrow, Driver, and Catteral (1987) studied dream recall from early and late awakenings in 17 patients with asthma. Each patient slept 3 nonconsecutive nights in the laboratory. Dream recall was as frequent in the men as in the women.

Hirsch et al. (1981) looked at dream-content categories and dream-recall frequency in a self-report study comparing 21 patients with asthma to 21 patients without asthma having obstructive lung disease, in an attempt to control for illness. The content items examined included typical dreams (e.g., being naked in a crowd) and content items supposedly related to issues in patients with asthma (e.g., water, drowning, and mother). The order of frequencies of the content items in the two groups was positively corrected ($r = .84$, $p = .001$). Recall for a recent dream was the same for the two groups, 52.4% for those with asthma and 66.7% for controls. A gender comparison was not statistically significant. The dream content and recall of patients with asthma and patients without asthma but with obstructive lung disease were not found to be statistically different.

Using patients with asthma as the test group, Hirsch et al. (1981) were not able to accept the finding that alexithymia patients have a significant impairment in experiencing or recalling a dream experience. Nightmare frequency was increased in patients with asthma, and content categories were similar to other patients with respiratory disease. Gender differences were not well supported. Working in therapy with patients with anorexia nervosa, another alexithymia group, Wilson (1983) found that dream reporting occurred and could be used in therapy.

To explore directly the effect of a somatic stimulus on dreaming, Gross and Lavie (1994) examined the dreams of patients with obstructive sleep apnea, comparing the dreams from REM periods of those with and without apneas. They studied a group of 33 patients who had a laboratory diagnosis of obstructive sleep apnea and had been successfully treated with nasal continuous positive air pressure. The participants subsequently slept for 2 nights in the laboratory, one with and one without continuous positive air pressure with the order counterbalanced. From the 26 patients who contributed to the final database, Gross and Lavie obtained 78 dream reports from the REM sleep awakenings of participants without apneas and 72 dream reports from the REM sleep awakenings of participants with apnea. The mean number of apneas in the apnea condition was 9.5 (SD = 5), with a mean apnea length of 28 s (SD = 12 s). Two raters scored dream-content data using the Dream Fantasy Scale of Foulkes, selected scales from the Hall–Van de Castle system, a set of 14 content categories related to content changes with altered breathing that might occur in the laboratory, and a global rating scale for scoring the dream content as positive, negative, or neutral. For 30 dreams, the Spearman correlation was .91.

Dream recall tended to be higher in participants with apnea than those without apnea (72% vs. 60%, p = .09), and dream reports were significantly longer (24 words vs. 16 words, p = .05; Gross & Lavie, 1994). When the researchers compared the content categories after a word length correction, no systematic incorporation of the apnea experience could be demonstrated. Dreams after apneas were more negative than dreams after healthy sleep (p = .01). The tendency for dream recall to show an increase in the apnea condition may be related to the patient's sleeping more lightly in the apnea condition and having more arousals during REM (the mean percentage stage at 3/4 sleep in the apnea condition was 4%, nonapnea 19%, p = .01). The global negative quality of the dream content in the apnea condition may be related to the attitude or expectation these patients had that sleeping without the device that had provided them with improvement would lead to poor sleep. Again, no support was demonstrated for the direct or indirect incorporation of a somatic stimulus into the dream.

AIDS and Rheumatoid Arthritis

There are also anecdotal reports of dreams from such diseases as rheumatoid arthritis and AIDS. These are interesting but because they are anecdotal are only suggestive. Levitan (1981) reported on his psychotherapeutic work with 25 women whom he saw in consultation in a rheumatoid arthritis clinic and who remained in treatment with him. Of these, 21 women (84%) reported dreams containing aggressive acts; the other 4 did not report dreams. Almost 56% reported repetitive oral sadistic dreams, all of which commenced before the onset of the illness. Levitan speculated that because the women were the victims of brutal attacks in their dreams, this dream trauma, in which the ego's self-protective devices failed, contributed to the disruption of physiological systems and may be effective in producing a stress disease. This highly speculative, unsubstantiated, but interesting idea is supported by the effects seen in REM behavior disorder (Schenck, Bundlie, Ettinger, & Mahowold, 1986) when REM state motor inhibition is lost and the dream is acted out. Is the traumatic experience inhibited in the rheumatoid patient?

The dreams of patients with AIDS have been used to facilitate their understanding of the dying process (Muff, 1996b) because dreams can be used to facilitate the dreamer's view of any intense life experience. The themes found in their dreams (e.g., wake-up dreams, reassurance dreams, dreams of opposition, separation or coming together dreams, transformation dreams, and spiritual or archetypal dreams; Muff, 1996a) do appear to reflect the dreamer's life circumstance and do not appear to be disease specific.

Dream Formation and the Brain

The brain must be involved in the dreaming process. What changes in dreaming occur with lesions in the brain? In an elegant neuropsychological study directed at establishing what brain structures and brain functions are involved in normal dreaming, Solms (1997) examined the dreaming and neuropsychological functions of 332 neurological and neurosurgical patients with a variety of lesions in different parts of their brain and compared them with 29 control participants with nonbrain nervous system pathology. Solms characterized changes in dreaming by using a clinical interview that inquires about the presence or absence of dreams, quality of sleep, vivacity of dream imagery, affective tone of the dreams, dream frequency, and so forth. He characterized clinical state by routine neurological and neuropsychological work up and classified it in accordance with standard nosological criteria. He established lesion type and site with computerized tomography and magnetic resonance imagery with template projection. Solms identified typical patterns of changes in dreaming and correlated them with clinical signs and symptoms and with site and type of pathology.

It is striking that in Solms's (1997) study, no patients with sensory motor symptoms arising from focal damage to the primary and secondary cortical areas, except the secondary visual cortex, experienced any gross sensory motor symptoms in their dreams. Cortically blind patients could see in their dreams, motor aphasia patients spoke normally in their dreams, and hemiplegic patients experienced normal movement in their dreams. Again, even central somatic stimuli were not the source of alterations in dream content, except in the secondary visual cortex, which is directly involved in dream formation.

Twenty-two of the patients had a lesion localized to the brain stem core, an area that would be critical to the regulation of REM sleep (Solms, 1997). Eighteen of these patients reported the preservation of dreaming. The other 4 patients had hydrocephalus. In 3 other patients with hydrocephalus and a core brain stem lesion who were not able to dream, relief of the hydrocephalus by shunting led to a return of dreaming in 4 weeks. If REM sleep were essential to dreaming, it would be expected that these patients with a core brain stem lesion would report the cessation of dreaming. In a review of the literature, Solms (1997) found no report that core brain stem lesions or the cessation of REM sleep is accompanied by dreaming cessation.

Sixty-four of the patients who reported cessation of dreaming had focal lesions (Solms, 1997). The first group had 55 cases that involved the parietal lobe, particularly the inferior parietal lobule of either hemisphere. This site discriminated significantly between dreaming and nondreaming patients ($p = .0003$). The nondreamers and dreamers had no disturbance of recent or remote memory. The second group of 9 nondreamers had bilateral frontal lobe involvement, where the critical site was the white matter that surrounded the anterior horns of the frontal ventricles ($p = .05$). No other sites discriminated between dreamers and nondreamers. The literature confirms the cessation of dreaming in patients with parietal and frontal lesions (Solms, 1997).

Nondreaming patients reported significantly disturbed sleep when compared with dreaming participants ($p = .01$). This finding by Solms (1997) is consonant with Freud's (1900/1955) view that dreams are the protector rather than the disturber of REM sleep. Two of Solms's patients reported the loss of visual dream imagery with the preservation of dreaming itself. They dreamed in sensations or words rather than pictures. These patients had a waking visual image deficit state as well. Similar cases have been reported in the literature. The site of the lesion in these two patients was medial occipitotemporal.

Nine cases with damage in the area of anterior limbic structures reported difficulty distinguishing dreams from reality, and nine cases with recurring stereotypical nightmares had temporal lobe involvement (Solms, 1997). In these latter cases, the nightmares were seizure equivalents that responded to seizure treatment with a disappearance of the nightmares. Both types of cases have been described in the literature.

Twelve patients with normal dreaming had focal lesions involving the dorsolateral frontal lobe convexity. Ten of the control participants had completely normal dreaming. A picture of normal dream function begins to emerge from Solms's (1997) study of focal brain lesions. His work points out that (a) damage to the brain stem core does not lead to the absence of dream reports, which suggests that REM mechanisms are not essential to psychological dreaming, and (b) damage to the frontal dorsolateral convexity, the executive center for goal-directed motor activity and thought, is not involved and may be inhibited during dreaming.

Patients with damage to the deep medial bifrontal area who did not recall dreaming showed changes in affect regulation, inhibition, and impulse control, whereas nondreamers who had inferior parietal lobule damage if left sided had impaired symbolic operations and if right sided had impaired spatial thought (Solms, 1997). Those with bilateral medial occipital temporal lesions had nonvisual dreaming.

Solms (1997) formulated the view that anything that disturbs sleep can give rise to a dream. Arousing stimuli proceed toward the motor system. During sleep, these centers are inhibited. If the stimulus does not overwhelm the inhibition in the center in the dorsolateral frontal convexity, it is deflected toward the perceptual system and proceeds toward hallucination. The control mechanism is mediated by mediobasal frontal and anterior limbic systems, areas essential for affect regulation, impulse control, and reality testing. They act as a form of censorship. If they break down, an awakening with anxiety and nightmares occurs. If the mediobasal frontal limbic area is functioning, the arousal process is deflected toward the perceptual system. The inferior parietal lobules are activated, providing symbolic (left) and spatial (right) aspects of the dream. The visual contribution occurs last, with the activation of the medial occipital temporal area.

Solms's (1997) study provides a theory that has a cortical rather than brain stem location and provides a striking concordance with Freud's (1900/1955) views of dream formation and function. Solms found dreaming related to the affective aspects rather than the goal-directed aspects of mental functioning. However, this theory needs to be tested in the sleep laboratory.

Heather-Greener, Comstock, and Joyce (1996) noted that negative affect is linked to the occurrence of a migraine and that clinical observations support a relationship between dreams and migraine headaches. However, as the reports were all anecdotal, they undertook a more systematic investigation. They recruited 97 volunteers with migraine headaches to participate in a study of dreaming. The volunteers received four seminars on the physiology of migraine headaches, and then they were asked to participate in a study in which they would record the next five dreams they had before a migraine and the next five dreams they recalled that were not followed by a migraine. Thirty-nine volunteers agreed to participate, and 37 provided usable dream data. Thirty-five of the 37 volunteers were women. The researchers scored dream content using five scales of the Hall–Van de Castle dream-content scoring system. An overall multiple analysis of variance with an alpha of 0.15 indicated significance between migraine and nonmigraine conditions on the five dependent variables ($p = .01$). Invariant F tests showed four of the five variables contributed to the overall effect, namely, anger, misfortune, apprehension, and aggressive interactions but not failure. Heather-Greener et al. concluded that their findings demonstrate that dreams reflecting strong emotions associated with stressful dream content precipitate migraines.

Unfortunately, this study of dreaming in migraine sufferers, as is much of the dream-content literature in physical illness, does not demonstrate what it purports. Heather-Greener et al. (1996) did not state the basis for calling the participants migraine patients, did not indicate the number and reliability of the dream-content scale, did not indicate the length of the dreams, did not include positive dream-content categories, did not limit their conclusions to women, and did not recognize that causation could not be inferred from a correlational study. The effect of a word length correction could alter some or all of their results, as it did in the studies conducted by Monday et al. (1987) and Gross and Lavie (1994).

A discrepancy between dreaming and waking mentation is captured in reports of the dreams of patients with amputations and phantom limb sensations (Frank & Lorenzoni, 1989). These patients reported that half the time they had a different phantom limb in their dreams than what they experienced awake. The conceptual and representational process rather than a simple continuity between waking and dreaming experiences is supported by these observations.

Changes in dreaming can be the result of alterations in sleep. In narcolepsy, there is the experience of vivid dreaming, hypnagogic hallucinations, that accompany the transition to sleep. This is thought to be the result of changes in the control of REM sleep (Douglass, Hays, Pazderka, & Russell, 1991; Lee, Bliwise, Lebret-Bories, Guilleminault, & Dement, 1993). Nightmares, which occur at times of emotional distress in adults (Kramer et al., 1984b), occur more often in women (Ohayon, Morselli, & Guilleminault, 1997), decrease with age (Klink & Quan, 1987), increase following surgery (Brimacome & Macfie, 1993), may begin following the development of illness or the starting or stopping of a medication (Pagel 1989), and can be treated effectively with behavioral techniques (Krakow, Kellner, Neidhart, Pathak, & Lambert, 1993; Palace & Johnson, 1989; Pellicer, 1993). REM behavior disorder is a condition in which the dream is acted out and results from a loss of the motor inhibition that generally accompanies dreaming (Dyken, Lin-Dyken, Seaba, & Yamada, 1995; Schenck et al., 1986).

Can changes in dreaming cause death? Alterations in sleep length in either direction covary with decreased longevity (Kripke et al., 1979). The experience of repetitive traumatic dreams that involve injury to the body may contribute to the production of illness in psychosomatic patients (Levitan, 1980). Reports of death during sleep in Hmong refugees suggest that a frightening dream may "explain" the sudden unexplained death syndrome (Adler, 1994, 1995; Tobin & Friedman, 1983).

Conclusion

There is a long history and continued interest in the relationship between dreams and illness, both mental and physical. The psychodynamic (Freudian) view of the dream as protecting sleep by responding to disturbing stimuli during sleep is supported by experimental work with dreams and neuropsychological investigations of patients with localized brain damage. The content of the dream is altered in psychiatric illness and perhaps in some physical illnesses. Changes in dream content and dream recall may contribute to the success or failure of the adaptational process in illness.

References

Adler, S. (1994). Ethnomedical pathogenesis and Hmong immigrants' sudden nocturnal deaths. *Cultural Medicine and Psychiatry, 18,* 23–59.

Adler, S. (1995). Refugee stress and folk belief: Hmong deaths. *Social Science and Medicine, 40,* 1623–1629.

Antrobus, J. (1993). Dreaming: Could we do without it? In A. Moffitt, M. Kramer, & R. Hoffmann (Eds.), *The functions of dreaming* (pp. 549–558). Albany: State University of New York Press.

Aserinsky, E. (1971). Rapid eye movement and density and pattern in the sleep of normal young adults. *Psychophysiology, 8,* 361–375.

Beck, A. T., & Hurvich, M. S. (1959). Psychological correlates of depression: I. Frequency of masochistic dream content in a private patient sample. *Psychosomatic Medicine, 21,* 50–55.

Breger, L. (1967). The functions of dreams. *Journal of Abnormal Psychology Monograph, 72,* 1–18.

Breger, L., Hunter, I., & Lane, R. (1971). The effect of stress on dreams. *Psychological Issues,* 7(3), *1,* 214.

Brimacome, J., & Macfie, A. (1993). Peri-operative nightmares in surgical patients. *Anesthesia, 48,* 527–529.

Castaldo, V., & Holzman, R. (1969). The effects of hearing one's voice on dreaming content: A replication. *Journal of Nervous and Mental Disease, 148,* 78–82.

Clyde, D. (1963). *Manual for the Clyde Mood Scale.* Miami, FL: University of Miami, Biometric Laboratory.

Douglass, A., Hays, P., Pazderka, F., & Russell, J. (1991). Florid refractory schizophrenias that turn out to be treatable variants of HLA-associated narcolepsy. *Journal of Nervous and Mental Disease, 179,* 12–18.

Dyken, M., Lin-Dyken, D., Seaba, P., & Yamada, T. (1995). Violent sleep-related behavior leading to subdural hemorrhage. *Archives of Neurology, 52,* 318–321.

Ekstrand, B., Barrett, T., West, J., & Maier, W. (1977). The effect of sleep on human long-term memory. In R. Drucker-Colin & J. L. McGaugh (Eds.), *Neurobiology of sleep and memory* (pp. 419–438). New York: Academic Press.

Epstein, A. (1964). Recurrent dreams: Their relationship to temporal lobe seizures. *Archives of General Psychiatry, 10,* 49–54.

Firth, H. (1974). Sleeping pills and dream content. *British Journal of Psychiatry, 124,* 547–553.

Fox, R., Kramer, M., Baldridge, B., Whitman, R., & Ornstein, P. (1968). The experimenter variable in dream research. *Diseases of the Nervous System, 29,* 698–701.

Frank, B., & Lorenzoni, E. (1989). Experiences of phantom limb sensations in dreams. *Psychopathology, 22,* 182–187.

Freemon, F. (1972). *Sleep research: A critical review.* Springfield, IL: Charles C Thomas.

French, T. (1952). *The integration of behavior* (Vol. 1). Chicago: University of Chicago Press.

French, T. (1953). *The integration of behavior* (Vol. 2). Chicago: University of Chicago Press.

French, T. (1958). *The integration of behavior* (Vol. 3). Chicago: University of Chicago Press.

French, T., & Fromm, E. (1964). *Dream interpretation.* New York: Basic Books.

Freud, S. (1955). *The interpretation of dreams.* New York: Basic Books. (Original work published 1900)

Freud, S. (1957). A metapsychological supplement to the theory of dreams. In J. Strachey (Ed. & Trans.), *The standard edition of the complete psychological work of Sigmund Freud* (Vol. 14, pp. 217–235). London: Hogarth Press. (Original work published 1917)

Frosch, J. (1976). Psychoanalytic contributions to the relationship between dreams and psychosis—A critical survey. *International Journal of Psychoanalytic Psychotherapy, 5,* 39–63.

Gross, M., & Lavie, P. (1994). Dreams in sleep apnea patients. *Dreaming, 4,* 195–204.

Hall, C., & Van de Castle, R. (1966). *The content analysis of dreams.* New York: Appleton-Century-Crofts.

Hauri, P., & Linde, S. (1990). *No more sleepless nights.* New York: Wiley.

Heather-Greener, G., Comstock, D., & Joyce, R. (1996). An investigation of the manifest dream content associated with migraine headaches: A study of the dreams that precede nocturnal migraines. *Psychotherapy and Psychosomatics, 65,* 216–221.

Hirsch, N., Kramer, M., & Kinney, L. (1981). Specificity of dream content and dream recall in asthma sufferers. *Sleep Research, 10,* 164.

Jackson, J. H. (1958). *Selected writings of John Hughlings Jackson* (J. Taylor, G. Holmes, & F. Wolse, Eds.; Vol. 2). New York: Basic Books. (Original work published 1911)

Johnson, B., Kramer, M., Bonnet, M., Roth, T., & Jansen, T. (1980). The effect of ketazolam on ocular motility during sleep. *Current Therapeutic Research, 28,* 792–799.

Johnson, L. C., Spinweber, C. L., Gomez, S. A., & Matteson, L. T. (1990). Daytime sleepiness, performance, mood, and nocturnal sleep: The effect of benzodiazepine and caffeine on their relationships. *Sleep, 13,* 121–135.

Jung, C. G. (1974). *Dreams.* Princeton, NJ: Princeton University Press.

Kinney, L., & Kramer, M. (1985). Sleep and sleep responsivity in disturbed dreamers. *Sleep Research, 14,* 178.

Kinney, L., Kramer, M., & Bonnet, M. (1981). Dream incorporation of meaningful names. *Sleep Research, 10,* 157.

Klinger, E. (1971). *Structure and functions of fantasy.* New York: Wiley–Interscience.

Klink, M., & Quan, S. (1987). Prevalence of reported sleep disturbance in a general adult population and their relationship to obstructive airways disease. *Chest, 91,* 540–546.

Krakow, B., Kellner, R., Neidhart, J., Pathak, D., & Lambert, L. (1993). Imagery rehearsal treatment of chronic nightmares: With a thirty month follow-up. *Journal of Behavioral and Experimental Psychiatry, 24,* 325–330.

Kramer, M. (1981). The function of psychological dreaming: A preliminary analysis. In W. P. Koella (Ed.), *Sleep 1980, Fifth European Congress Sleep Research, Amsterdam, 1980* (pp. 182–185). Basel, Switzerland: Karger.

Kramer, M. (1982). The psychology of the dream: Art or science? *Psychiatric Journal of the University of Ottawa, 7,* 87–100.

Kramer, M. (1992). Mood change from night to morning. *Sleep Research, 21,* 153.

Kramer, M. (1993). The selective mood regulatory function of dreaming: An update and revision. In A. Moffit, M. Kramer, & R. Hoffmann (Eds.), *The functions of dreaming* (pp. 139–195). Albany: State University of New York Press.

Kramer, M. (in press). Dreams and psychopathology. In M. Kryger, T. Roth, & W. Dement (Eds.), *Principles and practices of sleep medicine* (3rd ed.). Philadelphia: Saunders.

Kramer, M., Baldridge, B., Whitman, R., Ornstein, P., & Smith, P. (1969). An exploration of the manifest dream in schizophrenic and depressed patients. *Diseases of the Nervous System, 30*(Suppl.), 126–130.

Kramer, M., Brunner, R., & Trinder, J. (1971). Discussion of Miller, J., & Buckley, P., *Dream changes in a manic-depressive cycle.* In J. H. Masserman (Ed.), *Science and psychoanalysis* (pp. 148–151). New York: Grune & Stratton.

Kramer, M., Hlasny, R., Jacobs, G., & Roth, T. (1976). *Do dreams have meaning?* An empirical inquiry. *American Journal of Psychiatry, 133,* 778–781.

Kramer, M., Kinney, L., & Scharf, M. (1983a). Dream incorporation and dream function. In W. P. Koella (Ed.), *Sleep 1982, Sixth European Congress on Sleep Research, Zurich, 1982* (pp. 369–371). Basel, Switzerland: Karger.

Kramer, M., Kinney, L., & Scharf, M. (1983b). Sex differences in dreams. *Psychiatric Journal of the University of Ottawa, 8,* 1–4.

Kramer, M., McQuarrie, E., & Bonnet, M. (1980). Dream differences as a function of REM period. *Sleep Research, 9,* 155.

Kramer, M., McQuarrie, E., & Bonnet, M. (1981). Problem solving in dreaming: An empirical test. In W. P. Koella (Ed.), *Sleep 1980, Fifth European Congress on Sleep Research, Amsterdam, 1980* (pp. 357–360). Basel, Switzerland: Karger.

Kramer, M., Moshiri, A., & Scharf, M. (1982). The organization of mental content in and between the waking and dream state. *Sleep Research, 11,* 106.

Kramer, M., Roehrs, T., & Roth, T. (1972a). Mood change and the physiology of sleep. *Comprehensive Psychiatry, 17,* 161–165.

Kramer, M., Roehrs, T., & Roth, T. (1972b). The relationship between sleep and mood. *Sleep Research, 1,* 193.

Kramer, M., & Roth, T. (1973a). A comparison of dream content in dream reports of schizophrenic and depressive patient groups. *Comprehensive Psychiatry, 14,* 325–329.

Kramer, M., & Roth, T. (1973b). The mood-regulating function of sleep. In W. P. Koella & P. Levin (Eds), *Sleep: Physiology, biochemistry, psychology, pharmacology, and clinical implications. First European Congress on Sleep Research, Basel, 1972* (pp. 563–571). Basel, Switzerland: Karger.

Kramer, M., & Roth, T. (1979). Dreams in psychopathology. In B. Wolman (Ed.), *Handbook of dreams: Research, theories and applications* (pp. 361–387). Von Nostrand–Reinhold.

Kramer, M., & Roth, T. (1980). The relationship of dream content to night–morning mood change. In L. Popoviciv, B. Asgarn, & E. Badin (Eds.), *Sleep 1978, Fourth European Congress on Sleep Research, Tigre-Migres, 1978* (pp. 621–624). Basel, Switzerland: Karger.

Kramer, M., Roth, T., Arand, D., & Bonnet, M. (1981). Waking and dreaming mentation: A test of their interrelationship. *Neuroscience Letters, 221,* 83–86.

Kramer, M., Roth, T., & Cisco, J. (1977). The meaningfulness of dreams. In W. Koella & P. Levin (Eds.), *Sleep 1976, Third European Congress on Sleep Research, Montpellier, 1976* (pp. 314–316). Basel, Switzlerland: Karger.

Kramer, M., Roth, T., & Czaya, J. (1975). Dream development within a REM period. In P. Levin & W. Koella (Eds.), *Sleep 1974, Second European Congress on Sleep Research, Rome, 1974* (pp. 406–408). Basel, Switzerland: Karger.

Kramer, M., Roth, T., & Palmer, T. (1976). The psychological nature of the REM dream report and T.A.T. stories. *Psychiatric Journal of the University of Ottawa, 1,* 128–135.

Kramer, M., Schoen, L., & Kinney, L. (1984a). The dream experience in dream-disturbed Vietnam veterans. In B. van der Kolk (Ed.), *Posttraumatic stress disorders: Psychological and biologic sequelae* (pp. 81–95). Washington, DC: American Psychiatric Press.

Kramer, M., Schoen, L. S., & Kinney, L. (1984b). Psychological and behavioral features of disturbed dreamers. *Psychiatric Journal of the University of Ottawa, 9,* 102–106.

Kramer, M., Trinder, J., & Roth, T. (1972). Dream content analysis of male schizophrenic patients. *Canadian Psychiatric Association Journal, 17,* 251–257.

Kramer, M., Trinder, J., Whitman, R., & Baldridge, B. (1969). The incidence of masochistic dreams in the night collected dreams of depressed subjects. *Psychophysiology, 16,* 250.

Kramer, M., Whitman, R., Baldridge, B., & Lansky, L. (1964). Patterns of dreaming: The interrelationship of the dreams of a night. *Journal of Nervous and Mental Disease, 139,* 426–439.

Kramer, M., Whitman, R., Baldridge, B., & Ornstein, P. (1968). Drugs and dreams. III. The effects of imipramine on the dreams of the depressed. *American Journal of Psychiatry, 124,* 1385–1392.

Kramer, M., Winget, C., & Whitman, R. (1971). A city dreams: A survey approach to normative dream content. *American Journal of Psychiatry, 127,* 1350–1356.

Kripke, D., Simmons, R., Garfinkel, L., & Hammond, E. (1979). Short and long sleep and sleeping pills. *Archives of General Psychiatry, 36,* 103–116.

Lee, J., Bliwise, D., Lebret-Bories, E., Guilleminault, C., & Dement, W. (1993). Dream disturbed sleep in insomnia and narcolepsy. *Journal of Nervous and Mental Disease, 181,* 320–324.

Levitan, H. (1980). Traumatic events in dreams of psychosomatic patients. *Psychotherapy and Psychosomatics, 33,* 226–232.

Levitan, H. (1981). Patterns of hostility revealed in the fantasies and dreams of women with rheumatoid arthritis. *Psychotherapy and Psychosomatics, 35,* 34–43.

Lutz, T., Kramer, M., & Roth, T. (1975). The relationship between mood and performance. *Sleep Research, 4,* 152.

Lysaght, K., Kramer, M., & Roth, T. (1979). Mood differences before and after sleep: A test of its generalizability. *Sleep Research, 8,* 168.

Lysaght, R., Roth, T., Kramer, M., & Salis, P. (1978). Variations in subjective state and body temperature across the day. *Sleep Research, 7,* 308.

Meier, C. A. (1967). *Ancient incubation and modern psychotherapy.* Evanston, IL: Northwestern University Press.

Mellen, R., Duffey, T., & Craig, S. (1993). Manifest content in the dreams of clinical populations. *Journal of Mental Health Counseling, 15,* 170–183.

Miller, L. (1986–1987). Is alexithymia a disconnection syndrome? A neuropsychological perspective. *International Journal of Psychiatry in Medicine, 16,* 199–209.

Monday, J., Montplaisir, J., & Malo, J. (1987). Dream process in asthmatic subjects with nocturnal attacks. *American Journal of Psychiatry, 144,* 638–640.

Muff, J. (1996a). From the wings of night: Dream work with people who have acquired immunodeficiency syndrome. *Holistic Nursing Practice, 10,* 69–87.

Muff, J. (1996b). Images of life on the verge of death: Dreams and drawings of people with AIDS. *Perspectives in Psychiatric Care, 32,* 10–22.

Nielsen, T., Quelle, T., Warnes, H., Malo, J., & Montplaisir, J. (1997). Alexithymia and impoverished dream recall in asthmatic patients: Evidence from self-report measures. *Journal of Psychosomatic Research, 42,* 53–59.

Ohayon, M., Morselli, P., & Guilleminault, C. (1997). Prevalence of nightmares and their relationship to psychopathology and daytime functioning in insomnia subjects. *Sleep, 20,* 340–348.

Pagel, J. (1989). Nightmares. *American Family Physician, 39,* 145–148.

Palace, E., & Johnson, C. (1989). Treatment of recurrent nightmares by the dream reorganization approach. *Journal of Behavioral and Therapeutic Psychiatry, 20,* 219–226.

Pellicer, X. (1993). Eye movement desensitization treatment of a child's nightmares: A case report. *Journal of Therapeutic and Experimental Psychiatry, 24,* 73–75.

Piaget, J. (1962). *Play, dreams and imitation in childhood.* New York: Norton.

Piccione, P., Jacobs, G., Kramer, M., & Roth, T. (1977). The relationship between daily activities, emotions and dream content. *Sleep Research, 6,* 133.

Piccione, P., Thomas, S., Roth, T., & Kramer, M. (1976). Incorporation of the laboratory situation in dreams. *Sleep Research, 5,* 120.

Rechtshaffen, A., Bergman, B., Everson, C., Kushida, C., & Gilland, M. (1989). Sleep deprivation in the rat. X. Integration and discussion of the findings. *Sleep, 12,* 68–87.

Rimon, R., Fujita, M., & Takahata, N. (1986). Mood alterations and sleep. *Japanese Journal of Psychiatry and Neurology, 40,* 153–159.

Roehrs, T., Kramer, M., Lefton, W., Lutz, T., & Roth, T. (1973). Mood before and after sleep. *Sleep Research, 2,* 95.

Rosa, R., Bonnet, M., & Kramer, M. (1983). The relationship of sleep and anxiety in anxious subjects. *Biological Psychiatry, 16,* 119–126.

Rosa, R., Bonnet, M., Warm, J., & Kramer, M. (1981). Recovery of performance during sleep following sleep deprivation. *Sleep Research, 10,* 264.

Ross, R., Ball, W., Sullivan, K., & Caroff, S. (1989). Sleep disturbance as the hallmark of posttraumatic stress disorder. *American Journal of Psychiatry, 146,* 697–707.

Roth, T., Kramer, M., & Lutz, T. (1976). The effects of sleep deprivation on mood. *Psychiatric Journal of the University of Ottawa, 1,* 136–139.

Roth, T., Kramer, M., & Roehrs, T. (1976). Mood before and after sleep. *Psychiatric Journal of the University of Ottawa, 1,* 123–127.

Schenck, C., Bundlie, S., Ettinger, M., & Mahowold, M. (1986). Chronic behavioral disorders of REM sleep: A new category of parasomnia. *Sleep, 9,* 293–308.

Schiller, F. (1985). The inveterate paradox of dreaming. *Archives of Neurology, 42,* 903–906.

Schoen, L., Kramer, M., & Kinney, L. (1984). Auditory thresholds in the dream disturbed. *Sleep Research, 13,* 102.

Schrotter, K. (1951). Experimental dreams. In D. Rappaport (Ed.), *The organization and pathology of thought* (pp. 234–248). New York: Columbia University Press. (Original work published 1912)

Schwartz, J., Kramer, M., & Roth, T. (1974). Triazolam: A new benzodiazepine hypnotic and its effect on mood. *Current Therapeutic Research, 16,* 964–970.

Shafton, A. (1995). *Dream reader: Contemporary approaches to the understanding of dreams.* Albany: State University of New York Press.

Shapiro, C., Borrow, S., Driver, H., & Catteral, J. (1987). Dream recall in male and female asthmatic patients. *Sleep Research, 16,* 262.

Silberer, H. (1951). Auto symbolic phenomenon. In D. Rappaport (Ed.), *The organization and pathology of thought* (pp. 195–207). New York: Columbia University Press. (Original work published 1909)

Smith, E. (1988). Concepts and thought. In R. Sternberg & E. Smith (Eds.), *The psychology of human thought* (pp. 19–49). Cambridge, England: Cambridge University Press.

Smith, R. (1987). Do dreams reflect a biological state? *Journal of Nervous and Mental Disease, 175,* 201–207.

Solms, M. (1997). *The neuropsychology of dreams: A clinico-anatomical study.* Mahwah, NJ: Erlbaum.

Sternberg, R., & Smith, E. (Eds.). (1988). *The psychology of human thought.* Cambridge, England: Cambridge University Press.

Tart, C. T. (1979). From spontaneous event to lucidity: A review of attempts to consciously control nocturnal dreaming. In B. Wolman (Ed.), *Handbook of dreams* (pp. 226–288). New York: Van Nostrand–Reinhold.

Taub, J., Kramer, M., Arand, D., & Jacobs, G. (1978). Nightmare dreams and nightmare confabulations. *Comprehensive Psychiatry, 19,* 285–291.

Tobin, J., & Friedman, J. (1983). Spirits, shamans, and nightmare death: Survivor stress in a Hmong refugee. *American Journal of Orthopsychiatry, 53,* 439–448.

Vaccarino, P., Rosa, R., Bonnet, M., & Kramer, M. (1981). The effect of 40 and 64 hours of sleep deprivation and recovery on mood. *Sleep Research, 10,* 269.

Whitman, R., Kramer, M., & Baldridge, B. (1963a). Experimental study of supervision of psychotherapy. *Archives of General Psychiatry, 9,* 529–535.

Whitman, R., Kramer, M., & Baldridge, B. (1963b). Which dream does the patient tell? *Archives of General Psychiatry, 8,* 277–282.

Whitman, R., Pierce, C., Mass, J., & Baldridge, B. (1962). The dreams of the experimental subject. *Journal of Nervous and Mental Diseases, 134,* 431–439.

Whitmont, C., & Perera, S. (1989). *Dreams as a portal to the source.* New York: Routledge.

Wilkinson, W. (1968). Sleep deprivation: Performance tests for partial and selective sleep deprivation. In L. Abt & B. Reiss (Eds.), *Progress in clinical psychology* (Vol. 17, pp. 28–43). New York: Grune & Stratton.

Wilson, C. (1983). Dream interpretation. In C. Wilson (Ed.), *Fear of being fat* (pp. 245–254). New York: Aronson.

Witkin, H. A., & Lewis, H. B. (1967). Presleep experiences and dreams. In H. Witkin & H. Lewis (Eds.), *Experimental studies of dreaming* (pp. 148–201). New York: Random House.

Chapter

4

Scriptotherapy: The Effects of Writing About Traumatic Events

Joshua M. Smyth and Melanie A. Greenberg

Accumulating evidence suggests that highly stressful or traumatic events, even those experienced in early childhood, can have long-lasting negative consequences on both mental and physical health (e.g., Felitti, 1991; Golding, Cooper, & George, 1997; Kessler & Magee, 1993). The desire to confide in another after highly emotional experiences occurs across eras and cultures (Rimé, 1995). Such interpersonal disclosure may reduce the negative sequelae of traumatic events. In many cases, however, emotions surrounding traumatic events are not expressed to others.

Various personality styles can impede one's ability or willingness to disclose. Patients with alexithymia lack the ability to identify and verbalize their emotional states (Taylor et al., 1988). People who are repressive copers do not readily acknowledge their negative affect (Weinberger, Schwartz, & Davidson, 1979). Some people have a characteristic tendency to self-conceal and keep secrets from others (Larson & Chastain, 1990), whereas others may refrain from disclosure because they are ambivalent and uncertain about the consequences of emotional expression (King & Emmons, 1990).

Even when individuals want to express or discuss traumatic events, social constraints may force them not to (Lepore, Silver, Wortman, & Wayment, 1996; Pennebaker & Harber, 1993). Social constraints that inhibit disclosure come in many forms. Certain cultures and religions value stoicism and consider disclosure of negative affects to be inappropriate. Certain traumatic experiences, such as rape, abuse, or HIV disease, may have a social stigma attached to them. Some people may lack sympathetic or supportive listeners to whom they can disclose. Others may attempt to talk to friends or family but receive responses that are inappropriate or insensitive. Such listeners may, for instance, minimize the event, resort to glib responses (e.g., "it could be worse"), or respond judgmentally. Many people choose not to disclose their traumas to avoid hearing such unhelpful responses. Social networks may abandon people experiencing traumas during times of crisis; this is particularly common in cases of "irrevocable" stressors, such as death or terminal illness, when support providers may feel helpless (Lehman, Wortman, & Williams, 1987). Recently, managed care policies and organizational cost cutting have placed severe restrictions on the number and duration of patient visits to health care providers. Consequently, providers have insufficient time for in-depth discussions with patients about traumatic events. These social constraints can produce a tension between the desire to confide and the fear of negative social consequences should one disclose.

It is important to investigate alternative modalities of expression for use with those who characteristically refrain from interpersonal disclosure or are in circumstances where responsive social support is not readily available. Written disclosure may thus fill a very important niche, providing a mechanism of emotional expression in circumstances where interpersonal expression is not viable or desirable.

Before investigating the empirical evidence for the health benefits of disclosure, we review several early theories derived from the clinical literature that explain adverse reactions to trauma. These theories are not intended to be exhaustive but rather to provide a historical background for writing intervention, which is discussed later. Selections from two broad categories of theory are presented: (a) *abreaction theories*, which explain adverse reactions to traumas as resulting from suppression or repression of affective reactions to traumatic memories and which suggest that recovery of the original memory and release of the appropriate affect are necessary and sufficient to alleviate posttraumatic symptoms, (b) *psychodynamic–cognitive processing theories*, which place adverse reactions to trauma within a broader context of personality dynamics and developmental issues and which attribute negative posttraumatic reactions to inadequate cognitive–affective processing, schematic integration of trauma memories, or both. These theories conceptualize treatment for posttraumatic symptoms as necessitating other elements besides the release of repressed emotions, for example, acquisition of insight into the subjective meanings of the trauma, cognitive integration of the trauma into existing schemas, or development of self-soothing capacities and emotion modulation skills. One theory (Grinker & Spiegel, 1945) has both abreactive and psychodynamic–cognitive processing components, in that it ties neurotic symptomatology to repression but also considers developmental issues and regards abreaction as being insufficient for a cure without the attainment of insight.

Abreaction Theories

Breuer and Freud's Theory of Hysteria

Breuer and Freud's (1893/1966) ideas regarding the effects of trauma on psychological functioning were laid out in *Studies on Hysteria*. Strangulated affect associated with past traumas was the hypothesized cause of hysterical symptoms. They defined trauma in terms of the individual's subjective reaction to the event rather than in terms of objective event characteristics.

> In traumatic neuroses the operative cause of the illness is not the trifling physical injury but the affect of fright—the psychical trauma. Any experience which calls up distressing affects—such

> as those of fright, anxiety, shame, or physical pain—may operate as a trauma of this kind. (Breuer & Freud, 1893/1966, p. 40)

Although Freud (1910) regarded hysterical symptoms as "residues precipitates, they might be called—of emotional experiences" (p. 14), he stated that emotional shock alone was not sufficient to produce hysterical symptoms. There also had to exist circumstances that precluded the emotional expression. Most of Freud's hysterical patients reported experiencing traumas, such as the nursing of sick and dying relatives and incestuous sexual abuse. These types of events typically involve circumstances that may actively impede emotional ventilation.

Breuer and Freud's (1893/1966) theory assumes a hydraulic model of emotional functioning in which traumatic events give rise to fixed quantities of excess psychic energy that seek release. Psychic energy that is not released accumulates and eventually finds pathological substitute modes of expression in physical or psychological symptoms. Breuer and Freud (1893/1966) specified appropriate modes of release.

> The injured person's reaction to a trauma only exercises a cathartic effect if it is an adequate reaction—as, for instance, revenge. But language serves as a substitute for action; by its help, an affect can be "abreacted" almost as effectively. (pp. 42–43)

Thus, Breuer and Freud (1893/1966) considered verbal expression to be an adequate means of expressing affective reactions to traumatic experiences. This assumption formed the basis for a therapeutic technique known as "abreaction" or the "talking cure." As Breuer and Freud (1893/1966) stated,

> for we found, to our great surprise at first, that each individual symptom immediately and permanently disappeared when we had succeeded in bringing to light the memory of the event by which it was provoked and in arousing its accompanying affect, and when the patient had described the event in the greatest possible detail and had put the affect into words. (pp. 40–41)

Thus, Breuer and Freud postulated three sufficient conditions for symptom elimination by abreaction: (a) remembering or thinking about all of the events associated with the onset of a particular symptom, (b) arousing the affect associated with these events, and (c) describing the affect in words.

Breuer and Freud's (1893/1966) seminal work on abreaction greatly contributed to psychology by linking current psychological and physical symptoms to past stressful experiences and proposing a structured psychotherapeutic method for treating patients with unresolved past traumas. Abreaction theory is difficult to test empirically, however, because the concepts are so broad. Definitions of abreaction range from simple, involuntary responses to complex behaviors: "the whole class of voluntary and involuntary reflexes —from tears to acts of revenge—in which, as experience shows us, the affects are discharged" (Breuer & Freud, 1893/1966, p. 42). Although the translation of affect into words forms a prominent part of their method, Breuer and Freud's theory is ambiguous as to the value of nonverbal expressions of affect. Although the talking cure involves only verbal expression, the quotation above suggests that physiological and behavioral forms of discharge might constitute adequate abreaction. Another issue concerns what intensity of affect was required for adequate abreaction. Scheff (1979) suggested that "by 'arousal of affect' they [Breuer and Freud] are usually referring to a very low level of emotional arousal (e.g., animated talk)" (p. 74). This raises the issue of whether more intense affective arousal might also produce or even enhance abreaction.

Scheff's Catharsis Theory

Scheff (1979) proposed a novel variant of abreaction theory, which he termed "catharsis theory." Scheff concurred with Breuer and Freud (1893/1966) that inhibited emotions associated with past stressors could produce physical and psychological symptoms. He argued that distressing, affect-arousing experiences are a normal part of development. Because of societal proscriptions against affective expression, negative emotions are frequently suppressed at the time of the event rather than appropriately expressed and discharged. The result is a continuing build-up of bodily tension that manifests itself in physical symptoms and psychopathology. Thus, like Breuer and Freud, Scheff adopted a hydraulic model of emotion, which assumes that discharge of emotional distress is necessary and sufficient to alleviate symptoms.

Scheff's (1979) view of how emotion should be discharged differed from Breuer and Freud's (1893/1966) however. In Breuer and Freud's talking therapy, each separate traumatic scene associated with the development of a symptom has to be consciously remembered and verbally described. Scheff (1979) suggested an alternative interpretation of Breuer and Freud's findings, namely, "a repeated discharge of emotional tension with which exactly the same scene is charged" is needed (p. 75). To support this argument, Scheff pointed to Breuer and Freud's description of the treatment of Mathilde H., a 19-year-old female patient suffering from depression. Breuer and Freud (1893/1966) wrote the following about Mathilde.

> She was very easily put into a state of deep somnambulism, and I [gave] her commands and suggestions at every visit. She listened to these in deep sleep, to the accompaniment of floods of tears. . . . One day . . . she told me that the cause of her depression was the breaking off of her engagement. . . . I did not succeed in inducing the girl to talk again. I continued to address her while she was in deep somnambulism and saw her burst into tears each time without ever answering me; and one day, round about the anniversary of the engagement, her whole state of depression passed off. (pp. 204–205)

Scheff (1979) argued, based on this case study, that contrary to Breuer and Freud's (1893/1966) thinking, a verbal recounting of the details of a precipitating traumatic event and their accompanying affect is not necessary. Instead, he suggested that intense nonverbal affective expression is sufficient for symptom alleviation. Scheff argued that it is not necessary for patients to remember the precipitating event that caused their distress for catharsis to be effective. Scheff (1979) wrote that

> in most cathartic laughing and crying, the individual is unaware of the unconscious source of distress, as in the case of the cathartic process that takes place in an audience at a theater. Most of the members of the audience, most of the time, do not make any connection between the powerful emotional experiences

> they undergo and events in their own lives. They usually think of their reactions as caused by the events in the drama. (pp. 68–69).

Scheff (1979) described the cathartic process as follows: There should be an arrangement of stimuli that is "optimally distanced." By optimally distanced, Scheff meant that the individual, while re-experiencing the affects associated with a past trauma, should simultaneously be aware of a "context of present safety." Thus, there should be a balance of distressing and reassuring stimuli. In this setting, participants experience a sense of control over the emotional outburst rather than fear that it will go on forever or destroy them. This response can be contrasted with "underdistancing," in which the participant actually re-experiences past affects, and with "overdistanced responding," an intellectualized style involving minimal affective experience. The actual catharsis, signaled by intense emotional displays, such as sobbing with tears or shivering in a cold sweat, results in a sense of relief, decreases in muscle tension, feelings of renewed energy or exhilaration, and clarity of thought.

Scheff's (1979) concept of optimal distance is useful to explain how a patient's re-experiencing of a trauma during therapy may have different, or even opposite, effects compared with the trauma experience. What makes the difference is the sense of present safety, which induces a sense of control, in contrast to the helplessness that the event initially evoked or that may be evoked during the intrusive re-experiencing of the trauma in flashbacks or nightmares. Unfortunately, the environmental conditions that facilitate optimal distancing are not clearly specified, which limits the testability of this hypothesis. It is also not specified whether catharsis is an appropriate method of treatment for normal and clinical populations.

Scheff's (1979) ideas provide creative insights into how intense emotional arousal might enhance physical health and psychological functioning, and they represent a fruitful source of hypotheses for empirical study. For example, a more recent finding of a positive association between frequency of weeping and self-esteem (Vingerhoets, Croon, & van Heck, 1992) indirectly supports

Scheff's proposition that intense emotion has psychological benefits.

Grinker and Spiegel's Psychosomatic Approach

Grinker and Spiegel (1945) explained the neurotic reactions of certain soldiers to combat stress during World War II using both abreaction and psychodynamic–cognitive processing principles. The abreaction component focuses on physical and psychological symptoms resulting from a repression of emotional reactions to combat. The psychodynamic component conceptualizes neurotic symptoms that are due to the dynamic struggles of the ego against the anxiety induced by combat. The cognitive-processing component focuses on abreaction as a precursor to achieving insight and cognitive integration during therapy for posttraumatic reactions.

The theory hypothesizes that combat experience arouses realistic anxiety associated with the threat to life and triggers anxiety associated with unresolved psychic issues, such as dependency needs or control of hostile impulses. In addition, external circumstances contribute to these reactions. Neurotic reactions are more likely when the ego is weakened by illness, fatigue, or repeated exposure to trauma or when the individual's identification with his or her combat unit is weakened. Individuals with more rigid personality types are also more likely to develop and sustain neurotic reactions.

Grinker and Spiegel (1945) outlined five types of neurotic reactions potentially resulting from combat: free anxiety states, depression, phobias, conversion reactions, and psychosomatic disturbances. Free anxiety states occur when the ego is unable to master severe anxiety. Depression is the result of an intense superego reaction in which the person feels unrelieved guilt over such issues as surviving when others did not or having hostile feelings toward authority figures. Phobias, conversion reactions, and psychosomatic disturbances are the ego's defenses against anxiety. In phobias, the anxiety is circumscribed and limited to a few aspects of the trauma, thus reducing anxiety in other situations. Conversion reactions are deficits in physical functioning (e.g., blindness, deafness) that have a symbolic connection to an aspect of the trauma situation. Psychosomatic disturbances are diverse physical symptoms resulting from repressed anxiety, hostility, or both.

The theory expands on the nature and origins of psychosomatic disturbances. In these disturbances, "a persistent or recurrent emotion is only recognized through those activities that normally accompany that emotion, consciousness of the emotion in the form of subjective feeling being absent" (Grinker & Spiegel, 1945, p. 253). In other words, conscious awareness of emotions is repressed, and emotions are experienced as lower level visceral sensations. In 330 psychosomatic cases studied by Grinker and Spiegel, almost half of the patients had gastrointestinal symptoms, and cardiac, dermatological, and joint and muscle symptoms were each reported by more than 10% of the patients.

This theory differs slightly from Breuer and Freud's (1893/1966) abreaction theory in its explanation of why repression occurs. Abreaction theory proposes that emotional repression occurs when external circumstances preclude appropriate emotional expression. In Grinker and Spiegel's (1945) theory, repression occurs when the individual regards conscious experience of the relevant emotion as unacceptable. This may result from external circumstances, such as commanding officers' labeling those who express fear as cowards. Alternatively, internal forces may preclude such expression. For example, to preserve ideal self-images of autonomy, soldiers may repress emotions related to their longing for their family.

Grinker and Spiegel (1945) differentiated between temporary and more severe neurotic reactions. In the former, symptoms subside when soldiers returned home and external dangers were removed. In the latter, symptoms persisted, even when the precipitating stressor was terminated. Prolonged symptomatology was associated with the soldier's deficient ability to discriminate present safety from past danger. Therefore, brief psychotherapy was indicated to uncover repressed reactions and strengthen the ego.

A cornerstone of Grinker and Spiegel's (1945) therapeutic technique is the use of sodium pentathol to induce abreaction of the repressed memories. Pentathol creates a sedative effect, reducing anxiety to manageable levels. The supportive presence of a therapist further strengthens patients' tolerance of the affect associated with reliving the event. Therefore, a good transference relationship is a prerequisite for effective treatment.

In contrast to Breuer and Freud (1893/1966), Grinker and Spiegel (1945) did not regard the re-experiencing of affective memories as sufficient for symptom reduction. Instead, abreaction was a precondition to the subsequent working through, attainment of insight, and cognitive integration of these experiences. They called the treatment "narcosynthesis" to emphasize the synthesis of previously unconscious material into the ego. Using the words of Kubie (1943), Grinker and Spiegel (1945) described the mechanism of therapeutic change as follows:

> It is not merely the recovery of the event which releases the patient, nor merely the recovery of the event plus the feelings and desires which derive from that event. It is the discovery of the totality of the purposes, the hopes, the fears, the loves, the hates which animated the individual at the moment of the event, plus what the event did to those purposes, loves and fears and hates, and how these were deviated by that event from their initial pathway onto another. (Kubie, cited in Grinker & Spiegel, 1945, p. 372)

Grinker and Spiegel's (1945) comprehensive theory conceptualizes neurotic and psychosomatic symptoms as defenses against severe anxiety caused by the trauma, namely, combat. They attributed these reactions to both external conditions and personality vulnerabilities. The external conditions were well described, but the specific personality vulnerabilities were less clear. These authors developed an innovative treatment, using drugs to hasten the pace of abreaction, which fit with the army's need for brief treatment. Their explanation of the mechanism of change in therapy adds to Breuer and Freud's approach by giving a more prominent role to the therapeutic relationship and cognitive changes stemming from abreaction.

Summary

Breuer and Freud (1893/1966) suggested that the cure for psychosomatic disturbances lay in the expression of previously suppressed affect associated with past traumas. They also noted the potential importance of language and verbal representation of emotion in coming to terms with past stressful experiences. Scheff

(1979) made explicit and questioned the assumptions underlying Breuer and Freud's abreaction theory. He suggested that physical and psychological symptoms are not always due to extreme trauma but can result from ongoing and habitual affective inhibition in response to diverse life stressors. He also claimed that verbal descriptions of trauma-related events and affects are not necessary for symptom alleviation; intense nonverbal expression could be as effective, providing the client experienced the expressive situation as safe. These hypotheses have yet to be tested empirically. Grinker and Spiegel (1945) integrated Breuer and Freud's early ideas with more modern psychodynamic theory, suggesting that emotional suppression is most likely to occur when individuals evaluate their initial emotional responses as unacceptable. They developed a treatment approach in which drug-induced abreaction was combined with therapeutic interpretation to enhance cognitive assimilation and insight.

Psychodynamic–Cognitive Processing Theories

The theories below are psychodynamic because they deal with both conscious and unconscious processes and regard personality structures and life patterns as determined by early life experiences. The cognitive-processing aspects of these theories focus on how individuals assimilate cognitive and emotional information about past traumas. Inadequate insight and assimilation are hypothesized to result in longer term psychological deficits.

Janet's Theory of Dissociation

Pierre Janet (1909) emphasized the potentially debilitating effects of trauma. His ideas have been translated from the French and elaborated on by van der Kolk, Brown, and van der Hart (1989). Like the psychodynamic theorists who came after him, Janet emphasized the effects of trauma on personality formation and development. He also emphasized cognitive integration of the trauma into existing worldviews.

His theory hypothesizes that experiences that are not actively dealt with by the individual evoke "vehement emotions" (Janet, 1919). Because intense emotional arousal interferes with appropriate memory storage, highly stressful events are dissociated from consciousness and stored as "unconscious fixed ideas," which are accessible under hypnosis. Dissociated events are subsequently re-experienced in involuntary forms, such as fragmentary images, emotional states, physical symptoms, and behavioral enactments. Traumatized individuals respond automatically to current stressful situations with thoughts, feelings, and behaviors more appropriate to the degree of threat involved in the trauma than to current environmental contingencies.

Memory, according to Janet's (1919) theory, is the "action of telling a story" (p. 661). Memorizing is the process of verbally representing novel experiences and organizing and interpreting these experiences to fit with existing concepts. Posttraumatic amnesias are failures to transform traumas into "less frightening narratives" (Janet, 1904). Such failures allegedly result in individuals' becoming "attached to the trauma. . . . It is . . . as if their personality which definitely stopped at a certain point cannot enlarge any more by the addition or assimilation of new elements" (Janet, 1911, p. 532). Thus, repression of traumatic experiences impedes normal psychological development. Because continued repression requires large expenditures of psychological resources, few resources remain available for the patient's responding to current stressors or developmental hurdles.

This theory has much in common with Breuer and Freud's (1893/1966) abreaction theory. Traumas are defined subjectively as events that overwhelm the psyche by producing intense emotional reactions. Translating traumas into narratives is thought to be curative. Janet (1919) identified many features of posttraumatic stress disorder (PTSD), including memory disturbances, unbidden repetitions, and impaired affect modulation. Some claims, such as the idea that the development of the psyche becomes severely arrested after the repression of a trauma, are stated in an overly broad manner and are difficult to test empirically. Despite the limitations, these ideas concerning the workings and importance to psychological health of conscious memory have inspired later theorists, including Horowitz (1986) and van der Kolk (1987), and form the basis for more modern approaches to trauma.

Krystal's Theory of Catastrophic Trauma

Krystal (1978, 1988) studied the long-term effects of trauma in Holocaust survivors and developed an influential psychoanalytic model of the psychological effects of catastrophic stress. Most interesting to the current discussion are his views regarding how trauma affects emotional functioning. Like Breuer and Freud (1893/1966) and Janet (1911), Krystal defined trauma not in terms of objective stressor characteristics but by the individual's psychological response. He defined catastrophic psychic trauma as a "surrender to what is experienced as unavoidable danger of external or internal origin" (Krystal, 1988, p. 154). Krystal postulated a progression of trauma response from anxiety and hypervigilance when the trauma is appraised as potentially avoidable to the "catatonoid reaction," involving helpless passivity and a blocking of emotional and cognitive reactions in the face of unavoidable danger.

Krystal (1988) compared massive adult trauma to severe infantile trauma and noted that the two differ in phenomenology but are similar in aftereffects. Infants' psyches are immature; therefore, their responses are primarily intense undifferentiated somatic sensations or affective precursors. For infants, the overwhelming affects themselves constitute a trauma, whereas for adults, strong affects can be tolerated, but the experience of helplessness and passivity defines the situation as traumatic.

Krystal (1988) argued that both infantile trauma and extreme adult trauma result in pervasive deficits in the ability to identify, tolerate, and regulate affect:

> Among the direct effects of severe childhood trauma in adults is a lifelong dread of the return of the traumatic state and an expectation of it. Emotions are frequently experienced as trauma screens; hence, there is a fear of one's emotions and an impairment of affect tolerance. (p. 147)

In adults, also, there exists "the expectation of the return of the traumatic *state* and, in particular, the return of the unbearable affective reaction" (p. 159, emphasis in original). One potential aftereffect of severe adult or infantile trauma is alexithymia. This involves a "dedifferentiation of affects," such that emotions are experienced in diffuse, somatized form, without a cognitive or meaning component. Patients with alexithymia cannot verbalize what they feel, differentiate between discrete emotions, or link their bodily states to events in their lives. They experience emotions as sudden floods of undifferentiated affect and psychosomatic symptoms.

Krystal's (1988) theory, perhaps the most comprehensive early psychodynamic account of trauma, is consistent with the extremes of emotional numbing and flooding that characterize patients with PTSD. The idea that the return of the traumatic state, rather than the traumatic event, is feared can help clarify why affective constriction occurs long after the trauma has ended, even in cases where a reoccurrence of the trauma is unlikely. Despite the quality of the ideas, Krystal's writing is difficult to follow, unless one is well versed in psychodynamic theory. The theory suggests that trauma results inevitably in patients with severe deficits. In actuality, reactions to trauma may vary widely, with some people demonstrating successful adaptation and even personal growth following adverse events. Trauma may result in people finding new sources of meaning and mastery, redefining their values and priorities in positive ways, or embarking on new life paths (Greenberg, 1995; Tedeschi, Park, & Calhoun, 1998).

Horowitz's Theory of Stress Responses

Horowitz's (1986) theory of response to stressful events is based on extensive laboratory and fieldwork and clinical observation. His theory has both psychodynamic and cognitive-processing components. The psychodynamic aspect of the theory emphasizes unconscious processes as sources of motivation. The cognitive-processing aspect focuses on memory structures and processes, using cognitive psychology terms such as schemas. Horowitz proposed general response tendencies that appear after a variety of qualitatively and quantitatively different stressful events. Stress responses may persist long after the termination and resolution of an external event, whereas some may appear after a symptom-free interval. One response mode is the intrusive repetition of thought, emotion, or behavior. Because states of intrusion are inherently painful, a second response mode develops, which involves attempts to suppress these intrusions using ideational denial, emotional numbing, and behavioral listlessness. Horowitz's model involves four phases of response: (1) outcry or initial realization that the stressor has occurred, (2) denial and numbness, (3) mixed phase of denial and intrusive repetition, and (4) working through and acceptance. These phases may overlap, and people may go through phases for varying time intervals and in varying sequences.

Horowitz (1975) explained why memories of stressful events recur by referring to two aspects of psychoanalytic theory: a purposeful or egolike function, which serves the purpose of mastery, and an instinctive idlike function, described by Freud as the compulsion to repeat. Horowitz described the workings of this instinctual function in terms of cognitive operations and suggested three basic propositions: (a) Active (short-term) memory storage will repeatedly represent its contents in consciousness, (b) representation will continue until the contents are no longer stored in active memory, and (c) when cognitive processing of the event is complete, the memory will move from active to long-term memory.

Horowitz (1975) argued that in contrast to ordinary events,

> stress events, by definition, will impose some strain on cognitive processing. That is, the working out of how this new information is to be matched and integrated with old information about the self and the world will be hard or time consuming. For a time, there will not be a good enough match. Eventually, schemata of self, objects, attitudes, and expectations will have been revised so that the new memories fit adequately. (p. 1462)

Horowitz and Kaltreider (1980) distinguished between normal and pathological patterns of response to stressful events. In the normal pattern, individuals "dose" themselves with tolerable levels of intrusion, so that they can work through the personal meanings of the event. Thus, the pattern is one of the progressive oscillations between intrusive and avoidant states of decreasing magnitude, leading to a completion of the response. Some individuals, however, develop pathological stress response "syndromes."

> Pathology is not usually the result of some qualitatively different response, but rather of responses that are of such magnitude that the person requires help, or they are responses that do not

> progress towards adaptive completion over an extended time. (Horowitz & Kaltreider, 1980, p. 165)

Pathology occurs when the person's cognitive controls are unsuccessful at regulating intense affective reactions to the event. Controls are broadly defined as "inhibition and facilitation," (Horowitz, 1986, p. 102) and are specifically defined as selecting (a) the topic and ways of thinking about it, (b) schemas of self and others from which to view the information, and (c) information about the topic to focus on or ignore. Pathological stress response syndromes occur when controls are either too rigid or too ineffective. Zilberg, Weiss, and Horowitz (1982) suggested three different forms of stress response syndromes, namely, frozen avoidance, undercontrolled intrusion, and oscillations between states of high intrusion and high avoidance.

In summary, the work of Horowitz and his colleagues (Horowitz, 1975, 1986; Horowitz & Kaltreider, 1980) is conceptually rich and has substantially enhanced theoretical understanding of how people respond to stressful events. This theory can also explain variability in response to trauma and the presence of both normal and pathological reactions. Unfortunately, the different stages in processing a trauma are vaguely defined and lack empirical support. The theory also does not specify the circumstances leading to diverse forms of pathology (e.g., frozen avoidance vs. undercontrolled states). Despite these limitations, research on the relationship of intrusive thoughts to adjustment supports many of Horowitz's ideas (see Greenberg, 1995, for a review).

Summary

Each of the theorists mentioned in this section made an important contribution to trauma theory. Janet (1911) delineated the important role memory and cognitive processing play in promoting adaptation to traumatic events and identified many features of posttraumatic disorder. Krystal's (1978, 1988) model, based on reactions to infantile trauma and extreme stress, highlights the potentially deleterious long-term effects of trauma on emotional functioning. He hypothesized that patients who have experienced trauma fear the return of the psychic state that accompanied the trauma and, as a result, block their experience of emotion. He also observed alexithymia deficits in these patients. Horowitz (1975, 1986) elaborated Janet's general statements about memory into a well-defined theory of cognitive processing associated with stressful events. He suggested that pathological responses to stressful events may be variants of normal responses. He also identified intrusion and avoidance as universal responses to trauma.

Contribution of Theories to Understand Trauma and Implications for Intervention

The early theories were among the first to describe the pervasive effects of trauma on cognitive, affective, and somatic functioning and presaged many of the current diagnostic symptoms criteria for acute stress disorder and PTSD (American Psychiatric Association, 1994). Krystal (1988) observed dissociative symptoms (e.g., numbing, detachment) at the time of the event. Janet (1911) and Horowitz (1975, 1986) described re-experiencing symptoms (e.g., flashbacks, intrusive thoughts); they also noted avoidance. Janet and Krystal noted hyperarousal (e.g., hypervigilance, startle responses). These theories linked traumas to physical or psychosomatic symptomatology, a relationship consistent with subsequent research. Research links past traumas to poorer health status in both the general population (e.g., Golding et al., 1997) and patients with gastrointestinal disorders (Leserman, Zhming, Yuming, & Drossman, 1998; Scarinci, McDonald-Haile, Bradley, & Richter, 1994).

In addition to describing pathological symptoms that can result from trauma, these theories hypothesize various mechanisms mediating symptom formation and reduction. The abreaction theorists have attributed psychosomatic symptoms to repressed affective reactions associated with past traumas and stressors. They have differed in stipulations of the necessary and sufficient conditions for symptom alleviation: Scheff (1979) considered intense emotional discharge occurring in a safe context to be sufficient, even if this was not integrated with verbal and factual memories; Breuer and Freud (1893/1966) considered an integrated recollection of facts and feelings to be sufficient; whereas Grinker and Spiegel (1945) proposed that a cognitive shift had to accompany such abreaction to produce a cure.

Common to the psychodynamic–cognitive processing theories is the assumption that maladjustment following trauma is the result of overly intense or constricted affective responding. Janet (1911) and Krystal (1988) postulated impairments in the ability to tolerate and regulate affect as the mechanism mediating between traumas and symptoms. Horowitz (1975, 1986) postulated that pathology occurs when individuals do not adequately use cognitive controls to regulate their thoughts and feelings about a trauma and to balance intrusive and avoidant phases.

The theorists above all believed that the cure for posttraumatic symptoms involved a cognitive integration of reactions associated with past traumas. For Krystal (1978, 1988), treatment involved teaching patients to put their feelings into words and to manage intense emotional and physiological responses. Janet (1919) advocated for not only the verbal description of feelings but also the translation of the sensory memory fragments of the trauma into an organized narrative that fits with pre-existing concepts and ideas. Similarly, Horowitz (1986) emphasized the need to modulate intense affect, so that the personal meanings of the trauma could be processed and assimilated into the schemas of self and world.

Taken together, these theories suggest that the following conditions should promote adjustment to trauma, symptom reduction, or both: (a) actively confronting the memory of the trauma and associated feelings, (b) putting the feelings associated with the trauma into words, (c) experiencing strong affect, (d) perceiving that one's current affective experience occurs in a safe context, (e) regulating intense physiological arousal so that feelings can be identified and thoughts can be sequentially organized, (f) organizing the sensations and perceptions associated with the trauma into a coherent narrative, (g) gaining insight into the personal meanings of the trauma, and (8) cognitively shifting one's view of the trauma so that it fits with pre-existing schemas.

Although these conditions may best be met in psychodynamic or cognitive–behavioral psychotherapy, a recent, brief expressive writing intervention contains many of these elements and should therefore also be efficacious in facilitating adjustment to trauma. Participants are instructed to write about their deepest thoughts and feelings about a past trauma or ongoing stressor. In so doing, they confront the memory of the trauma, experience and verbalize the associated affect, experience the safety of anonymous disclosure (without a social response), and disclose in a format that promotes sequential organization of thoughts and narrative formation. Disclosing in this format may also promote new insights and cognitive shifts. In the next section, we discuss the evidence regarding the efficacy of expressive writing as a treatment for stress and trauma. Finally, we present a theoretical framework linking the writing manipulation to current research regarding physiological, cognitive, and emotional consequences of trauma.

Writing as a Form of Treatment for Stressful or Traumatic Experiences

Expressive writing has been used to promote good health in controlled studies (Donnelly & Murray, 1991; L'Abate, Boyce, Fraizer, & Russ, 1992; Murray & Segal, 1994). Journal writing has long been used for a variety of goals, from personal exploration to facilitating communication between client and therapist. Progoff's (1977) method of intensive process journaling, for example, has been widely taught and used as a creative process to bring the conscious and unconscious self into alignment. Although this method is popular, we are unaware of any research that examines the efficacy of this method. A brief, written emotional expression task, developed by Pennebaker (e.g., Pennebaker & Beall, 1986), calls for experimental participants to write essays expressing their feelings about traumatic experiences (e.g., "write about your deepest thoughts and feelings about the most traumatic or stressful event you can remember"), while control participants write about innocuous topics (e.g., "write about your plans for the day"). Participants typically write for 20–30 minutes each session on 3–5 consecutive days and are instructed to write continuously, without regard to spelling or grammar.

One of the first questions about the use of this writing task was if people asked to write about highly personal and upsetting material would do so. We have consistently been amazed at the willingness of people to disclose through writing. The topics people write about are serious; rape, family violence, suicide attempts, drug problems, and other traumatic issues are common. Conversely, participants asked to write about neutral topics produce essays on the investigator-selected topics that lack emotion and are, in fact, dull. Three essays are presented in the appendix to give a sense of what—and how—people write about when asked to perform this task. These essays are from the first of three 20-minute writing sessions; the topics were continued for two more writing sessions. Two experimental essays and one control essay are included (essays were transcribed verbatim after identifying information was removed or altered).

Effect of This Writing Task

Researchers using this writing task have examined the effects of written expression on diverse outcomes, including health center visits, affect, immune measures, grade point average (GPA), and re-employment status, and consistently found improvements in individuals writing about traumas, relative to controls. That a brief, written emotional expression task can affect psychological well-being, physical health, and general adaptation several months later is a controversial finding. Interest in the topic has resulted in numerous articles in both prestigious scientific journals and lay publications.

The investigation of the effects of written expression seems especially important, given this widespread publicity. For instance, entering students at a major university are routinely asked to perform this writing task. Any number of people may be "self-prescribing" this writing task, based on lay reports and publications. *American Health,* for instance, published articles entitled "Writing Your Wrongs" (Pennebaker, 1991) and "Writing Off the Unemployment Blues" (Wilenski, 1993), both lauding the benefits of writing about emotional events. Several articles on written expression have appeared in *USA Today* and *Psychology Today.*

The recent popularity and use of this writing task raise a number of important questions, each of which is addressed here. First, is there adequate evidence that emotional writing about traumatic or stressful events produces health benefits? Second, if writing does produce health benefits, how large are the benefits produced, and are those benefits clinically meaningful? Third, what outcomes are influenced by writing? Fourth, what factors are related to or influence the effects produced by this writing task? Fifth, how does writing influence emotional, cognitive, and biological states, and how does this relate to the theories of posttraumatic functioning discussed earlier? Sixth, what can we conclude about this writing task and its potential value as a therapeutic process?

Clinical Benefits

Reviews of research regarding the writing task generally conclude that experimental participants (those who write about traumatic or stressful topics) are superior to control participants (who write about neutral topics) on a variety of measures over the next few months after a trauma (e.g., Pennebaker, 1993). These reviews use the narrative method, in which studies are grouped, the direction and significance of findings are noted, and conclusions are drawn from the number and consistency of the findings. Evaluating numerous or complicated studies, however, quickly becomes overwhelming and can lead to errors (Cooper & Hedges, 1994). This is further exacerbated when individual studies present equivocal results. For example, participants may improve on some measures but not on others. Similarly, some studies reveal dramatic improvements, whereas others show only moderate or no benefit. Accordingly, conclusions from narrative reviews must be taken cautiously.

Several additional questions cannot be addressed by the narrative method. What is the effect size produced by the writing task; that is, what is the size of the relationship between writing and subsequent good health? It is possible that the health improvements, although reliable, are so small as to be negligible. Can written expression meaningfully affect well-being, health, and general adaptation?

The advent of statistical methods for the aggregation and examination of research literature, typically called meta-analysis or research synthesis, provides a more sophisticated and comprehensive process for evaluating a complicated research literature (Cooper & Hedges, 1994). Research synthesis consists of statistical methods for generating an estimate of the effect under observation (in this case, the writing task) by the cumulation of information from all available studies. Furthermore, these methods explicitly place more "weight" on studies of higher quality. Quality is based on such factors as a large sample size, randomized designs, and similar methodological strengths. Although this method is not always appropriate, the use of research synthesis to evaluate new interventions is advocated and is especially warranted when experimental studies exist (Yeaton, Langenbrunner, Smyth, & Wortman, 1995).

The results of a quantitative meta-analysis demonstrate that emotional writing about traumatic or stressful events produces significant health benefits in healthy participants (Smyth, 1998). Thirteen experimental studies, comprising data from over 800 participants, were included in this analysis. The participants in these studies were psychologically and physically healthy—a point we return to later. The binomial effect size display (BESD) is a method of showing the practical importance of an effect size and is presented as the difference in outcome rates between experimental and control groups (Rosenthal & Rubin, 1982). The overall effect size of written expression, in terms of a BESD, is a 23% improvement in the experimental group over the control group. For example, in a population that normally has a 61% chance of catching the flu, experimental participants would have only a 38% (61–23%) chance of catching the flu. Similarly, experimental participants would be 23% more likely to find re-employment after layoffs. Although the outcomes assessed in these studies (e.g., health center visits or short-term immunological status) are not as critical as those assessed in many medical trials (e.g., mortality and morbidity), an effect size of 23% seems clinically important by established medical standards. For example, the effect of written expression on health outcomes has the same magnitude as the effect of azidothymidine on the survival of AIDS patients, a treatment with profound social, policy, and medical implications (Barnes, 1986). Although it is not strictly valid to compare effect sizes between studies with dissimilar outcome measures, this approach can suggest that the effects produced by the writing task are substantial and similar in magnitude to the effects of other psychological interventions.

During the evaluation of the clinical relevance of this intervention, it may be more illustrative to compare this writing task with other psychological, behavioral, and educational treatments. (For ease in comparison, all effect size estimates have been translated into BESD.) In a landmark meta-analysis of psychotherapy outcomes, Smith and Glass (1977) reported an average 32% improvement for those receiving psychotherapy over those who did not. Although their analyses of subgroups (i.e., particular psychotherapeutic orientations) has been challenged, the overall effect size of 32% is comparable, albeit somewhat larger, with the 23% improvement achieved by writing. More recent analyses of psychosocial interventions report similar or smaller effect sizes than that of written expression. Individuals receiving remediation (e.g., drug–alcohol counseling) for driving while intoxicated showed an 8–9% lower recidivism rate than did individuals not receiving remediation (Wells-Parker, Bangert-Drowns, McMillen, & Williams, 1995). A meta-analysis of the effects of psychosocial interventions with adult cancer patients shows improvements ranging from 9% to 14% across various outcome measures (Meyer & Mark, 1995). Lipsey and Wilson (1993) examined effect sizes from 302 meta-analyses of behavioral and educational interventions and reported a 23% average improvement for experiments using random assignment of participants to experimental conditions—the same procedure used in most written expression experiments.

Outcome Benefits

The breadth of the benefits produced by the writing task is revealed through an examination of the various outcomes showing improvements in research. Outcomes include, but are not limited to, depression, anxiety, medical service use (e.g., going to the doctor), immune system function (e.g., natural killer cell activity), academic performance (e.g., GPA), re-employment after layoffs, and reports of upper respiratory illness (colds and influenza). Outcomes comprise four major categories: reported physical health, psychological well-being, physiological functioning, and general adaptation. All outcomes improved at follow-up (typically, 1–4 months postwriting), and the magnitude of effect on any particular outcome did not significantly differ from the effect of writing overall. Another type of outcome, health behaviors, has also been assessed. Health behaviors are behaviors or lifestyles known to affect health and include drinking, smoking, and exercise. These do not seem to be significantly influenced by writing—a fact we return to below.

The improvement in reported physical health, psychological well-being, physiological functioning, and general adaptation after the writing task indicates that the overall effect of writing is not dependent solely on any one outcome type. That is, if one subgroup of outcomes (e.g., subjective well-being) were responsible for the entire effect, other outcome types would not improve. There were, however, differences across various outcomes in the benefits of writing (Smyth, 1998). Psychological well-being and physiological functioning improved more than reported health, which improved more than general adaptation. Although not measured as a health outcome, short-term distress (i.e., pre- to postwriting) also increased after written disclosure.

The effects of writing on psychological well-being and physiological functioning are consistent with theories and research regarding posttraumatic functioning, which we discuss later in this chapter. The impact of writing on reported health outcomes may be lower than on physiological functioning because overall health is only partially mediated by physiological competence. For example, immune function is only one influence on the resistance to disease; diet and exercise also play a part. Similarly, the impact of writing on general adaptation may be even lower because it is mediated by the changes in well-being, reported health, and physiological function. Re-employment may be more likely for individuals with improved well-being (who may be more pleasant), whereas GPA may be higher for those who are healthier (who do not miss classes). This is partially supported by Pennebaker, Mayne, and Francis (1997), who found that higher general adaptation outcomes (GPA and re-employment) were consistently associated with better physical health outcomes. The relationship among all four outcome types is likely to be dynamic. Changes in mood (possibly resulting from changes in well-being), for example, are known to affect the immune system (Knapp, 1990). Improved health can enhance well-being.

The meta-analysis by Smyth (1998) reveals that benefits of the writing task on health behaviors are negligible, indicating that the effects of writing are not achieved through changes in health behaviors. This is somewhat surprising in light of the extensive changes evoked by written expression in other domains. Research suggests that a successful change in health behaviors requires a complex set of conditions, including both the intent to change and the behavioral execution of these intentions (Miller, Shoda, & Hurley, 1996). Health behaviors thus seem to be more influenced by commitment than by emotional factors, although the importance of situational and personal factors is noted (Miller et al., 1996).

Smyth (1998) also found that short-term distress consistently increases from pre- to postwriting sessions. In fact, an unpleasant mood experienced immediately after writing (discussed next) may specifically undermine successful health behavior change. Individuals reported more unpleasant moods, reported fewer positive moods, and showed heightened physiological arousal (e.g., increased blood pressure). Although short-term distress during disclosure has been postulated to predict long-term improvement ("no pain, no gain"), no direct relationships were found. Although all studies report mean increases in distress, participants experiencing relative more intense short-term distress did not benefit more from writing. The universality of short-term distress supports the view of Foa, Riggs, Massie, and Yarczower (1995), who argued that the trauma-relevant fear network must be activated (i.e., fear and anxiety must be experienced) for improvements to be made. The lack of a relationship between short-term distress and longer term improvements suggests that there may be a threshold of distress necessary for improvement, but once this threshold is reached, additional increments in distress do not convey added benefits.

Factors Related to Improvement

One of our goals in this chapter is to evaluate factors that are related to or influence the effect produced on an individual by writing about his or her trauma. Smyth's (1998) meta-analysis reveals that the effects of writing about trauma are moderated by numerous variables, several of which we discuss below.

Student participants improved more on well-being outcomes than nonstudents (although overall improvement did not differ). Student participants were 1st year or transfer students who wrote about the stress or coming to college. Much of this stress may have involved personal insecurity and issues of self-esteem. Nonstudents, however, often wrote about serious, stressful topics, including isolation and loneliness, loss of family, and even thoughts of suicide (Smyth, 1998). Because the nonstudent participants were much older on average, it is tempting to believe they had had more rigidly defined views of the self, which were less susceptible to change during writing. When participants in all studies were examined, however, age was unrelated to improvements in well-being. This suggests that some other aspects unique to the students led to the enhanced improvements in well-being. It is interesting to note that college adjustment has positive as well as negative aspects, in that it brings individuals closer to their life goals and thus may be uniquely related to well-being. Additionally, adjustment to college often consists of ongoing, daily hassles that may have more immediate influences on mood.

Male participants benefited more from writing than did the female participants. Because traditional sex roles make it less likely for men to disclose a trauma or express emotion than women, they may experience greater benefit due to lower prewriting levels of emotional expression (Ptacek, Smith, & Zanas, 1992). Men tend to use more problem-focused coping, thus writing may provide them with alternative strategies, such as cognitive reframing (Ptacek et al., 1992). Although this gender difference is not well understood, it does underscore the importance of not overgeneralizing these findings to samples not adequately represented in existing research (e.g., individuals of various races and of religious beliefs).

The amount of time over which the writing intervention was spaced is positively related to health benefits, implying that the more days that elapse between writing sessions, the stronger the effects (Smyth, 1998). That is, writing once each week over 1 month may be more effective than writing four times within a single week. The number (ranging from 1 to 5) and length of writing sessions, however, seem unrelated to improvement. This suggests that the benefits of writing may occur not only during the 20- or 30-minute session but also in the intersession interval, as participants continue to think about and react emotionally to what they wrote. There is currently no research examining the effect of manipulating the interwriting interval, so this effect must be taken cautiously, but it is certainly an exciting area for future research.

It is also interesting to note that several conceptually important variables, including age, education, and social class, do not predict improvement from the writing task (Pennebaker, 1993; Smyth, 1998). The writing task has been successfully used in groups of varying education, in several languages, and in multiple countries. One compelling example is that writing about traumatic experiences has produced similar benefits for adult professionals with advanced educational degrees (Spera, Buhrfeind, & Pennebaker, 1994) and maximum security prisoners with little education (Richards, Pennebaker, & Beall, 1995). Clearly, more research on individual differences in response to the writing task is needed, but it appears to be a robust intervention that produces benefits in a variety of people.

A Potential Therapeutic Intervention

Although this writing task produces health benefits in healthy participants, it is not known whether there are negative interactions with other treatments or a negative impact on a subset of participants (e.g., those with pre-existing psychopathology). Several ongoing program researchers are evaluating the effects of written expression in clinical samples with both psychological (e.g., PTSD) and somatic (e.g., patients with HIV disease) disorders. Using writing as a therapeutic intervention may also be limited by a hesitation to foster short-term distress in the absence of support resources (e.g., a therapist) because exposure therapy can have negative effects on some participants (Pitman et al., 1991) and writing produces exposure but lacks the possibility of a control provided by a therapist. Conversely, very few (healthy) participants in other studies reported a difficulty in dealing with the negative emotions evoked by writing. A recent examination of the safety of the writing task suggests the negative mood state engendered by writing does not exceed typical levels of distress and is short lived (Hockemeyer, Smyth, Anderson, & Stone, 1999). Although more research on this topic is clearly needed, preliminary data suggest that the writing task is unlikely to produce extreme levels of distress in those writing about traumatic experiences.

Mechanism Links to Health Benefits

Originally, writing was conceptualized to allow individuals to confront upsetting topics, reducing the constraints or inhibitions associated with not talking about the event. As discussed earlier, it was thought that people might wish to disclose traumas but would actively hold back from doing so because of inhibiting personality styles or constraining social environments. From existing animal and psychophysiological literatures, the active inhibition of thoughts, feelings, and behaviors is conceptualized as a form of physiological work. This inhibitory work is reflected in autonomic and central nervous system arousal.

The autonomic nervous system is the part of the nervous system that controls internal organs. It has two parts or branches: the sympathetic branch, which mobilizes the body, and the parasympathetic branch, which conserves the body's energy. When one encounters an environmental stressor or threat, the sympathetic system may react by preparing to fight or flee. The primary effects of the sympathetic branch are to increase the heart rate, inhibit digestion, increase lung flow, dilate the pupils, inhibit saliva flow (dry mouth), release stored energy, and stimulate the production of catecholamines. The primary effects of the parasympathetic branch are antagonistic to the sympathetic branch: It slows heart rate, stimulates digestion, and so forth. The autonomic arousal arising from inhibition can be viewed as a chronic low-level stressor. This prolonged stress response could then cause or exacerbate psychosomatic processes, increasing the risk of illness and other stress-related problems. Just as constraining thoughts, feelings, and behaviors linked to a traumatic event are stressful, disclosing thoughts and feelings about these experiences should, in theory, reduce the stress of inhibition.

Findings to support the inhibition model of psychosomatics are growing. Individuals who conceal their gay status (Cole, Kemeny, Taylor, & Visscher, 1996) or their previous traumatic experiences (Pennebaker, 1993) or who are considered inhibited or shy by others (Kagan, Reznick, & Snidman, 1988) exhibit more health problems than those less inhibited. Although inhibition may contribute to long-term health problems, the idea that disclosure through writing reduces inhibition and should therefore improve health is not as well supported. Greenberg and Stone (1992) found no differences in the health effects of participants writing about traumas of which they had told others, compared with traumas that they had kept secret. Inhibitory personality styles or reports of how inhibited participants feel before and after writing do not consistently relate to health benefits of disclosure. At this point, the role of inhibition in promoting health within the paradigm of writing about trauma is not fully understood.

A complementary theoretical framework can be drawn from traumatic stress and memory research. Traumatic stress research often notes the distinction between memories for ordinary events and those for traumatic events; memories for traumatic events seem immutable and are more emotional and perceptual than declarative (Terr, 1993). They are often initially experienced as sensory fragments of the original event, without verbal descriptors. Visual, olfactory, auditory, and even kinesthetic sensations, as well as intense feelings thought to represent those sensations at the time of the traumatic event, are typically reported (van der Kolk & van der Hart, 1991).

Memories for traumatic events are also thought to be encoded differently than those of nontraumatic events; perhaps this is due to a restricted attentional focus or altered hippocampal memory function due to extreme arousal (van der Kolk, 1994). When under stress, endogenous stress hormones are secreted that influence the strength of memory consolidation (storage). Emotionally charged material, stored in a state of arousal, is more easily recalled during subsequent states of arousal (so-called "state-dependent recall"). Traumatized individuals appear to have lost some discriminatory function of retrieval; trauma-related memory traces are accessed too easily, thus cuing the remembering of the trauma inappropriately. Most notably, the trauma is recalled when it is not relevant to the person's current experience (Pitman & Orr, 1990).

When an individual is intensely upset about a traumatic event, memories cannot be integrated into a personal narrative, resulting in the memory being stored as sensory perceptions, obsessional ruminations, or behavioral re-enactments (e.g., promiscuity in a sexual abuse survivor; Janet, 1909; van der Kolk & van der Hart, 1991). McFarlane (e.g., 1992) and others have noted that it is the persistence of intrusive and distressing symptoms, avoidance, and hyperarousal, not the traumatic memory itself, that result in observed psychological and biological dysfunction.

Traumatized individuals often narrow their attentional focus to be "on guard" for sources of potential threat. Hence, they are prepared for action (fight or flight); they will likely have increased heart rate, sweaty palms, and other symptoms of autonomic arousal. This phenomenon can be experienced too much of the time (chronic physiological overarousal)—a state particularly inappropriate because there is often no current threat to be concerned with. Because this physiological arousal is similar to the physiological state that was present during the onset of the traumatic memory (i.e., during the experience itself), the individual will more readily recall memories of the traumatic event (state-dependent recall). This can result in the experience of involuntary intrusions of the traumatic event, which further increases physiological arousal. This vicious cycle clearly perpetuates both the negative physiological and psychological aspects of traumatic memories.

One goal in treating traumatic memories thus is to facilitate cognitive processing (Foa, Rothbaum, & Molnar, 1995). Foa and Riggs (1993) noted that such memories are particularly disorganized, and treatments to facilitate organization should therefore be particularly effective (because more organized memories should be easier to integrate into existing schemas). This hypothesis is supported by work with both clinical and healthy populations. DeSavino et al. (1993) analyzed victims' trauma-related narratives during exposure and found that decreasing disorganization over time was associated with clinical improvement. Similarly, Pennebaker et al. (1997) found that increased coherence and focus over writing sessions was associated with increased health benefits. Van der Kolk and Fisler (1995) found traumatized individuals initially had no narrative memories of traumatic events and developed narratives over time as they became aware of more elements of the traumatic experience.

Because traumatic memories lack verbal components, they cannot be effectively communicated or organized. Rauch et al. (1996) found a decrease in the activation of Broca's area (the area most involved in the transduction of subjective experience into speech) during the provocation of traumatic memories and a simultaneous increase of the activation in areas of the right hemisphere thought to process intense emotions and visual images. It seems that the lack of a linguistic representation interferes with the development of a personal narrative and the assimilation of traumatic memories. Writing about the traumatic event may force the transduction of the memories from sensory–affective components into an organized, linguistic format (Pennebaker et al., 1997).

Writing about traumatic events may thus facilitate several processes considered central in the treatment of traumatic memory, specifically the deconditioning of memories related to the traumatic event from sensory–physiological responses and the restructuring of dissociated traumatic memories from intrusive reexperiencing of feelings and sensations into a personal, integrated narrative (Foa & Kozak, 1986). Language may be necessary (either through writing or talking) because the deconditioning of traumatic memories and responses does not occur merely by a person's re-experiencing fragments of the trauma (e.g., intrusions, ruminations). The reason for this is that affective and sensory elements of the trauma remain separate from the rest of memory. This separation prevents the creation of an integrated memory that is no longer a trigger for conditioned (fear) responses (van der Kolk, 1997).

The process of emotional writing about traumatic or stressful events may produce positive effects by initially forcing the encoding of the traumatic memory into narrative language. Although the process may initially increase distress, it should modify the cognitive fear structure (or schema) associated with the trauma, in turn facilitating the integration of the traumatic memory. A more integrated memory should reduce intrusive re-experiencing and attenuate conditioned fear responses. This, in turn, should ameliorate chronic hyperarousal, thereby facilitating a reduction of both psychological and physiological symptomatology.

Changes in psychological well-being may result from cognitive shifts after the individual writes either about the trauma itself or about its continued impact on him or her. Pennebaker et al. (1997) analyzed the language that individuals use in writing about emotionally traumatic topics. Certain features of essay writing predicted long-term health improvements, most notably the transition from an unstructured representation to a coherent narrative or story. The increased usage of insight words across writing sessions (e.g., *understand, realize*) was also associated with more health improvement. Improved insight may reduce the long-term anxiety associated with memories of the trauma (i.e., assimilation of the traumatic memory and deconditioning of fear responses).

The clear physiological consequences of writing support its biological impact. As mentioned, writing on emotional topics may free physiological resources previously used for inhibition, resulting in observed changes in physiological measures. It is also known that traumas and their associated memories can alter a variety of biological systems. Although space considerations preclude a full discussion of this issue, these reactions to traumatic stress can be grouped into four main areas: psychophysiologic, neurohormonal, neuroanatomical, and immunological effects. Psychophysiological effects include strong autonomic responses both to memories of trauma and to other intense stimuli that are not trauma related. Neurohormonal effects include alterations in a variety of neurohormonal functions (e.g., cortisol secretion, norepinephrine levels) and downregulation ("disactivation") of adrenergic receptors. Neuroanatomical effects include decreased hippocampal volume, amygdala activation, suppression of Broca's area in traumatic memory flashbacks, and right hemispheric lateralization. Finally, a variety of changes in immunological parameters are noted that suggest less effective immune function in terms of disease resistance (see van der Kolk, 1994, for a complete discussion of these issues).

Writing may also promote the formation of a narrative and cognitive assimilation of the traumatic memory. Such assimilation may reduce intrusions and hyperreactivity provoked by internal and external reminders of the trauma, ultimately attenuating physiological responses and alterations. More research is clearly needed, however, to elucidate the undoubtedly complex relations among ongoing intrusive thoughts, assimilation, and physiological functioning.

Relationship Between Theoretical Perspective and Early Trauma Theories

The theoretical perspective was drawn from research on the physiological and cognitive sequelae of trauma, yet these findings are surprisingly consistent with the early clinical insights of the early trauma theorists. In some cases, these theories directly influence the research. For example, van der Kolk and Fisler (1995) wrote that their study on the sensory, nonverbal nature of traumatic memory "merely confirmed Janet's century-old clinical observations" (p. 520). We attribute the benefits of writing to the translation of sensory–physiological responses into language and the construction of narratives, which provide structure and therefore facilitate cognitive integration with pre-existing ideas and concepts. Our theoretical perspective is essentially an integration and elaboration of ideas derived from Janet (1909, 1919) and Horowitz (1986). Researchers and theorists developing the scriptotherapy intervention are indebted to these theorists.

Conclusion

Both subjective and quantitative evaluations of the evidence support the conclusion that written expression about traumatic or stressful events benefits both somatic and psychological health. The amount of benefit depends on the outcome measure used, perhaps due to varying association with underlying mechanism(s) or the dynamic relationships between the various outcome types. The degree to which someone improved after writing was related to several factors, including gender, student status, and intervention parameters. Because such individual differences in response to writing exist, extant research cannot easily be generalized to subgroups who were not well represented. A theoretical explanation of how these changes may occur was presented, focusing primarily on how writing may promote the formation of a structured narrative out of previously unstructured sensory fragments. This new structure should lead to the cognitive assimilation of traumatic memories and subsequent biological alterations. This explanation is consistent with older, cognitive-processing theories of posttraumatic functioning, most notably, those of Janet (1909, 1919) and Horowitz (1986). Note that although plausible, this model is speculative and must be tested in future research.

Future Research Directions

The health benefits of writing about emotionally traumatic events seem clear for healthy individuals. Future research studies should examine the efficacy of writing for clinical patients. We can speculate that writing might be a useful adjunct to insight-oriented psychotherapy. Writing could provide the opportunity for patients to explore their reactions to past events without having to explain their actions or feelings to others or face social judgment. Furthermore, writing gives clients the freedom to face painful emotions at their own pace. Thus, this technique may be an important initial exposure for avoidant patients who are hesitant to discuss trauma-related affects with their therapist. Patients can also be encouraged to write down their dreams and intrusive thoughts and feelings about past traumas as they occur and to bring these diaries into therapy. The immediacy and emotional salience of this material makes it a potentially valuable therapeutic tool. Finally, writing could help patients to organize new insights that emerge during therapy. Writing down these new interpretations and contrasting them with their previous perspectives should enhance their salience and emotional significance. Furthermore, writing could facilitate the construction of narratives, integrating new understandings with prior self- and worldviews.

Clinical trials are needed to examine the efficacy of written disclosure for diverse populations. Kelly, Lumley, and Leisen's (1997) controlled study demonstrates that verbal disclosure of reactions to stressful events are associated with reduced reports of affective disturbance and physical disability in patients with rheumatoid arthritis. It would be important to replicate these results using written disclosure, large samples, and alternative measures of health status. Furthermore, it would be desirable to test the effects of written disclosure in patients with diseases for which research shows a link between emotional inhibition and health status. These include cancer and asthma. Grinker and Spiegel (1945) observed that gastrointestinal, cardiac, dermatological, and joint and muscle symptoms were associated with unresolved past traumas, suggesting the potential applicability of written disclosure for patients with these disorders. Written disclosure may also be relevant to populations who face social stigma and therefore may chronically inhibit important aspects of their identity or experience. These include ethnic minorities, gay men and lesbians, and women who have been raped or sexually abused. Future researchers should also examine whether written disclosure is effective with individuals from other cultures. In some cultures, for example, open expression of negative emotions is regarded as unacceptable. This attitude may make people less willing to engage in disclosure and may limit the benefits obtained. Finally, the efficacy of disclosure for individuals facing a change in social roles should be explored. Research shows that disclosure enhances the participants' adjustment to college and unemployment, suggesting that it might also enhance a person's adjustment to other developmental transitions or life crises, including marriage, pregnancy, divorce, and bereavement.

References

American Psychiatric Association. (1994). *Diagnostic and statistical manual of mental disorders* (4th ed.). Washington, DC: Author.

Barnes, D. (1986). Promising results halt trial of anti-AIDS drug. *Science, 234,* 15–16.

Breuer, J., & Freud, S. (1966). *Studies on hysteria.* New York: Avon Books. (Original work published 1893)

Cole, S. W., Kemeny, M. W., Taylor, S. E., & Visscher, B. R. (1996). Elevated health risk among men who conceal their homosexuality. *Health Psychology, 15,* 243–251.

Cooper, H., & Hedges, L. (1994). *The handbook of research synthesis.* New York: Russell Sage Foundation.

DeSavino, P., Turk, E., Massie, E., Riggs, D., Penkower, D., Molnar, C., & Foa, E. (1993, November). *The content of traumatic memories: Evaluating treatment efficacy by analysis of verbatim descriptions of the rape scene.* Paper presented at the 27th annual meeting of the Association for the Advancement of Behavior Therapy, Atlanta, GA.

Donnelly, D., & Murray, E. (1991). Cognitive and emotional changes in written essays and therapy interviews. *Journal of Social and Clinical Psychology, 10,* 334–350.

Felitti, V. J. (1991). Long-term medical consequences of incest, rape, and molestation. *Southern Medical Journal, 84,* 328–331.

Foa, E. B., & Kozak, M. J. (1986). Emotional processing of fear: Exposure to corrective information. *Psychological Bulletin, 99,* 20–35.

Foa, E. B., & Riggs, D. S. (1993). Posttraumatic stress disorder in rape victims. *American Psychiatric Press Review of Psychiatry, 12,* 273–303.

Foa, E. B., Riggs, D. S., Massie, E. D., & Yarczower, M. (1995). The impact of fear activation and anger on the efficacy of exposure treatment for posttraumatic stress disorder. *Behavior Therapy, 26,* 487–499.

Foa, E. B., Rothbaum, B., & Molnar, C. (1995). Cognitive–behavioral treatment of posttraumatic stress disorder. In M. Friedman, D. S. Charney, & A. Y. Deutch (Eds.), *Neurobiological and clinical consequences of stress: From normal adaptation to posttraumatic stress disorder* (pp. 483–494). New York: Raven Press.

Freud, S. (1910). *Five lectures on psychoanalysis.* London: Hogarth.

Golding, J. M., Cooper, M. L., & George, L. K. (1997). Sexual assault history and health perceptions: Seven general population studies. *Health Psychology, 16,* 417–425.

Greenberg, M. A. (1995). Cognitive processing of traumas: The role of intrusive thoughts and reappraisals. *Journal of Applied Social Psychology, 25,* 1262–1296.

Greenberg, M. A., & Stone, A. A. (1992). Emotional disclosure about traumas and its relation to health: Effects of previous disclosure and trauma severity. *Journal of Personality and Social Psychology, 63,* 75–84.

Grinker, R. R., & Spiegel, J. P. (1945). *Men under stress.* York, PA: Blakiston.

Hockemeyer, J., Smyth, J., Anderson, C., & Stone, A. (1999, March). *Is it safe to write? Evaluating the short-term distress produced by writing about emotionally traumatic experiences.* Poster session presented at the annual meeting of the American Psychosomatic Society, Vancouver, British Columbia, Canada.

Horowitz, M. J. (1975). Intrusive and repetitive thoughts after experimental stress. *Archives of General Psychiatry, 32,* 1457–1463.

Horowitz, M. J. (1986). *Stress response syndromes* (2nd ed.). Northvale, NJ: Aronson.

Horowitz, M. J., & Kaltreider, N. B. (1980). Brief psychotherapy of stress response syndromes. In T. B. Karasu & L. Bellak (Eds.), *Specialized techniques in individual psychotherapy.* New York: Brunner/Mazel.

Janet, P. (1904). L'amnesie et la dissociation des souvenirs par l'emotion [Amnesia and the dissociation of memories by emotion]. *Journal de Psychologie, 1,* 417–453.

Janet, P. (1909). *Les névroses* [The neuroses]. Paris, France: Flammarion.

Janet, P. (1911). *L'etat mental des hysteriques* [The mental state of hysterics] (2nd ed.). Paris, France: Alcan.

Janet, P. (1919). *Les medications psychologiques* [The psychological medications] (Vols. 1–3). Paris, France: Alcan.

Kagan, J., Reznick, J. S., & Snidman, N. (1988). Biological bases of childhood shyness. *Science, 240,* 167–171.

Kelly, J. E., Lumley, M. A., & Leisen, J. C. (1997). Health effects of emotional disclosure in rheumatoid arthritis patients. *Health Psychology, 16,* 331–340.

Kessler, R. C., & Magee, W. J. (1993). Childhood adversities and adult depression: Basic patterns of association in a U.S. national survey. *Psychological Medicine, 23,* 679–690.

King, L. A., & Emmons, R. A. (1990). Conflict over emotional expression: Psychological and physical correlates. *Journal of Personality and Social Psychology, 58,* 864–877.

Knapp, P. (1990). Short-term immunological effect of induced emotion. *Psychosomatic Medicine, 52,* 246–252.

Krystal, H. (1978). Trauma and affect. *Psychoanalytic Study of the Child, 33,* 81–116.

Krystal, H. (1988). *Integration and self-healing: Affect, trauma, alexithymia.* Hillsdale, NJ: Analytic Press.

Kubie, L. S. (1943). The nature of psychotherapy. *Bulletin of the New York Academy of Medicine, 19,* 183.

L'Abate, L., Boyce, J., Fraizer, R., & Russ, D. (1992). Programmed writing: Research in progress. *Comprehensive Mental Health Care, 2,* 45–62.

Larson, D. G., & Chastain, R. L. (1990). Self-concealment: Conceptualization, measurement, and health implications. *Journal of Social and Clinical Psychology, 9,* 439–455.

Lehman, D., Wortman, C., & Williams, A. (1987). Long-term effects of losing a spouse or child in a motor vehicle crash. *Journal of Personality and Social Psychology, 52,* 218–231.

Lepore, S., Silver, R., Wortman, C., & Wayment, H. (1996). Social constraints, intrusive thoughts, and depressive symptoms among bereaved mothers. *Journal of Personality and Social Psychology, 70,* 271–282.

Leserman, J., Zhming, L., Yuming, J. B. H., & Drossman, D. A. (1998). How multiple types of stressors impact on health. *Psychosomatic Medicine, 60,* 175–181.

Lipsey, M., & Wilson, D. (1993). The efficacy of psychological, educational, and behavioral treatment: Confirmation from meta-analysis. *American Psychologist, 48,* 1181–1209.

McFarlane, A. (1992). Avoidance and intrusion in posttraumatic stress disorder. *Journal of Nervous and Mental Disease, 180,* 439–445.

Meyer, T., & Mark, M. (1995). Effects of psychosocial interventions with adult cancer patients: A meta-analysis of randomized experiments. *Health Psychology, 14,* 101–108.

Miller, S., Shoda, Y., & Hurley, K. (1996). Applying cognitive–social theory to health-protective behavior: Breast self-examination in cancer screening. *Psychological Bulletin, 119,* 70–94.

Murray, E. J., & Segal, D. L. (1994). Emotional processing in vocal and written expression of feelings about traumatic experiences. *Journal of Traumatic Stress, 7,* 391–405.

Pennebaker, J. W. (1991, January–February). Writing your wrongs. *American Health, 10,* 64–67.

Pennebaker, J. W. (1993). Putting stress into words: Health, linguistic, and therapeutic implications. *Behaviour Research and Therapy, 31,* 539–548.

Pennebaker, J. W., & Beall, S. (1986). Confronting a traumatic event: Toward an understanding of inhibition and disease. *Journal of Abnormal Psychology, 95,* 274–281.

Pennebaker, J., & Harber, H. (1993). A social stage model of collective coping: The Loma Prieta earthquake and the Persian Gulf War. *Journal of Social Issues, 49,* 125–146.

Pennebaker, J., Mayne, T., & Francis, M. (1997). Linguistic predictors of adaptive bereavement. *Journal of Personality and Social Psychology, 72,* 863–871.

Pitman, R., Altman, B., Greenwald, E., Longpre, R., Macklin, M., Poire, R., & Steketee, G. (1991). Psychiatric complications during flooding therapy for posttraumatic stress disorder. *Journal of Clinical Psychiatry, 52,* 17–20.

Pitman, R. K., & Orr, S. P. (1990). The black hole of trauma. *Biological Psychiatry, 27,* 469–471.

Progoff, I. (1977). *At a journal workshop: The basic text and guide for using the Intensive Journal.* New York: Dialogue House Library.

Ptacek, J., Smith, R., & Zanas, J. (1992). Gender, appraisal, and coping: A longitudinal analysis. *Journal of Personality, 60,* 747–770.

Rauch, S. L., van der Kolk, B. A., Fisler, R. E., Alpert, N. M., Orr, S., Savage, C., Fischman, A., Jenike, M., & Pitman, R. (1996). A symptom provocation study of posttraumatic stress disorder using positron emission tomography and script-driven imagery. *Archives of General Psychiatry, 53,* 380–387.

Richards, J., Pennebaker, J., & Beall, W. (1995). *The effects of criminal offense and disclosure of trauma on anxiety and illness behavior in prison inmates.* Unpublished manuscript, Southern Methodist University, Austin, TX.

Rimé, B. (1995). Mental rumination, social sharing, and recovery from emotional exposure. In J. Pennebaker (Ed.), *Emotion, disclosure, and health* (pp. 271–291). Washington, DC: American Psychological Association.

Rosenthal, R., & Rubin, D. (1982). A simple, general purpose display of magnitude of experimental effect. *Journal of Educational Psychology, 74,* 166–199.

Scarinci, I. C., McDonald-Haile, J., Bradley, L. A., & Richter, J. E. (1994). Altered pain perception and psychosocial features among women with gastrointestinal disorders and a history of abuse: A preliminary model. *American Journal of Medicine, 97,* 108–118.

Scheff, T. J. (1979). *Catharsis in healing, ritual, and drama.* Berkeley: University of California Press.

Smith, H., & Glass, G. (1977). Meta-analysis of psychotherapy outcome studies. *American Psychologist, 32,* 752–760.

Smyth, J. M. (1998). Written emotional expression: Effect sizes, outcome types, and moderating variables. *Journal of Consulting and Clinical Psychology, 66,* 174–184.

Spera, S. P., Buhrfeind, E. D., & Pennebaker, J. W. (1994). Expressive writing and coping with job loss. *Academy of Management Journal, 37,* 722–733.

Taylor, G. J., Bagby, R. M., Ryan, D., Parker, J. D. A., Doody, K., & Keefe, P. (1988). Criterion validity of the Toronto Alexithymia Scale. *Psychosomatic Medicine, 50,* 500–509.

Tedeschi, R. G., Park, C. L., & Calhoun, L. G. (Eds.). (1998). *Posttraumatic growth: Positive changes in the aftermath of crisis.* Mahwah, NJ: Erlbaum.

Terr, L. (1993). *Unchained memories: True stories of traumatic memories, lost and found.* New York: Basic Books.

van der Kolk, B. (1987). *Psychological trauma.* Washington, DC: American Psychiatric Press.

van der Kolk, B. (1994). The body keeps the score: Memory and the evolving psychobiology of posttraumatic stress. *Harvard Review of Psychiatry, 1,* 253–265.

van der Kolk, B. (1997). The psychobiology of posttraumatic stress disorder. *Journal of Clinical Psychiatry, 59*(Suppl. 9), 16–24.

van der Kolk, B. A., Brown, P., & van der Hart, O. (1989). Pierre Janet on post-traumatic stress. *Journal of Traumatic Stress, 2,* 365–378.

van der Kolk, B., & Fisler, R. (1995). Dissociation and the fragmentary nature of traumatic memories: Review and experimental confirmation. *Journal of Traumatic Stress, 8,* 505–525.

van der Kolk, B., & van der Hart, O. (1991). The intrusive past: The flexibility of memory and the engraving of trauma. *American Imago, 48,* 425–454.

Vingerhoets, A., Croon, M., & van Heck, G. (1992, April). *Weeping and personality.* Poster session presented at the annual meeting of the American Psychosomatic Society, New York.

Weinberger, D. A., Schwartz, G. E., & Davidson, R. J. (1979). Low-anxious, high-anxious, and repressive coping styles: Psychometric patterns and behavioral and physiological responses to stress. *Journal of Abnormal Psychology, 88,* 369–380.

Wells-Parker, E., Bangert-Drowns, R., McMillen, R., & Williams, M. (1995). Final results from a meta-analysis of remedial interventions with drink/drive offenders. *Addiction, 90,* 907–926.

Wilenski, D. (1993, June). Writing off the unemployment blues. *American Health, 12,* 35.

Yeaton, W., Langenbrunner, B., Smyth, J., & Wortman, P. (1995). Exploratory research synthesis: Methodological considerations for addressing limitations in data quality. *Evaluation and the Health Professions, 18,* 283–303.

Zilberg, N. J., Weiss, D. S., & Horowitz, M. J. (1982). Impact of Event Scale: A cross-validation study and some empirical evidence supporting a conceptual model of stress response syndromes. *Journal of Consulting and Clinical Psychology, 50,* 407–414.

Appendix
Experimental Essay 1

The most stressful time in my life happened many years ago. My oldest son made his first communion—as well as five or six other neighborhood children. There were a few individual parties going on but we were having one together with good friends down the block. (I have three boys—my youngest at the time was going to turn 2 in a week.) Since there was so much going on in the neighborhood, I felt that the biggest possible danger was the roads—cars were parked up + down the sides + it would be difficult to see if anyone were to run out from between the cars. The children were all playing in J's back yard—it was equipped with a play house, sand box, jungle gym, and above ground pool which of course wasn't opened yet. I let David (my baby) go out to play with the older children, thinking that he would be safe with his older brothers with him—I checked to make sure that the gates were secure + went back in the house. After about 30 min the children started coming back in + I didn't see David with them. I went out back to check on him—checking the gates first—+ eventually finding him floating in the water on top of the pool cover. To this day I can't figure out how he got in the pool—there was no ladder, stool, chair around. There happened to be a beach ball floating on the water so I guess he was trying to get it. I don't even know how I got in the pool (my upper body strength was never strong enough to pull my weight up + over the 4 foot pool before). When I got to David he wasn't breathing + was already turning a strange color of blue. I couldn't get both of us out of the pool without dropping him so I sat there trying to scream. I'm not sure if any sound came out—because it seemed like forever before anyone heard me. I didn't know CPR at the time so I didn't know that I could have been helping David while we were still in the pool. When help finally arrived—David was put on the ground + CPR was started. J was the first one to start—he wasn't responding so someone suggested getting help.

Experimental Essay 2

One of the most stressful times of my life was the death of my husbin—after years of his illness.

It was hard coping with him when I hurt also. Many times I wanted to walk away—but couldn't. This lasted for 8 years. Back + fourth to the Hosp. He always insisted I stay with him but I wanted to get away. Wanting me to get the nurses when he couldn't get them on the Buzzer. He was always so—impatient. It imbarised me to bother them because I knew they were doing everything they could for him.

My life as a farm wife was very stressful. Rasing 4 children who hated it also. They had to work also especily the 2 Boys. One left home as soon as he could after getting out of school. Didn't see him for 4 years. Now he come back after he married and my Husbin retired from farm. They never got close.

Control Essay

Got up at 6 am, got ready for work. Fixed breakfast, lunch, walked 10 mins. on treadmill, ate, fed dog went to work. Spoke with boss on phone (he's away on business). Cleared messages on lotus notes, gave people locker info, answered phones, tried to get some work done. At 11:30 went to work with Volunteer Services for one hour planting bulbs + plants. Back in office I did some more work, answered phones. Then at 1:30 went for a 1 mi walk with friends. Came back to office + had a call from my son. Some good news regarding his compensation situation. Worked on incoming mail, took care of some mail. Worked on P's party arrangements for tomorrow's party. Four new people signed up. Called restaurant with new amount of people. Talked to 2nd boss, J regarding arrangements—whether or not we can do a cake on Monday for employee D, who's turning 80. We all say "yes" J says "no." We overruled her decision—she's the Business Mgr—D get's a birthday cake on Monday at Staff Meeting. Talked to P regarding Monday; Columbus Day. I was to be off all day, but I should be at Staff Mtg for D's cake. Will probably work 1/2 day Mon + 1/2 day Tuesday. Assigned work to student worker, M., regarding classes. A few things needed to be corrected on my data base. Talked to J about P's party—did they get the sweatshirt that was ordered—(yes) what about a flowers (she'll take care of that).

Chapter

5

The Assumed Necessity of Working Through Memories of Traumatic Experiences

George A. Bonanno and Stacey Kaltman

One of the cornerstones of early psychoanalytic theory and now axiomatic within the broader disciplines of psychology and psychiatry is the assumption that memories for painful or traumatic experiences must be *worked through* (i.e., they must be re-experienced, expressed, and talked about) and that the failure to do so ultimately results in poor adjustment or increased somatic distress. In this chapter, we begin by examining Freud's original exposition of the working through assumption and its theoretical dependency on the construct of repression. We note the conceptual limitations of the idea of repression and suggest that the assumed importance of working through memories of traumatic experience can be explained to some extent as a product of assumptions inherent in late 19th-century Western culture. We next review recent research and theory in the cognitive neuroscience that illuminates both the ways normal, everyday events are processed and integrated into existing memory structures and the ways that highly stressful or traumatic experiences tend to disrupt memory consolidation. On the basis of these data, we suggest that traumatic memories are relatively inaccessible and difficult to control, not because of repression but because of limited encoding.

In the next section, we review two bodies of recent experimental evidence on the direct consequences of the working through process. One set of studies provides important evidence for the health benefits of writing about traumatic memories. However, these studies are best explained as cognitive restructuring, even in cases when personal memory contents are not involved. A second set of studies show that attempts to work through the death of one's spouse are generally ineffective, suggesting that the efficacy of working through may depend on the specific situational context. Finally, we conclude by proposing that rather than working through memories of their traumatic past, people who have experienced trauma would be better served by working toward the construction of a new narrative meaning that incorporates the traumatic event within a broader life narrative.

Cultural and Historic Assumptions

The Repression Model

Although Freud modified his theories countless times in a continual effort to expand and advance psychoanalytic thought (Erdelyi, 1985; Gay, 1989), the crucial role played by repression and the assumed importance of working through traumatic memories remained at the core of his theorizing. Essentially, Freud (Breuer & Freud, 1893/1955) assumed that distressing or traumatic experiences, sexual or otherwise, are stored in memory as near-exact replicas of the antecedent traumatic event. Because of the intolerable emotion with which they are associated, these memories are prohibited from re-entering conscious awareness by an unconscious "censor," who wields the powerful mechanism of repression (Freud, 1915/1957, 1917/1966). Once barred from conscious experience in their original form, the traumatic memories and the libidinal energy with which they are bound seek expression in other forms. They typically disguise themselves to fool the censor and gain expression indirectly, frequently in the form of a somatic symptom linked by way of an association to the contents of the original trauma (Freud, 1926/1966). Divining the meaning or "sense of the symptom" associated with the somatic complaints is a primary task of the psychoanalyst and provides important keys to the original traumatic experience. After a lengthy exploration using the psychoanalytic method, the psychoanalyst can identify the original traumatic experience; the patient can then accept it into his or her conscious experience. When this occurs, the unconscious somatic disguise is assumed to be no longer necessary and the somatic symptoms should cease.

There are a number of serious conceptual problems with the idea of somatic symptoms as disguised traumatic memories. Most significant, the key assumptions of this view, namely, repression, the spatial metaphor for "the" unconscious, and the compatible assumption of a censor or gatekeeper, are based on circular reasoning (Bonanno & Keuler, 1998; J. M. G. Williams, Watts, MacLeod, & Mathews, 1988). By its own logic, the hydraulic-repression concept assumes that if one's conscious mind cannot bear to process certain thoughts or memories, then the censor's decision to keep these thoughts and memories repressed in the unconscious can only take place unconsciously. Consequently, the unconscious must be an autonomous entity, a sort of inner "homunculus" that knows what is best for the conscious self. However, a century of research in psychology and the neurosciences has yet to reveal anything remotely similar to such an omnipotent mechanism. Indeed, an abundant corpus of contemporary research on unconscious processes suggests, if anything, the opposite: Nonconscious processing by itself, that is, processing that occurs in the complete absence of conscious awareness, appears to be at best crude and to have a dramatically limited capacity (Bargh, 1989; Bonanno & Keuler, 1998; Greenwald, 1992; Greenwald, Klinger, & Liu, 1989; LeDoux, 1996).

We review the contemporary empirical evidence in greater detail in the next section. Before this review, however, we must address the important questions of why the repression-hydraulic model gained such popularity in the first place and why it has endured for so long as the justification for the working through of traumatic memories. The best answer to these questions is that the ideas fit well with certain cultural and historic assumptions of late 19th- and early 20th-century Western-European culture. Historical and cultural changes may also explain the fact that this idea is now strongly challenged.

Birth of the Psychoanalytic Idea

Clearly, even a cursory review of the political and social climate of Western culture in the late 19th century would exceed the space limits of this chapter. However, several key points may illuminate the context in which the working through assumption was born. Perhaps the key ingredient was the profound and rapid industrialization taking place throughout Western Europe and North America in that era as well as the equally rapid and profound transition from what had been primarily a rural, agrarian economy to an urban, wage-based economy. From a psychological perspective, these changes were intimately linked with a comparable shift away from the larger community and the common interplay with and dependence on other people toward an increasing emphasis first on smaller and smaller family units and ultimately on the autonomy of the single individual (Dizard & Gadlin, 1990; Weinstein & Platt, 1989).

Weber (1904/1976) linked Western industrial growth to a "reversal of what we should call the natural relationship" (p. 53). Weber was particularly struck by the gradual but dramatic shift away from the general communal goal of material security (having enough to satisfy the material needs of one's self, family, and community) toward the capitalist ideal of accruing wealth as a goal itself. As Weber wrote, the "dreamy" ideals of romanticism that had dominated most of the 19th century were giving way to a more mercenary, secular view of life, which he termed "worldly asceticism." Individual prosperity and financial success had become life's "ultimate purpose" (Weber, 1904/1976, p. 53). As a new, almost religious ideal,

> the earning of money within the modern economic order is, so long as it is done legally, the result and the expression of virtue and proficiency of a calling . . . an obligation which the individual is supposed to feel and does feel toward the content of his professional activity. (p. 54)

In Weber's view, the emerging worldly asceticism that increasingly characterized Western capitalism separated the individual from the security and unconscious identity of the greater community. As a result, 19th-century Western Europe experienced the "unprecedented inner loneliness of the single individual" (p. 104) and the removal of the self from the "magic" salvation of communal ritual and safety.

Homans (1989) more recently advanced a similar argument to explain the social origins of psychoanalysis. In his view, psychoanalysis, and in particular the idea of working through painful or traumatic ideation, arose in response to the Western world's loss of community and cultural meaning. Extending Weber's analysis, Homans (1989) viewed the psychological impact of industrialization as "diminishing the capacity of individuals to invest representative persons in their communities with the same quality of primitive and unconscious affect which, today, tends to be associated with the nuclear family" (p. 121). This resulted, near the end of the 19th century, in a kind of "mourning" for the "lost spontaneity and immediacy which the social formations and symbols of Western religious culture had built up and guaranteed" (p. 26). As a result and in part a response to this dilemma, the psychoanalytic idea was born. According to Homans, the major tenets of psychoanalysis were first and foremost "a creative response to disillusionment and disenchantment, for in its farthest reaches [psycho]analysis is nothing less than the injunction to give up many of the illusions or 'enchantments' which traditional culture had praised" (p. 27). Thus, the process of working through one's troubled memories offers a systematic method for severing oneself from the traditional, culturally shared symbols and institutions of the dependent, communal past and emerging as a more fully autonomous and economically viable individual.

The Working Through Assumption in a Cultural Context

The axiomatic role of the working through assumption in Western psychological theory suggests it is a universal feature of human psychological functioning. It is important to note that in non-Western cultures, which account for nearly two-thirds of the world's population, the idea of working through personal memories or reactions to difficult or aversive events is literally a foreign idea (Bonanno, 1998). Whereas Western-European cultures emphasize individual understanding and working through personal crises to resolution, non-Western cultures tend to de-emphasize the personal experiences of the individual and instead affirm a person's belongingness to the larger community. Indeed, in preindustrial, non-Western cultures, the so-called "primitive" healing rites are almost always communal rather than individual and typically involve the individual's entire extended family or village (Ellenberger, 1970; Price & Price, 1991).

These patterns show an obvious consistency with the general association of non-Western cultures with "collectivism" (Triandis, Bontempo, Villareal, Asai, & Lucca, 1988). Western "individualist" cultures are characterized generally by an emphasis on personal goals, preferences, and interests, and these tend to be "relatively free of the dictates of family, neighbors, or others to whom one might be linked in traditional role relations" (Ross & Nisbett, 1991, p. 181). In contrast, for non-Western or collectivist societies, the relations and values of the family and community, rather than the individual, "are the primary sources of demands and rewards, and the primary arbiters of what is desirable, what is permissible, and what is unthinkable" (p. 181). Non-Western cultures are often referred to as "other focused" because in these cultures, the primary task is to maintain harmony with others, even if this means deferring personal feelings, desires, and needs (Triandis, 1995).

The collectivism of non-Western cultures is clearly at odds with the Western concept of working through as a means of recovering from painful or traumatic experiences (Bonanno, 1998; M. Stroebe, Gergen, Gergen, & Stroebe, 1992). For example, Asian cultures traditionally de-emphasize the experience and expression of distress in response to stressful life events. In Chinese culture in particular, the expression of intensely negative or disturbing emotions is viewed as shameful to the self and the family (Kleinman & Kleinman, 1985). Indeed, traditional Chinese medicine considers the expression of a distressing emotion as a potential cause of illness (Tseng, 1974). It would be incorrect to assume that individuals in non-Western cultures are unable to focus on their emotional or bodily reactions. Instead, it is a question of the selective allotment of attention. Because non-Western cultures are typically collectivist, attention is usually aimed externally toward the behavior and responses of others. Information about the self is simply less important in the negotiation of cultural norms and expectations (Kitiyama & Markus, 1995; Suh, Diener, Oishi, & Triandis, 1998), so it is given less attention.

A particularly intriguing aspect of the individualistic–collectivist cultural distinction concerns psychological dysfunction. In this context, collectivist cultures bear a striking resemblance to preindustrial Western Europe. In the late 19th century, when Freud began his career, psychological difficulties were commonly manifest in the form of somatic symptoms. Perhaps the most common psychosomatic malady presented to the physicians of late 19th-century in Western Europe and North America, neurasthenia is characterized by a general physical and mental exhaustion, emotional malaise, and a garden variety of somatic complaints, such as headaches, sleeplessness, and loss of appetite (Ellenberger, 1970). In an "autobiographical study" published late in his career, Freud (1925/1989) noted that he first came to terms with the many and varied people with neurasthenia who visited his office by exploring their sexual lives. Through the process of uncovering his patients' sexual pasts, Freud (1925/1989) felt he could gradually untangle "the confused jumble of clinical pictures covered by the name of neurasthenia" (p. 15) and establish a broader etiologic taxonomy of hysteria-like disorders. Freud's success was based on the elaboration of the etiological significance of past experiences; in fact, he replaced the umbrella term, neurasthenia, with increasingly more differentiated constructs, first splitting the category into hypochondriacal symptoms and anxiety neuroses and then into an ever-increasing array of types of psychosexual dysfunction.

As Western-European psychologists progressed into the 20th century with an increasing emphasis on the individual, neurasthenic difficulties eventually gave way to the range of diagnostic categories currently in use. Indeed, in contemporary Western culture, neurasthenia is virtually unknown. There have been occasional reports of related types of difficulties, as evidenced in such recent emergences as the so-called "chronic fatigue syndrome," but such difficulties are typically viewed with great suspicion or dismissed as malingering.

In striking contrast, stressful events in non-Western or collectivist cultures are still manifested as increases in general somatic complaints or "somatizing" (Draguns, 1993; Kleinman & Kleinman, 1985; Marsella, 1979). As compared with the myriad categories of mental difficulties currently used in Western psychiatry, non-Western countries typically report markedly reduced prevalence rates for virtually all forms of mental illness. For example, a relatively recent epidemiological study in China reveals prevalence rates for various mental illness that are three to five times less frequent than in Western countries (Lee & Kleinman, 1997). It is interesting to note that the most common form of mental difficulty in China is neurasthenia. Furthermore, since China opened itself to the West some 15 years ago and with it allowed a rapid influx of individual-oriented media, products, and ideas, there has been a dramatic rise in depressive and anxiety disorders and a comparable decrease in neurasthenia-like symptoms (Lee & Kleinman, 1997).

It is difficult to say which is a more desirable response to stress, global neurasthenic difficulties or a wider range of more clearly defined mental difficulties. Although the cultural evidence is indirect and subject to numerous re-interpretations and methodological criticisms, it does raise the rather compelling argument that working through traumatic memories may be less a universal discovery and more a cultural and historical construction.

The Brain

In this section, we consider the working through of memories of traumatic experience in the context of recent developments within cognitive neuroscience. Research in this area provides important information about the psychological processes underlying memory for normal, everyday events. It is important to note that research in this area also provides a theoretical alternative to repression as the conceptual underpinning of the working through assumption. Whereas repression theory assumes that traumatic memories are unavailable because they are intolerable, from a cognitive neuroscience perspective traumatic memories appear relatively inaccessible and difficult to control because stressful or traumatic experiences may disrupt normal encoding processes.

Declarative and Nondeclarative Memory

The idea that traumatic experiences can disrupt human memory systems is not new. As early as the late 1800s and several years before Freud's first published work appeared, Janet (1889) identified a number of differences that set memories of trauma apart from other (typical) memories. He observed that when an individual is overwhelmed with emotion during a traumatic experience, the memory for this event cannot be transformed into what he called a "neutral narrative." The individual is "unable to make the recital which we call narrative memory, and yet he remains confronted by [the] difficult situation" (Janet, 1919/1925, p. 660). This results in what Janet called a phobia of memory, which subsequently prevents the integration of traumatic events and dissociates traumatic memories from ordinary consciousness. Janet (1889) claimed that the memory traces of the trauma linger as what he termed "subconscious *idée fixe*" (fixed ideas). He chose the term subconscious to heighten the distinction between his views and the then-current conceptions of the "mystical" unconscious, popularized by 19th-century Romanticism (Hilgard, 1977). In Janet's (1889) view, subconscious fixed ideas represent dissociated fragments of the traumatic experience that remain autonomous and intrusive as long as they cannot be integrated into a personal narrative. Thus, Janet observed that extreme emotion at the time of memory encoding interferes with typical information processing and the storage of the memory in a narrative form and tends to produce a qualitatively distinct memory imprint. Although Janet's postulations regarding memory for traumatic events were made almost a century ago, they remain consistent with current research and understanding in this area (Bonanno & Keuler, 1998; Reviere, 1996; van der Kolk, 1996).

Contemporary views of human memory hold that a number of different memory systems can be catalogued into a variety of levels. Most memory systems can be subsumed by the overarching distinction between explicit or declarative memory and implicit or nondeclarative memory. Explicit or declarative memory involves "the acquisition, retention, and retrieval of knowledge that can be consciously and intentionally recollected" (Gabrieli, 1998, p. 89). This system encompasses numerous memory subsystems, including the memory for facts and common knowledge (semantic memory) and the memory for the occurrence of specific individual events (episodic memory). The declarative system is generally involved in the encoding, storage, and retrieval of memories for typical, everyday, nontraumatic experiences. In contrast, nondeclarative memory generally does not occur within the bounds of conscious awareness and encompasses memory subsystems related to automatic processes that do not necessarily require conscious awareness for their operation, including conditioned responses, priming, skills and habits, and procedural or sensorimotor learning (Squire, 1992). In terms of our concerns in this chapter and consistent with Janet's (1919/1925) nascent theorizing, it is now widely accepted that traumatic experiences interfere with the normal functioning of explicit memory and tend to be encoded at the level of implicit or nondeclarative memory (Schacter, 1997).

The differential involvement of the declarative and nondeclarative systems in the acquisition of a memory trace influences the type of information that an individual has access to on retrieval. Declarative memories for everyday experiences (episodic memories) are characterized by a narrative or story of what occurred during the event for which a memory was formed. In contrast, traumatic memories typically lack this episodic component. The intense and primitive emotional features of a trauma tend to produce "speechless terror" (van der Kolk, 1994, p. 258). Traumas are further characterized by confusion, disorganization, and the feeling of being frozen or immobilized, as if events had occurred out of sequence (Peterson, Prout, & Schwarz, 1991; T. Williams, 1988). Sometimes, traumas involve perceptual aberrations and result in a kind of tunnel vision in which selected aspects of the traumatic events are perceived in vivid, almost exaggerated detail, whereas other crucial aspects are not encoded. For example, people involved in a robbery sometimes become so transfixed by their assailant's weapon that they fail to attend to or recall crucial details of the event, such as the assailant's face. The phenomenon, known as "weapon focus," has also been demonstrated in more tightly controlled laboratory settings (Kramer, Buckhout, & Eugenio, 1990).

The confusion and narrowing of attention associated with traumatic experience is further exacerbated by the increased arousal and sensory readiness associated with the fight or flight response. As a result, traumatic memories tend to be dominated by intense waves of feeling; fragmented visual images; olfactory, kinesthetic, or auditory sensations; and primitive motor memories (Bonanno, 1990, 1995). People who have experienced a trauma often report that these sensory motor enactments and images replicate the feelings and sensations that were present during the trauma (van der Kolk, 1994). However, the confusion and lack of episodic detail make it difficult for people who have experienced a trauma to understand or talk about their experiences (Bonanno, 1990; Terr, 1994).

In one of the few empirical studies in this area, van der Kolk and Fisler (1995) used a structured interview to assess sensory, affective, and narrative components of traumatic and nontraumatic memories among individuals diagnosed with posttraumatic stress disorder (PTSD). When recalling everyday, nontraumatic experiences, none of the participants reported olfactory, visual, auditory, or kinesthetic memory components. In contrast, when they recalled traumatic memories, all reported that they initially recalled "somatosensory or emotional flashback experiences" (van der Kolk & Fisler, 1995, p. 517). In addition, none reported having a narrative for the traumatic experience during the initial recall of the event, whether they had continuous awareness of the experience or not.

Differences may also exist in the way traumatic and nontraumatic memories are activated. Episodic memory for nontraumatic events may be triggered by reminders or cues, but nontraumatic events can generally be retrieved through conscious and intentional effort. In contrast, memory for traumatic events is usually less accessible, thus not readily available to intentional recall. Instead, traumatic memories tend to be activated automatically in response to specific emotional and sensory triggers, which may be only loosely related to the trauma (van der Kolk, 1994). This gives memories for trauma an intrusive quality, not present for nontraumatic memories (Horowitz, 1986). For example, in response to a subsequent stressor, traumatized people may experience arousal similar to that felt during their prior traumatization, which serves "selectively to promote retrieval of traumatic memories, sensory information, or behaviors associated with previous traumatic experiences" (van der Kolk, 1994, p. 259). State-dependent recall of traumatic memories has also been demonstrated in laboratory experiments. In patients with PTSD, injections of lactate and yohimbine (medications that simulate autonomic arousal) resulted in flashbacks or reliving the experiences related to the trauma (Rainey et al., 1987; Southwick et al., 1993). Thus, traumatic memories are further distinguished from nontraumatic memories by their state-dependent recall and intrusive qualities.

Architecture of Traumatic Memories

The brain's memory architecture is remarkably complex, with various structures participating in the encoding, storage, and retrieval of memory. One such structure, the hippocampus, is now widely assumed to play a crucial role in consolidating or binding various aspects of experience in long-term memory. Specifically, the hippocampus serves to encode the spatial and temporal dimensions of an individual's experience (van der Kolk, 1994). Thus, explicit or declarative memory requires proper functioning of the hippocampus.

Squire et al. (1992) used positron emission tomography (PET) to demonstrate the importance of the hippocampus in explicit recall among normal participants. In another PET study (Schacter, Alpert, Savage, Rauch, & Albert, 1996), hippocampal activation was not observed during perceptual priming in normal participants, suggesting that the hippocampus is not involved in implicit or nondeclarative memory processes. This conclusion should be viewed cautiously because negative PET findings are not as easily interpreted as positive findings. Taken together, however, this research provides compelling evidence to suggest the primary involvement of the hippocampus in episodic memory.

In related research, several studies show that intense stress can disrupt hippocampal functioning (Diamond & Rose, 1994; McEwen & Sapolsky, 1995) and cause a shift to more primitive forms of memory encoding. Hippocampal activity decreases as a result of the stress-induced production of epinephrine, norepinephrine, and glucocorticoids (Sapolsky, 1996). Studies with rats show that exposure to excess glucocorticoids over a period of several weeks caused a reversible atrophy of hippocampal dendrites and that exposure to excess glucocorticoids over a period of several months resulted in the permanent loss of hippocampal neurons (Sapolsky, 1996). A study of Vietnam combat veterans with PTSD provides further evidence of the relationship between excessive exposure to glucocorticoids and hippocampal function (Bremner et al., 1995). Bremner et al. used magnetic resonance imaging to measure the hippocampal volume of 26 veterans and 22 matched control participants. The veterans with PTSD showed a significant 8% atrophy of the right hippocampus and a near statistically significant atrophy of the left hippocampus. Although this is an exciting finding, its implications are unclear because nonsignificant reductions to the amygdala, caudate nucleus, and temporal lobe were also observed. It is interesting to note that the duration of time spent in combat was negatively correlated with hippocampal volume. Sapolsky (1996) described a number of unpublished studies that show similar hippocampal atrophy, some of which correct for whole-brain volume.

Researchers now generally believe that the amygdala, another brain structure involved in the processing of memory, is involved in the evaluation of the emotional significance of incoming stimuli and helps determine the neural route this information will take in subsequent processing throughout the brain (LeDoux, 1996). One difficulty in studying the functioning of the amygdala is its proximity to the hippocampus. Both structures are often damaged in patients with amnesia. Urbach–Weithe syndrome, a rare congenital dermatological disorder associated with the mineralization of the amygdala while sparing the hippocampal function, offers an opportunity to study how the human brain functions without the involvement of the amygdala. Cahill, Babinsky, Markowitsch, and McGaugh (1995) demonstrated that whereas most individuals usually exhibit superior memory for emotionally disturbing stimuli relative to neutral stimuli, people with Urbach–Weithe syndrome fail to exhibit such an effect, suggesting that damage to the amygdala interferes with emotional processing. Similarly, Markowitsch et al.'s (1994) neuropsychological testing of these individuals reveals disturbed performance on memory tasks that were likely to have an emotional effect on the patients.

Neuroimaging studies demonstrate the involvement of the amygdala in explicit memory for aversive stimuli in people without Urbach–Weithe syndrome. Irwin et al. (1996) demonstrated amygdala activation during the presentation of affectively negative pictures but not affectively neutral pictures in three female participants. The authors concluded that the amygdala serves "as the neural structure responsible for extracting the affective content from stimuli in the environment" (Irwin et al., 1996, p. 1769). In a similar study, Lane et al. (1997) showed women pictures that had been previously shown to elicit pleasant, unpleasant, or neutral emotion. Using PET, the authors observed amygdala activation when participants saw unpleasant stimuli but not pleasant stimuli. Morris et al. (1996) found amygdala activation in PET and functional magnetic resonance imaging studies of the perception of fear-inducing facial expressions and scenes. Patients with amygdala lesions also show deficits in the identification of angry and fearful facial expressions (Adolphs, Tranel, Damasio, & Damasio, 1994). Together, this evidence suggests that the amygdala has "a widespread role in processing negatively salient stimuli" (Gabrieli, 1998, p. 93). In addition, numerous studies demonstrate the role of the amygdala in implicit memory for aversive stimuli through the examination of fear conditioning in rats (Davis, Hitchcock, & Rosen, 1987) and humans (Bechara et al., 1995; LaBar, LeDoux, Spencer, & Phelps, 1995).

The significant role of the amygdala in the processing of negative stimuli and in fear conditioning provides essential information for the understanding of memory for traumatic experiences. Because a trauma is considered to be an overwhelmingly aversive and fear-inducing experience, it is likely that traumatic learning and memories are characterized by the amygdala's processing of external signals (LeDoux & Muller, 1997). "Most of the evidence points to the amygdala as particularly important in the conditioning and extinction of sensory and cognitive associations to the original trauma and subsequent activation of traumatic memories" (Charney, Deutch, Krystal, Southwick, & Davis, 1993, p. 301). The amygdala's connections to all the sensory systems in the cortex can help explain how traumatic memories are recalled. "The functional interchange between the sensory cortices, where memories of each sense may be stored, and the amygdala may be critical for the ability of specific sensory input to elicit traumatic memories" (p. 301).

To summarize, there appear to be qualitative differences in memory for nontraumatic and traumatic events. Memory for everyday, nontraumatic events is characterized by an episodic narrative, primarily lexical and conceptual encoding, and generally easy accessibility to conscious, intentional recall. In contrast, traumatic memories are distinguished by prominent sensory and emotional components that are experienced as involuntary intrusions. This distinction is supported on a neurological level by the differential involvement of the hippocampus and the amygdala in explicit and implicit memory. Unlike theories of repression, this line of inquiry suggests that under conditions of extreme stress, memory is likely to be markedly incomplete and poorly organized in relation to the ongoing hierarchical structures used to catalogue everyday information and experiences. The fragmentary, emotional nature of traumatic memories accounts to some extent for their apparent autonomous, intrusive quality. In addition, because these memories are not and cannot be easily integrated and consolidated with other aspects of normal experience, they are not readily controlled or regulated by conscious volition. Finally, the relative incompleteness of traumatic memories suggests that attempts to work through, fill in, and otherwise complete a memory for the traumatic experience more often than not result in failure or, perhaps even worse, exacerbate the traumatic aspects of the experience (Bonanno, 1995; Ehrlich, 1988; Kinzie, 1988). In the next section, we consider this question further by reviewing research directly related to the working through assumption.

Experimental Studies

In this section, we first review studies of the health consequences of writing about traumatic events. This literature provides abundant evidence that writing about traumatic events can exert a salutary influence on the person's long-term health. Although this conclusion is consistent with Freud's (1917/1966) original speculations, this literature also suggests that the lifting of repression cannot fully explain this salutary effect but instead the findings can be ascribed to cognitive restructuring. We then review several recent studies pertaining to the working through of thoughts and emotions associated with the death of one's spouse or partner. In this case, we find virtually no supportive evidence. Thus, these findings suggest that the relative usefulness of working though traumatic memories may depend on the situational context and the particular demands of the stressor event.

Writing About Traumatic Events

An abundance of empirical data document the impact of writing about traumatic events on the person's health (reviewed in Smyth, 1998; see also Smyth & Greenberg, chap. 4, this volume). Much of these data come from the research of Pennebaker and colleagues. Although these studies consistently verify the salutary health consequences of writing about traumatic events, when all of this literature is considered, it becomes apparent that repression is not an adequate explanation. Indeed, in some of the more recent studies (e.g., Greenberg, Wortman, & Stone, 1996), researchers have underscored the important role played by cognitive restructuring and have suggested that this mechanism may lead to health improvements, regardless of whether personal traumatic memories are examined.

Pennebaker and O'Heeron (1984) asked a small group of bereaved individuals who had lost spouses either to suicide or accidental death how often they had talked about the spouse's death with close friends, counselors, or members of a support group. The amount that the bereaved individuals talked about their loss was not related to the type of loss. Furthermore, both of the bereaved groups reported significant increases in health problems after their loss, but health problems were unrelated to the degree that the bereaved individuals had talked about the loss with a counselor or support group. However, there was a clear relationship between talking about the loss with close friends and reduced health problems. In other words, talking with friends buffered the health costs of bereavement. This relationship remained significant even when the researchers statistically controlled for the number of friends. Similar links between the failure to disclose traumatic material and increased health difficulties were reported in relation to childhood sexual abuse (Pennebaker & Hoover, 1986) and traumatic experiences among white-collar workers (Pennebaker & Susman, 1988). However, as is often the case with research in a new area, these data suffer from a number of methodological limitations. First, because the data are correlational and retrospective, causal attributions regarding the role of disclosure are not appropriate. Second, the exclusive reliance on self-report means that the results may have been inextricably confounded with state-dependent memory biases.

More impressive findings were generated in a number of studies that use more controlled, prospective designs. For example, Pennebaker and Beall (1986) randomly assigned college undergraduate students to different groups and asked them to write about different topics on 4 consecutive nights. One group wrote about their emotional reactions to a prior trauma, defined as "a personally upsetting experience" (Pennebaker & Beall, 1986, p. 275). A second group wrote only about the facts associated with a prior trauma. A third group wrote about both trauma-related emotions and facts. Finally, a control group wrote about trivial topics each night. The researchers monitored participants' psychological and physiological reactions each day of the study. In addition, they collected self-reported health data 4 months later and records from the health and counseling centers for a period beginning 6 months prior to and 6 months following the writing of the essays. Overall, writing about traumatic experiences was associated with short-term increases in physiological arousal and negative mood. However, over the long term, writing about trauma resulted in decreased health problems. These findings were most pronounced for the students who wrote about their emotional reactions to the traumas.

To explain these findings, Pennebaker (1989) and colleagues rejected Freud's (1917/1966) repression model and proposed a physiologically based model of behavioral inhibition. According-ing to this view, the act of not disclosing or keeping private one's personal or emotional reactions to a traumatic event is a physical act. In other words, the body must work to inhibit the feelings, thoughts, and behaviors associated with the trauma. Over the long term, the repeated stress created by this type of physiological inhibition produces a cumulative stress on the body and an eventual increased vulnerability to stress-related illness (Selye, 1976).

Numerous subsequent studies add further support to this view. For instance, college students who discussed deeply personal and stressful events during a laboratory experiment evidenced lower skin conductance levels than those who were low disclosers (Pennebaker, Hughes, & O'Heeron, 1987). Pennebaker and Barger (1988) observed a similar relationship among Holocaust survivors who were interviewed about their wartime experiences. College students who wrote about traumatic and upsetting experiences that they had not previously discussed in detail with others had better immune functioning, as measured by two indexes of cellular immune function, and fewer health center visits than students who wrote about trivial topics (Pennebaker, Kiecolt-Glaser, & Glaser, 1988). In a similar study, medical students who wrote about emotional topics while being vaccinated for hepatitis B evidenced increasingly higher hepatitis B antibodies over time than did medical students who wrote about control topics (Petrie, Booth, Pennebaker, Davison, & Thomas, 1995). Esterling, Antoni, Fletcher, Margulies, and Schneiderman (1994) examined the effect of writing and talking about stressful events in patients' production of Epstein–Barr virus antibodies. Among Epstein–Barr seropositive undergraduates, both written and verbal disclosure groups evidenced significantly greater decreases in antibody titers than did control participants who wrote about trivial topics.

It is important to note, however, that although these findings appear to be consistent with the physiological inhibition hypothesis, the concept of physiological inhibition would obviously involve numerous complex processes that may not be fully captured in a small number of writing sessions. Perhaps more important, several researchers have failed to replicate Pennebaker's findings or to support the inhibition theory fully. For example, Greenberg and Stone (1992) compared undergraduates who were randomly assigned to write over a period of 4 days about a trauma that they had never previously discussed, a trauma that they had already discussed with others, or trivial events. The three groups did not differ on self-reported physical symptoms or visits to health professionals over time. However, participants who wrote about more severe traumas by their own subjective estimates reported fewer physical symptoms following the experiment than did participants who wrote about less severe traumas. Thus, in contradiction to the inhibition hypothesis, the health benefits for a person writing about traumatic material appear to be less related to disclosure than to the severity of the material.

Greenberg et al. (1996) provided an even more compelling challenge to the inhibition hypothesis in a subsequent study. They first preselected college students to ensure that they had actually experienced a trauma and then asked the students to provide the factual details of the traumatic event. As in previous studies, the researchers asked participants in one condition to write about their emotional reactions to the trauma, whereas they asked a second group to write about trivial events. However, in a clever variation on this procedure, participants in a third condition received the factual details of another person's traumatic experience; the researchers then asked them to imagine themselves having this experience and to write about their emotional reactions. Somewhat surprisingly, at a 1-month follow-up assessment, both participants who wrote about their own traumas and participants who wrote about their imaginary reactions to another person's trauma had fewer illness visits to doctors and fewer self-reported physical symptoms than did the control group. In other words, health benefits were associated with writing about traumatic material in general, regardless of whether participants had actually experienced the traumatic event or not.

This result is not easily explained by either Freud's repression hypothesis or Pennebaker's physiological inhibition hypothesis, unless it is assumed that writing about someone else's trauma allows individuals to lift their repression or stop inhibiting their own traumatic experiences, neither of which seem plausible. Instead, Greenberg et al. (1996) hypothesized that imagining another person's trauma may lead to healthy improvements because such a task may "foster self-empathy by allowing participants to observe their own emotional pain in the context uncontaminated by [the] knowledge of failed coping efforts and associated self-derogation" (p. 599) and, in doing so, may help people who have experienced a trauma understand and gain mastery over their reactions and thus construct more "resilient possible selves" (p. 599).

Pennebaker (1993) and colleagues have likewise attempted to expand their explanation for the salutary effects of writing about trauma to include the ways that writing helps individuals structure and ultimately understand their experiences. Pennebaker, Colder, and Sharp (1990) noted that in one study students transitioning to college who wrote about their experiences had not yet had time to be influenced by the long-term negative effects of inhibition yet evidenced similar health benefits to those in prior experiments who wrote about past traumas. Thus, Pennebaker et al. (1990) concluded, "the value of writing about thoughts and feelings . . . may have simply been to assimilate their leaving home with current college experiences. Assimilation rather than reduction in inhibition may have been the key variable that promoted health" (p. 535). Pennebaker (1993) analyzed the writing samples from several other studies and found that the participants who wrote about traumas and improved the most had done so using gradually increasing numbers of insightful, causal, and cognitive words over the course of several days of writing.

Working Through Bereavement: The Grief Work Assumption

The research reviewed above provides clear evidence that writing about traumatic events can lead to a person's improved health. However, neither Freud's repression model nor Pennebaker's physiological inhibition theory are fully compatible with these findings. Instead, the most parsimonious explanation is that writing allows traumatized individuals the opportunity to structure and potentially understand their experiences (Pennebaker, 1993) and to gain some distance from the immediacy of the experience, so they might explore images of more resilient, competent selves (Greenberg et al., 1996). In this section, we review evidence from another related area, the working through of emotional pain of interpersonal loss. In this case, however, there is little positive evidence for the benefits of working through.

The idea that a bereaved individual should work through the pain of a loss may be again traced to Freud. In his seminal work, "Mourning and Melancholia," Freud (1917/1957) described grieving as a process by which the mourner gradually reviews "each single one of the memories and hopes which bound the libido to the object . . . [until] . . . detachment of the libido from it (is) accomplished" (p. 254). Although Freud (1917) put forth these speculations cautiously and discussed bereavement primarily as a means of elucidating his views on depression, Deutsch (1937) and Lindemann (1944) in subsequent theorizing expanded on this metaphor of the "work of mourning," which eventually became the dominant perspective on bereavement (Belitsky & Jacobs, 1986; Bowlby, 1980; Cerney & Buskirk, 1991; Horowitz, Bonanno, & Holen, 1993; Lazare, 1989; Osterweis, Solomon, & Green, 1984; Parkes & Weiss, 1983; Raphael, 1983; Raphael, Middleton, Martinek, & Misso, 1993; Sanders, 1993).

Until recently, there has been little in the way of empirical data from which to evaluate the grief work assumption (W. Stroebe & Stroebe, 1987). However, within the past decade, bereavement researchers have turned their attention to this question. Initial attempts to evaluate the grief work assumption directly were largely inconclusive (Mawson, Marks, Ramm, & Stern, 1981; M. S. Stroebe & Stroebe, 1991). These researchers were unable to resolve the issue presumably because a process as complex as grief work could not be easily operationalized in a single study (Bonanno, 1998). More recently, bereavement investigators have found a more efficacious approach to define and examine operationally specific predictions of the grief work assumption in terms of basic cognitive and emotional processes. Somewhat surprisingly, the results of this approach are singularly unsupportive of the hypothesized necessity of working though grief (Bonanno & Kaltman, 1999).

In a series of studies from our own research program, Bonanno, Keltner, Holen, and Horowitz (1995) examined the experience and expression of emotion 6 months after the loss of a spouse by conducting a semistructured narrative interview in which bereaved individuals were asked to describe their prior relationship to the spouse and how they reacted to the loss of that relationship. During this task, the interviewer spoke sparingly and encouraged the bereaved participants to "try to relate as openly as possible whatever comes to . . . mind" (Bonanno, Keltner, Holen, & Horowitz, 1995, p. 979). Researchers also assessed participants using a separate clinical interview for grief severity. The grief interview provides a relatively objective index of the degree that the loss impeded general psychological functioning and has been validated against several standardized measures of grief and depression as well as clinical ratings of grief severity from an unaware and independent team of psychotherapists (Bonanno, 1995). In addition, participants provided self-reports of distress and somatic complaints. To allow assessment of the long-term consequences of grief work, the researchers obtained both the interview and self-reported outcome measures at the 6-month point and again at 14- and 25-months postloss.

Bonanno et al. (1995) examined emotional experience and emotional dissociation comparing self-reported emotion with long-term outcome. To test one prediction of the grief work hypothesis, the researchers operationally defined emotional avoidance as the reduced experience of distress while describing the lost relationship in conjunction with elevated levels of physiological arousal. This type of verbal-autonomic response dissociation is linked in other research on repressive–defensiveness (Asendorpf & Scherer, 1983; Newton & Contrada, 1992; Shedler, Mayman, & Manis, 1993; Weinberger & Davidson, 1994; Weinberger, Schwartz, & Davidson, 1979). The verbal-autonomic dissociation score also converged with clinician ratings of the avoidance of emotional awareness (Bonanno et al., 1995). In contrast to the predictions of the grief work approach, however, high levels of verbal-autonomic dissociation at the 6-month point in bereavement were associated with low levels of interviewer-rated grief at 25-months postloss, even when researchers statistically controlled initial levels of grief (Bonanno et al., 1995; Bonanno, Znoj, Siddique, & Horowitz, 1999). Some evidence for a physical cost of avoidance shows that verbal-autonomic dissociation at 6 months was associated with concurrent elevations in reported somatic symptoms. It is important to note, however, that this effect appears to be short lived. Over the course of 25 months of bereavement, verbal-autonomic dissociation was associated with low levels of somatic symptoms and, thus, was not linked to either a cumulative or delayed physical cost.

In another study from this same project, Bonanno and Keltner (1997) examined the expression of emotion early in bereavement by coding facial expressions of emotion. From participants who described their loss at the 6-month point in bereavement, the researchers tallied a range of facial expressions corresponding to different negative emotions. As consistent with the emotional dissociation findings and in contrast to the assumption that it is necessary to express one's reactions to a loss, the more participants showed negative facial expressions while describing the lost relationship, the greater their grief was at 14 and to a lesser extent 25 months postloss.

There are also important findings about the adaptive role of positive emotion during bereavement. Positive emotions have been largely ignored by researchers in the bereavement literature or, in some cases, assumed to indicate maladaptive denial (Bowlby, 1980; Raphael, 1983; Sanders, 1979). However, Keltner and Bonanno (1997) did readily observe facial expressions of positive emotions during participants' discussions of their lost relationship. Most important, expressing positive emotions predicted reduced grief over time. Subsequently, they examined the role of positive emotions during bereavement by distinguishing between genuine laughter and smiling, which involve the obicularis oculi muscles around the eye, and nongenuine or social laughs and smiles, which do not involve these same muscles and tend not to be associated with the experience of positive emotion. Only genuine laughs and smiles predicted reduced grief. Furthermore, genuine laughter during bereavement appeared to have clear social benefits. Laughter while talking about the lost relationship was associated with greater adjustment in the relationship with the deceased and less ambivalent relationships with other important people in the participants' lives and evoked more positive responses in observers. Expressions of genuine laughter were also more readily seen in those individuals who had also shown emotional dissociation, whereas individuals who did not evidence emotional dissociation tended to display only nongenuine or social laughter.

To take a different approach, Capps and Bonanno (in press) transcribed the bereaved participants' narrative descriptions of their loss and coded them for the degree that they involved positive and negative thoughts and emotions. In further support of the role of positive experiences during bereavement, positive thoughts and emotions associated with the loss were quite common. In addition, the presence of more negative thoughts and emotions while speaking about the lost relationship was associated with a more symptomatic long-term outcome, which again is in contrast with the grief work assumption. When the researchers used regression analyses to control for initial symptoms, covariance among narrative variables, perceived social support, and dyadic adjustment, negative thoughts significantly predicted increased grief at later dates and negative emotions significantly predicted increased somatic complaints at later dates.

Using a similar approach, Stein, Folkman, Trabasso, and Christopher-Richards (1997) interviewed bereaved gay men within the first month after their partners had died from AIDS. Consistent with evidence for the salutary impact of positive emotions, an analysis of the narratives from this project shows that gay men who early in bereavement made positive appraisals, such as a positive attitude toward death or a belief in self-growth from difficult events, had better morale, more positive states of mind, and less depression 12 months postloss than did gay men who did not have such positive aspects.

In another study from this project of particular relevance to the grief work assumption, Nolen-Hoeksema, McBride, and Larson (1997) coded the 1-month narratives of bereaved gay men for evidence of self-analysis; in this case, self-analysis was defined as the "participant's attempts to understand the loss and his own reaction to the loss" (p. 857) and included the participant's descriptions of his own personality, assessments of the relationship with the deceased partner, thoughts about dealing with life without the partner, statements about giving oneself time to adjust, lessons learned by the participant from the loss or how it had changed his own experience, and the means by which the participant found meaning or was trying to find meaning in his loss. Clearly, any of these aspects of self-analysis would be considered adaptive from the perspective of the grief work assumption. Yet Nolen-Hoeksema et al. found that self-analysis predicted increased depression and reduced positive morale at the 12-month point in bereavement, even when they statistically controlled for initial levels of depression and positive morale.

Conclusion: From Working Through to Working Toward

We began this chapter by reviewing the traditional concept of working through traumatic memories, which is based on the assumption that repressed contents seek expression symbolically in the form of somatic symptoms. We noted the conceptual limitations of that approach and its cultural and historic origins in the particular circumstances of Western society in the late 19th century. We next reviewed important evidence from the cognitive neurosciences, suggesting that traumatic experiences interfere with normal memory consolidation and tend to produce fragmentary traces that are not well integrated within other aspects of remembered experience. Thus, traumatic memories tend to be intrusive and difficult to control, not because they are repressed but because there is a relative paucity of information encoded. We then reviewed in numerous empirical studies how researchers directly examined the consequences of attempts to work through difficult or painful memories. In one set of studies, researchers consistently found writing about traumatic material to foster participants' health. However, these results were best explained in terms of cognitive processes associated with the restructuring of experience, rather than the lifting of repression. Indeed, writing about another person's trauma produced health benefits equally as salutary as writing about one's own trauma (Greenberg et al., 1996), a finding that could not easily be explained as the lifting of repression. In a second set of studies, pertaining to the specific situational context of the loss of a loved one, attempts to work through the emotional pain of the loss by experiencing or expressing emotion, describing painful thoughts to an interviewer, or engaging in self-analysis not only failed to produce benefits but actually predicted a worse long-term outcome. Furthermore, these studies pointed to the importance of positive emotions and appraisals in the recovery process, a factor for the most part ignored by theorists concerned with the working through process.

When considered together, these findings suggest that assumptions about the universal necessity of working through painful or traumatic memories are unfounded. Indeed, persistent attempts to work through fragmentary memories that are only partially encoded in episodic form may actually add to the distress of a traumatic experience or exacerbate memory disruption (Bonanno & Keuler, 1998; Ehrlich, 1988; Kinzie, 1988). This is not to say that traumatized individuals should be discouraged from reflecting on their traumatic experiences. Indeed, structuring and integrating these experiences with broader schematized beliefs and expectations about life is essential to maintain a healthy sense of self and buffer against further stresses and difficulties in life (Bonanno, 1995; Janoff-Bulman, 1992; McAdams, 1985, 1993).

How then might clinicians think about memories for traumatic experience? We propose a crucial distinction between working through the actual memory of a traumatic event, which would be unlikely to include extensive narrative or episodic elements and therefore remain elusive, and working toward the construction of a new narrative meaning that incorporates the traumatic event within a broader life narrative (Bonanno & Keuler, 1998). The distinction between working through past memories and working toward new meaning suggests a subtle but important shift in emphasis. Whereas working though focuses on the past and the aim of recovering lost experiences, working toward focuses on the present and future and the aim of moving on toward new goals and new challenges. Typically, treatment models for people who have experienced a trauma emphasize the exploration of the traumatic past. For instance, van der Kolk, van der Hart, and Marmar (1996) espoused an approach that first involves stabilizing patients and preparing them for approaching the traumatic memories and then identifying, exploring, and modifying the traumatic memory.

However, as noted earlier, traumatic experiences are generally disorganized and, when they are recollected, tend to emerge as fragmented bits and pieces of the event dominated primarily by sensory and motor representations. Thus, whereas each piece of information related to the traumatic event may capture some feature or form of the original traumatic experience, in isolation the traumatic memory lacks the narrative cohesion of normal episodic memories. This limited and relatively inaccessible aspect of traumatic memories suggests that too much emphasis on reviewing and recreating or modifying the traumatic past may only end in frustration and ultimately produce a confused and distorted sense of what really happened during the traumatic experience.

We agree that working toward the construction of new meaning may sometimes entail a process of translating the various fragments of traumatic experience into a unified and integrated representation of a single moment in time that makes sense in the person's larger narrative understanding. This process, which has elsewhere been termed "narrative revision" (Bonanno, 1990, 1995), would naturally occur gradually over time (van der Kolk & Fisler, 1995). However, the crucial concern in working toward new meaning is that the fragmentary pieces of the traumatic memory available are associated and integrated into a broader life narrative that allows the traumatized individual to accept the occurrence of the traumatic event as something that, however unfortunate, has actually happened but is over and is now in the past. Thus, it may not even be necessary to review the accuracy of the traumatic memory or to attempt to fill in the missing details. Instead, what is crucial is not the veridicality or the fullness of the traumatic memory but the act of telling the story of the trauma to supportive listeners.

Attempts to describe a traumatic event or events in the safe confines of the treatment situation or with supportive friends and family may, in and of itself, be enough to reduce the sense of fear and isolation that often accompanies traumatic reactions. From the perspective of human associative memory, this would occur by the building of associations between the fragmentary bits and pieces of traumatic memory and the supportive and understanding responses of others (Bonanno, 1995; Bonanno & Keuler, 1998). Over time, then, a fragmentary traumatic memory becomes to some extent unified and associated with a broader life narrative that accepts the inevitability of untoward events but nonetheless maintains the normative assumptions about the generally benign character of life events and the worthiness of the self and other people.

A safe and trusting environment, whether a clinical setting or a sense of belonging to a larger community of family or friends, would obviously foster this process (Bonanno, 1990, 1995; Silver,

1986; van der Kolk & Kadish, 1987). The bereavement research reviewed earlier also underscores the importance of maintaining, or even deliberately accentuating, positive experiences and appraisals, especially those that involve laughter. Numerous investigators have also pointed in general to the important role played by positive emotions in fostering coping (Bonanno & Kaltman, 1999; Lazarus, Kanner, & Folkman, 1980). Similarly, the concept of stress-related growth (Park, Cohen, & Murch, 1996; Tedeschi & Calhoun, 1996) suggests that even in the face of dreadful and disturbing traumatic memories, it is possible for a person to find something positive in having gone through such an experience. Thus, in contrast to a rigid emphasis on working through the traumatic past, which might ignore these more positive aspects of growth, the focus is on working toward a way to fit the traumatic past into an ongoing present and future. This action explicitly allows a traumatized individual to let go of the past if possible, to associate the untoward aspects of the event with the benign support of others, to focus on whatever positive aspects or implications of the experience that may be available, and to have hope for the future and the possibility of finding personal growth in having gone through such a painful experience.

References

Adolphs, R., Tranel, D., Damasio, H., & Damasio, A. (1994). Impaired recognition of emotion in facial expressions following bilateral damage to the human amygdala. *Nature, 372,* 669–672.

Asendorpf, J. B., & Scherer, K. R. (1983). The discrepant repressor: Differentiation between low anxiety, high anxiety, and repression of anxiety by autonomic-facial-verbal patterns of behavior. *Journal of Personality and Social Psychology, 45,* 1334–1346.

Bargh, J. A. (1989). Conditional automaticity: Varieties of automatic influence in social perception and cognition. In J. S. Uleman & J. A. Bargh (Eds.), *Unintended thought* (pp. 3–51). New York: Guilford Press.

Bechara, A., Tranel, D., Damasio, H., Adolphs, R., Rockland, C., & Damasio, A. R. (1995). Double dissociation of conditioning and declarative knowledge relative to the amygdala and hippocampus in humans. *Science, 269,* 1115–1118.

Belitsky, R., & Jacobs, S. (1986). Bereavement, attachment theory, and mental disorders. *Psychiatric Annals, 16,* 276–280.

Bonanno, G. A. (1990). Remembering and psychotherapy. *Psychotherapy, 27,* 175–186.

Bonanno, G. A. (1995). Accessibility, reconstruction, and the treatment of functional memory problems. In A. Baddeley, B. A. Wilson, & F. Watts (Eds.), *Handbook of memory disorders* (pp. 616–637). Sussex, England: Wiley.

Bonanno, G. A. (1998). The concept of "working through" loss: A critical evaluation of the cultural, historical, and empirical evidence. In A. Maercker, M. Schuetzwohl, & Z. Solomon (Eds.), *Posttraumatic stress disorder: Vulnerability and resilience in the life-span* (pp. 221–247). Göttingen, Germany: Hogrethe & Huber.

Bonanno, G. A., & Kaltman, S. (1999). Toward an integrative perspective on bereavement. *Psychological Bulletin, 125,* 760–776.

Bonanno, G. A., & Keltner, D. (1997). Facial expressions of emotion and the course of conjugal bereavement. *Journal of Abnormal Psychology, 106,* 126–137.

Bonanno, G. A., Keltner, D., Holen, A., & Horowitz, M. J. (1995). When avoiding unpleasant emotions might not be such a bad thing: Verbal-autonomic response dissociation and midlife conjugal bereavement. *Journal of Personality and Social Psychology, 69,* 975–989.

Bonanno, G. A., & Keuler, D. J. (1998). Psychotherapy without repressed memory: A parsimonious alternative based on contemporary memory research. In S. J. Lynn & K. M. McKonkey (Eds.), *Truth in memory* (pp. 437–463). New York: Guilford Press.

Bonanno, G. A., Znoj, H. J., Siddique, H., & Horowitz, M. J. (1999). Verbal-autonomic response dissociation and adaptation to midlife conjugal loss: A follow-up at 25 months. *Cognitive Therapy and Research, 23,* 605–624.

Bowlby, J. (1980). *Loss: Sadness and depression. Vol. 3: Attachment and loss.* New York: Basic Books.

Bremner, J. D., Randall, P., Scott, T. M., Bronen, R. A., Seibyl, J. P., Southwick, S. M., Delaney, R. C., McCarthy, G., Charney, D. S., & Innis, R. B. (1995). MRI-based measurement of hippocampal volume in patients with combat related posttraumatic stress disorder. *American Journal of Psychiatry, 152,* 973–981.

Breuer, J., & Freud, S. (1955). Studies on hysteria. In J. Strachey, A. Freud, A. Strachey, & A. Tyson (Eds. & Trans.), *The standard edition of the complete psychological works of Sigmund Freud* (Vol. 2). London: Hogarth Press. (Original work published 1893)

Cahill, L., Babinsky, R., Markowitsch, H. J., & McGaugh, J. L. (1995). The amygdala and emotional memory. *Nature, 377,* 295–296.

Capps, L., & Bonanno, G. A. (in press). Narrating bereavement: Thematic and grammatical predictors of adjustment to loss. *Discourse Processes.*

Cerney, M. W., & Buskirk, J. R. (1991). Anger: The hidden part of grief. *Bulletin of the Menninger Clinic, 55,* 228–237.

Charney, D. S., Deutch, A. Y., Krystal, J. H., Southwick, S. M., & Davis, M. (1993). Psychobiologic mechanisms of posttraumatic stress disorder. *Archives of General Psychiatry, 50,* 294–305.

Davis, M., Hitchcock, J. M., & Rosen, J. B. (1987). Anxiety and the amygdala: Pharmacological and anatomical analysis of the fear potentiated startle response. In G. Bower (Ed.), *The psychology of learning and emotion* (pp. 263–305). Orlando, FL: Academic Press.

Deutsch, H. (1937). Absence of grief. *Psychoanalytic Quarterly, 6,* 12–22.

Diamond, D. M., & Rose, G. (1994). Stress impairs LTP and hippocampal-dependent memory. *Annals of the New York Academy of Sciences, 746,* 411–414.

Dizard, J. E., & Gadlin, H. (1990). *The minimal family.* Amherst: University of Massachusetts Press.

Draguns, J. G. (1993). Abnormal behavior in Chinese societies: Clinical, epidemiological, and comparative studies. In M. H. Bond (Ed.), *The handbook of Chinese psychology* (pp. 412–428). New York: Oxford University Press.

Ehrlich, P. (1988). Treatment issues in the psychotherapy of Holocaust survivors. In J. P. Wilson & B. Kahana (Eds.), *Human adaptation to extreme stress* (pp. 285–304). New York: Plenum Press.

Ellenberger, H. E. (1970). *The discovery of the unconscious.* New York: Basic Books.

Erdelyi, M. H. (1985). *Psychoanalysis: Freud's cognitive psychology.* New York: Freeman.

Esterling, B. A., Antoni, M. H., Fletcher, M. A., Margulies, S., & Schneiderman, N. (1994). Emotional disclosure through writing or speaking modulates latent Epstein–Barr virus antibody titers. *Journal of Consulting and Clinical Psychology, 62,* 130–140.

Freud, S. (1957). Repression. In J. Strachey (Ed. & Trans.), *The standard edition of the complete psychological works of Sigmund Freud* (Vol. 14, pp. 146–158). London: Hogarth Press. (Original work published 1915)

Freud, S. (1957). Mourning and melancholia. In J. Strachey (Ed. & Trans.), *The standard edition of the complete psychological works of Sigmund Freud* (Vol. 14, pp. 243–258). London: Hogarth Press. (Original work published 1917)

Freud, S. (1966). Introductory lectures on psychoanalysis. In J. Strachey (Ed. & Trans.), *The standard edition of the complete psychological works of Sigmund Freud* (Vols. 15 & 16, pp. 146–158). London: Hogarth Press. (Original work published 1917)

Freud, S. (1966). Inhibition, symptoms and anxiety. In J. Strachey (Ed. & Trans.), *The standard edition of the complete psychological works of Sigmund Freud* (Vol. 20, pp. 87–172). London: Hogarth Press. (Original work published 1926)

Freud, S. (1989). An autobiographical study. In P. Gay (Ed.), *The Freud reader* (pp. 3–41). New York: Norton. (Original work published 1925)

Gabrieli, J. D. (1998). Cognitive neuroscience of human memory. *Annual Review of Psychology, 49,* 87–115.

Gay, P. (Ed.). (1989). *The Freud reader.* New York: Norton.

Greenberg, M. A., & Stone, A. A. (1992). Emotional disclosure about traumas and its relation to health: Effects of previous disclosure and trauma severity. *Journal of Personality and Social Psychology, 63,* 75–84.

Greenberg, M. A., Wortman, C. B., & Stone, A. A. (1996). Emotional expression and physical health: Revising traumatic memories or fostering self-regulation? *Journal of Personality and Social Psychology, 71,* 588–602.

Greenwald, A. G. (1992). New look 3: Unconscious cognition reclaimed. *American Psychologist, 47,* 766–779.

Greenwald, A. G., Klinger, M. R., & Liu, T. J. (1989). Unconscious processing of dichoptically masked words. *Memory and Cognition, 17,* 35–47.

Hilgard, E. R. (1977). *Divided consciousness: Multiple controls in human thought and action* (3rd ed.). New York: Wiley.

Homans, P. (1989). *The ability to mourn: Disillusionment and the social origins of psychoanalysis.* Chicago: University of Chicago Press.

Horowitz, M. J. (1986). *Stress response syndromes.* Northvale, NJ: Aronson.

Horowitz, M. J., Bonanno, G. A., & Holen, A. (1993). Pathological grief: Diagnosis and explanation. *Psychosomatic Medicine, 55,* 260–273.

Irwin, W., Davidson, R., Lowe, M. J., Mock, B. J., Sorenson, J. A., & Turski, P. A. (1996). Human amygdala activation detected with echo-planar functional magnetic resonance imaging. *Neuroreport, 7,* 1765–1769.

Janet, P. (1889). *L'automatisme psychologique* [Psychological automatism]. Paris, France: Librairie Félix Alcan.

Janet, P. (1925). *Psychological healing* (Vols. 1–2). New York: Macmillan. (Original work published 1919)

Janoff-Bulman, R. (1992). *Shattered assumptions: Towards a new psychology of trauma.* New York: Free Press.

Keltner, D., & Bonanno, G. A. (1997). A study of laughter and dissociation: Distinct correlates of laughter and smiling during bereavement. *Journal of Personality and Social Psychology, 73,* 687–702.

Kinzie, J. D. (1988). The psychiatric effects of massive trauma on Cambodian refugees. In J. P. Wilson, Z. Harel, & B. Kahana (Eds.), *Human adaptation to extreme stress* (pp. 305–318). New York: Plenum Press.

Kitayama, S., & Markus, H. (1995). Construal of the self as a cultural frame: Implications for internationalizing psychology. In N. R. Goldberger & J. B. Veroff (Eds.), *The culture and psychology reader* (pp. 366–383). New York: New York University Press.

Kleinman, A., & Kleinman, J. (1985). Somatization: The interconnections in Chinese society among culture, depressive experiences, and the meanings of pain. In A. Kleinman & B. Good (Eds.), *Culture and de-*

pression: Studies in anthropology and cross-cultural psychiatry of affect and disorder (pp. 429–490). Berkeley: University of California Press.

Kramer, T. H., Buckhout, R., & Eugenio, P. (1990). Weapon focus, arousal, and eyewitness memory: Attention must be paid. *Law and Human Behavior, 14,* 167–184.

LaBar, K. S., LeDoux, J. E., Spencer, D. D., & Phelps, E. A. (1995). Impaired fear conditioning following unilateral temporal lobectomy in humans. *Journal of Neuroscience, 15,* 6846–6855.

Lane, R. D., Reiman, E. M., Bradley, M. M., Lang, P. L., Ahern, G., Davidson, R. J., & Schwartz, G. E. (1997). Neuroanatomical correlates of pleasant and unpleasant emotion. *Neuropsychologia, 35,* 1437–1444.

Lazare, A. (1989). Bereavement and unresolved grief. In A. Lazare (Ed.), *Outpatient psychiatry: Diagnosis and treatment* (2nd ed., pp. 381–397). Baltimore: Williams & Wilkins.

Lazarus, R. S., Kanner, A. D., & Folkman, S. (1980). Emotions: A cognitive–phenomenological analysis. In R. Plutchik & H. Kellerman (Eds.), *Theories of emotion. Emotions: Theory, Research, and Experience* (Vol. 1, pp. 189–217). New York: Academic Press.

LeDoux, J. E. (1996). *The emotional brain.* New York: Simon & Schuster.

LeDoux, J. E., & Muller, J. (1997). Emotional memory and psychopathology. *Philosophical Transactions of the Royal Society of London—Series B: Biological Sciences, 352,* 1719–1726.

Lee, S., & Kleinman, A. (1997). Mental illness and social change in China. *Harvard Review of Psychiatry, 5,* 43–46.

Lindemann, E. (1944). Symptomatology and management of acute grief. *American Journal of Psychiatry, 101,* 1141–1148.

Markowitsch, H. J., Calabrese, P., Wurker, M., Durwen, H. F., Kessler, J., Babinsky, R., Brechtelsbauer, D., Heuser, L., & Gehlen, W. (1994). The amygdala's contribution to memory—A study on two patients with Urbach–Weithe disease. *Neuroreport, 5,* 1349–1352.

Marsella, A. (1979). Depressive experience and disorder across cultures. In H. Triandis & J. Draguns (Eds.), *Handbook of cross-cultural psychology* (Vol. 8, pp. 237–290). Boston, MA: Allyn & Bacon.

Mawson, D., Marks, I. M., Ramm, L., & Stern, L. S. (1981). Guided mourning for morbid grief: A controlled study. *British Journal of Psychiatry, 158,* 185–193.

McAdams, D. P. (1985). *Power, intimacy, and the life story: Personalogical inquiries into identity.* New York: Guilford Press.

McAdams, D. P. (1993). *The stories we live by: Personal myths and the making of the self.* New York: Morrow.

McEwen, B., & Sapolsky, R. (1995). Stress and cognitive functioning. *Current Opinion in Neurobiology, 5,* 205–216.

Morris, J. S., Frith, C. D., Perrett, D. I., Rowland, D., Young, A. W., Calder, A. J., & Dolan, R. J. (1996). A differential neural response in the human amygdala to fearful and happy expressions. *Nature, 383,* 812–815.

Newton, T. L., & Contrada, R. J. (1992). Repressive coping and verbal-

autonomic response dissociation: The influence of social context. *Journal of Personality and Social Psychology, 62,* 159–167.
Nolen-Hoeksema, S., McBride, A., & Larson, J. (1997). Rumination and psychological distress among bereaved partners. *Journal of Personality and Social Psychology, 72,* 855–862.
Osterweis, M., Solomon, F., & Green, F. (Eds.). (1984). *Bereavement: Reactions, consequences, and care.* Washington, DC: National Academy Press.
Park, C., Cohen, L. H., & Murch, R. L. (1996). Assessment and prediction of stress-related growth. *Journal of Personality, 64,* 71–105.
Parkes, C. M., & Weiss, R. S. (1983). *Recovery from bereavement.* New York: Basic Books.
Pennebaker, J. W. (1989). Confession, inhibition, and disease. *Advances in Experimental Social Psychology, 22,* 211–244.
Pennebaker, J. W. (1993). Putting stress into words: Health, linguistic, and therapeutic implications. *Behaviour Research and Therapy, 31,* 539–548.
Pennebaker, J. W., & Barger, S. D. (1988). *Autonomic and health effects of traumatic disclosure among survivors of the Holocaust.* Unpublished manuscript, Department of Psychology, Southern Methodist University, Dallas, TX.
Pennebaker, J. W., & Beall, S. K. (1986). Confronting a traumatic event: Toward an understanding of inhibition and disease. *Journal of Abnormal Psychology, 95,* 274–281.
Pennebaker, J. W., Colder, M., & Sharp, L. K. (1990). Accelerating the coping process. *Journal of Personality and Social Psychology, 58,* 528–537.
Pennebaker, J. W., & Hoover, C. W. (1986). Inhibition and cognition: Toward an understanding of trauma and disease. In R. J. Davidson, G. E. Schwartz, & D. Shapiro (Eds.), *Consciousness and self-regulation* (Vol. 4). New York: Plenum Press.
Pennebaker, J. W., Hughes, C. F., & O'Heeron, R. C. (1987). The psychophysiology of confession: Linking inhibitory and psychosomatic processes. *Journal of Personality and Social Psychology, 52,* 781–793.
Pennebaker, J. W., Kiecolt-Glaser, J. K., & Glaser, R. (1988). Disclosure of traumas and immune function: Health implications for psychotherapy. *Journal of Consulting and Clinical Psychology, 56,* 239–245.
Pennebaker, J. W., & O'Heeron, R. C. (1984). Confiding in others and illness rate among spouses of suicide and accidental-death victims. *Journal of Abnormal Psychology, 93,* 473–476.
Pennebaker, J. W., & Susman, J. R. (1988). Disclosure of traumas and psychosomatic processes. *Social Science and Medicine, 26,* 327–332.
Peterson, K. C., Prout, M. P., & Schwarz, R. A. (1991). *Post-traumatic stress disorder: A clinician's guide.* New York: Plenum Press.
Petrie, K. J., Booth, R. J., Pennebaker, J. W., Davison, K. P., & Thomas, M. G. (1995). Disclosure of trauma and immune response to a hepatitis B vaccination program. *Journal of Consulting and Clinical Psychology, 63,* 787–792.

Price, R., & Price, S. (1991). *Two evenings in Saramaka.* Chicago: University of Chicago Press.

Rainey, J. M., Aleem, A., Ortiz, A., Yaragani, V., Pohl, R., & Berchow, R. (1987). Laboratory procedure for the inducement of flashbacks. *American Journal of Psychiatry, 144,* 1317–1319.

Raphael, B. (1983). *The anatomy of bereavement.* New York: Basic Books.

Raphael, B., Middleton, W., Martinek, N., & Misso, V. (1993). Counseling and therapy of the bereaved. In M. S. Stroebe, W. Stroebe, & R. O. Hansson (Eds.), *Handbook of bereavement: Theory, research, and intervention* (pp. 427–456). Cambridge, England: Cambridge University Press.

Reviere, S. L. (1996). *Memory for childhood trauma.* New York: Guilford Press.

Ross, L., & Nisbett, R. E. (1991). *The person and the situation.* New York: McGraw-Hill.

Sanders, C. M. (1979). The use of MMPI in assessing bereavement outcome. In C. S. Newmark (Ed.), *MMPI: Clinical and research trends* (pp. 223–247). New York: Praeger.

Sanders, C. M. (1993). Risk factors in bereavement outcome. In M. S. Stroebe, W. Stroebe, & R. O. Hansson (Eds.), *Handbook of bereavement: Theory, research, and intervention* (pp. 255–270). Cambridge, England: Cambridge University Press.

Sapolsky, R. M. (1996). Why stress is bad for your brain. *Science, 273,* 749–750.

Schacter, D. L. (1997). The cognitive neuroscience of memory: Perspectives from neuroimaging research. *Philosophical Transactions of the Royal Society of London—Series B: Biological Sciences, 352,* 1689–1695.

Schacter, D. L., Alpert, N. M., Savage, C. R., Rauch, S. L., & Albert, M. S. (1996). Conscious recollection and the human hippocampal formation: Evidence from positron emission tomography. *Proceedings of the National Academy of Sciences of the United States of America, 93,* 321–325.

Selye, H. (1976). *The stress of life.* New York: McGraw-Hill.

Shedler, J., Mayman, M., & Manis, M. (1993). The illusion of mental health. *American Psychologist, 48,* 1117–1131.

Silver, S. M. (1986). An inpatient program for post-traumatic stress disorder. In C. R. Figley (Ed.), *Trauma and its wake. Vol. 2: Traumatic stress theory, research, and intervention* (pp. 213–231). Bristol, PA: Taylor & Francis.

Smyth, J. M. (1998). Written emotional expression: Effect sizes, outcome types, and moderating variables. *Journal of Consulting and Clinical Psychology, 66,* 174–184.

Southwick, S. M., Krystal, J. H., Morgan, A., Johnson, D., Nagy L., Nicolaou, A., Heninger, G. R., & Charney, D. S. (1993). Abnormal noradrenergic function in posttraumatic stress disorder. *Archives of General Psychiatry, 50,* 266–274.

Squire, L. R. (1992). Declarative and nondeclarative memory: Multiple

brain systems support learning and memory. *Journal of Cognitive Neuroscience, 4*, 232–243.
Squire, L. R., Ojemann, J. G., Miezin, F. M., Petersen, S. E., Videen, T. O., & Raichle, M. E. (1992). Activation of the hippocampus in normal humans: A functional anatomical study of memory. *Proceedings of the National Academy of Sciences of the United States of America, 89*, 1837–1841.
Stein, N. L., Folkman, S., Trabasso, T., & Christopher-Richards, A. (1997). Appraisal and goal processes as predictors of well-being in bereaved caregivers. *Journal of Personality and Social Psychology, 72*, 863–871.
Stroebe, M., Gergen, M. M., Gergen, K. J., & Stroebe, W. (1992). Broken hearts or broken bonds: Love and death in the historical perspective. *American Psychologist, 47*, 1205–1212.
Stroebe, M. S., & Stroebe, W. (1991). Does "grief work" work? *Journal of Consulting and Clinical Psychology, 59*, 479–482.
Stroebe, W., & Stroebe, M. S. (1987). *Bereavement and health.* Cambridge, England: Cambridge University Press.
Suh, E., Diener, E., Oishi, S., & Triandis, H. C. (1998). The shifting basis of life satisfaction judgments across cultures: Emotions versus norms. *Journal of Personality and Social Psychology, 74*, 482–493.
Tedeschi, R. G., & Calhoun, L. G. (1996). The posttraumatic growth inventory: Measuring the positive legacy of trauma. *Journal of Traumatic Stress, 9*, 455–471.
Terr, L. (1994). *Unchained memories.* New York: Basic Books.
Triandis, H. C. (1995). *Individualism and collectivism.* Boulder, CO: Westview Press.
Triandis, H. C., Bontempo, R., Villareal, M. J., Asai, M., & Lucca, N. (1988). Individualism and collectivism: Cross-cultural perspectives on self-ingroup relationships. *Journal of Personality and Social Psychology, 54*, 323–338.
Tseng, W. S. (1974). The development of psychiatric concepts of Chinese medicine. *Archives of General Psychiatry, 29*, 569–575.
van der Kolk, B. A. (1994). The body keeps the score: Memory and the evolving psychobiology of posttraumatic stress. *Harvard Review of Psychiatry, 1*, 253–265.
van der Kolk, B. A. (1996). Trauma and memory. In B. A. van der Kolk, A. C. McFarlane, & L. Weisaeth (Eds.), *Traumatic stress: The effects of overwhelming experience on mind, body, and society* (pp. 279–302). New York: Guilford Press.
van der Kolk, B. A., & Fisler, R. (1995). Dissociation and the fragmentary nature of traumatic memories: Overview and exploratory study. *Journal of Traumatic Stress, 8*, 505–525.
van der Kolk, B. A., & Kadish, W. (1987). Amnesia, dissociation, and the return of the repressed. In B. A. van der Kolk (Ed.), *Psychological trauma* (pp. 303–330). Washington, DC: American Psychiatric Press.
van der Kolk, B. A., van der Hart, O., & Marmar, C. R. (1996). Dissociation

and information processing in posttraumatic stress disorder. In B. A. van der Kolk, A. C. McFarlane, & L. Weisaeth (Eds.), *Traumatic stress: The effects of overwhelming experience on mind, body, and society* (pp. 303–330). New York: Guilford Press.

Weber, M. (1976). *The protestant ethic and the spirit of capitalism.* London: Unwin. (Original work published 1904)

Weinberger, D. A., & Davidson, M. N. (1994). Styles of inhibiting emotional expression: Distinguishing repressive coping from impression management. *Journal of Personality, 62,* 587–613.

Weinberger, D. A., Schwartz, G. E., & Davidson, J. R. (1979). Low-anxious and repressive coping styles: Psychometric patterns of behavioral and physiological responses to stress. *Journal of Abnormal Psychology, 88,* 369–380.

Weinstein, F., & Platt, G. M. (1989). *The wish to be free: Society, psyche, and value change.* Berkeley: University of California Press.

Williams, J. M. G., Watts, F. N., MacLeod, C., & Mathews, A. (1988). *Cognitive psychology and emotional disorders.* New York: Wiley.

Williams, T. (1988). Diagnosis and treatment of survivor guilt: The bad penny syndrome. In J. P. Wilson, Z. Harel, & B. Kahana (Eds.), *Human adaptation to extreme stress* (pp. 319–336). New York: Plenum Press.

Chapter

6

Death Can Be Hazardous to Your Health: Adaptive and Ironic Consequences of Defenses Against the Terror of Death

Jamie Arndt, Jamie L. Goldenberg, Jeff Greenberg, Tom Pyszczynski, and Sheldon Solomon

> Back of everything is that great specter of universal death, the all encompassing blackness. (James, 1910/1978, p. 139)

> There is one word which, if we only understand it, is the key to Freud's thought. That word is "repression". . . . The Freudian revolution is that radical revision of traditional theories of human nature and human society which becomes necessary if repression is recognized as a fact. (Brown, 1959, p. 3)

Psychoanalysis is an ambitious effort to elucidate the motivational underpinnings of human behavior, with the aim of the maximization of understanding the human condition to effect constructive individual and social change. In *On The History of the Psychoanalytic Movement*, Freud (1938/1966) concluded that repression is the conceptual cornerstone of the theory of psychoanalysis.

Responsibility for this chapter is shared equally among the authors. This work was generously supported by grants from the National Science Foundation, Ernest Becker Foundation, and Skidmore College.

It is interesting to note that Freud himself may have manifested a particularly compelling example of repression. Although he was obsessively and superstitiously preoccupied with the prospect of his own death (see, e.g., Becker, 1973), he made one clear intellectual recognition of the importance of the role of death in unconscious mental activity.

> Is it not for us to confess that in our civilized attitude towards death we are once more living psychologically beyond our means, and must reform and give truth its due? Would it not be better to give death the place in actuality and in our thoughts which properly belongs to it and to yield a little more prominence to that unconscious attitude towards death which we have hitherto so carefully suppressed? This hardly seems indeed a greater achievement but rather a backward step . . . but it has the merit of taking somewhat more into account the true state of affairs. (Freud, 1915/1939, pp. 316–317)

He never seriously considered the notion that the uniquely human awareness of death, and repression thereof, is a central dynamic force that instigates and directs a substantial proportion of human activity.[1]

Although most of Freud's followers were (and are) similarly oblivious to the role of death denial in human affairs, Otto Rank (1884–1939) became the first glaring and important exception. At age 17, Rank read Freud's work and soon developed a treatise on the creative expression of the artist, a theme that would pervade his entire career (Liberman, 1993). After seeing Rank's treatise, Freud was greatly impressed, and the two formed an intensely strong scholarly and personal relationship (Liberman, 1993). After about 15 years of close collaboration, however, Rank's ideas began to diverge from Freud's dogmatic reliance on sexual conflicts as the primary source of repression and consequent neuroses. Al-

---

[1]Of course, Freud (e.g., 1938) did focus on death in his conceptualization of *thanatos* (the death instinct). Freud proposed a basic drive toward death that operates in opposition to Eros, the basic drive for more life, stimulation, and pleasure. In sharp contrast, on the basis of Rank's (e.g., 1932/1989) and Becker's (e.g., 1973) work, we propose a basic drive to avoid and deny death. A full comparison of these two perspectives is outside the domain of this chapter (see Brown, 1959).

though Rank retained the Freudian ideas of repression and a dynamic unconscious, he argued that the fundamental human defense is against the possibility of a meaningless existence ending in absolute annihilation (e.g., Rank, 1929/1978, 1932/1989, 1936/1978, 1941/1958).

Norman O. Brown (in *Life Against Death,* 1959) later independently offered an interpretation of psychoanalysis completely congruent with Rank's; specifically, he argued that a fundamental incapacity to accept death impels human beings to strive for immortality through the creation of and participation in culture. Ernest Becker (1973) then attempted to synthesize Freud's ideas with Rank's and Brown's (and the ideas of a host of other thinkers from a variety of academic disciplines) in his Pulitzer Prize-winning *The Denial of Death.* In this work, Becker (1973) forcefully advanced the argument that fear of death "haunts the human animal like nothing else; it is a mainspring of human activity" (p. xvii) and is therefore the central psychological construct necessary to understand the human condition in general and issues surrounding mental and physical health in particular.[2]

Terror management theory (Greenberg, Pyszczynski, & Solomon, 1986; Solomon, Greenberg, & Pyszczynski, 1991) was initially developed to organize Becker's (e.g., 1973, 1975) ideas into a coherent theory of social behavior that could be used to generate testable hypotheses. The cumulative results of 10 years of research clearly indicate that the human awareness of mortality plays an important role in a variety of personal and interpersonal behaviors. Research findings have also led to refinements of the original theory, which have in turn produced new hypotheses, many of which are also supported by subsequent research (Greenberg, Solomon, & Pyszczynski, 1997). We believe that this kind of dialectical interplay between theory and research is the most productive way to ad-

[2]Robert Jay Lifton (*The Broken Connection: On Death and the Continuity of Life,* 1983) and Irvin Yalom (*Existential Psychotherapy,* 1980) also share Becker's sense that death awareness and denial play a central role in directing human affairs; before that Gregory Zilboorg (1943) and Rollo May (e.g., *Man's Search for Himself,* 1953) advanced ideas that are strikingly similar to those of his contemporaries, Brown and (to a lesser extent) Rank.

vance scientific knowledge (for extended discussions of this idea, see Greenberg, Solomon, Pyszczynski, & Steinberg, 1988; Laudan, 1977, 1984; and Solomon et al., 1991). We also believe that the juxtaposition of broad ambitious psychoanalytic theorizing with the highly sophisticated methods of experimental social psychology that characterize terror management research has allowed researchers to progress toward a powerful account of the motivational underpinnings of human behavior. This analysis, in turn, can inform efforts to understand and promote human health and well-being.

In this chapter, we explore the effects of the human awareness of mortality on physical and mental health. This exploration culminates in an analysis of both the adaptive and the ironic maladaptive consequences of the psychological defenses people use to manage the terror of death. To lay the groundwork for this analysis, we must begin with an overview of terror management theory, followed by a general description of a number of research programs and theoretical refinements produced as a result of the initial empirical findings. We then examine the implications of this theory and research for the understanding of mental health and physical well-being.

Terror Management Theory

> Civilization originates in delayed infancy and its function is security. It is a huge network of more or less successful attempts to protect mankind against the danger of object-loss, the colossal efforts made by a baby who is afraid of being left alone in the dark. (Roheim, 1943, p. 107)

Terror management theory is based on an examination, from an evolutionary perspective, of how humans are both similar to and different from other living things. In terms of similarity, humans share with all other creatures a fundamental biological predisposition toward self-preservation. "Staying alive," the biological prime directive and common denominator for all living organisms, facilitates the survival of the individual, thereby enhancing reproductive success and contributing to the perpetuation of the species.

Different forms of life, however, vary immensely in specific structural and functional adaptations that have rendered them eligible for continued membership in the gene pool (e.g., turtle shells, fish gills, owls' eyesight, peacocks' strut). In this regard, the primary difference between humans and all other life is the inordinately sophisticated personal and interpersonal activities made possible by the unique structure of the human brain, which facilitates the survival of the species.

In *The Birth and Death of Meaning*, Ernest Becker (1962, 1971) argued that cognitive complexity functions to provide *freedom of reactivity* (the ability to separate an organism's responses from the stimuli that initiated them). So, for example, whereas simple-minded amoebas are limited to moving toward or away from a glucoselike substance, their more cognitively adroit human counterparts have much greater latitude when confronted with the same situation. They can "slurp" the glucoselike substance down immediately, delay gratification and slurp it later, or even decide to stuff it in some angel food cake and make a Twinkie. Thus, human adaptation consists in large measure of the capacity to think abstractly, namely, to think in terms of a past, present, and future and to imagine things that have not yet occurred and attempt to transform those visions into reality, culminating in a conscious and self-conscious creature with a linguistically constructed self that regulates thoughts, feelings, and behaviors (i.e., Duval & Wicklund, 1972; Mead, 1934/1968). Freedom of reactivity through abstract and symbolic thought provides humans with remarkable advantages in navigating through the world and is surely responsible for their survival and prosperity in a variety of environmental circumstances.

However, as Becker (1973) and Rank (1929/1978) before him (and Kierkegaard, 1844/1957, before Rank) pointed out, there are also some unsettling consequences of cognitive complexity. Humans, aware of their own existence, are necessarily aware of the inevitability of death. They also know they can perish at any time for reasons that cannot be anticipated or controlled; that is, life can be snatched away by the mouth of a lion, the eye of a hurricane, the foot of a ninja, or the nose of a scud missile. For a species endowed with a biological proclivity for self-preservation, the awareness that death is always potentially imminent and ultimately inevitable creates the potential for a profoundly debilitating and uniquely human anxiety—a notion that has been around for some time.

> For in much wisdom is much grief: and he that increaseth knowledge increaseth sorrow. . . . The wise man's eyes are in his head; but the fool walketh in darkness: and I myself perceived also that one event happeneth to them all. . . . For there is no remembrance of the wise more than of the fool for ever; seeing that which now is in the days to come shall all be forgotten. And how dieth the wise man? as the fool. (*Ecclesiastes, The Preacher*, n.d.)

As film director John Cassavetes succinctly observed in his film *Shadows*, "it is perfectly obvious—man, in contrast to other animals, is conscious of his own existence and therefore conscious of the possibility of nonexistence; ergo, he has anxiety" (McMendree & Cassavetes, 1960).

Because this uniquely human "existential paradox"—that humans are creatures with a God-like imagination that is capable of conceiving of immortality but are housed in defecating, copulating, degenerating bodies destined to die and are capable of conceiving of that too—is an emergent consequence of the exquisitely adaptive capacity for symbolic thought, it is not surprising that the human evolutionary reaction to this problem is also symbolic. We posit that cultural worldviews are humanly created beliefs about the nature of reality shared by groups of people that are developed as a means by which the people manage the potential for terror (hence our term terror management) engendered by the human awareness of mortality. One of the primary functions of cultural worldviews is the repression of the awareness of death to obliterate, or at least to attenuate, the terror that such awareness would otherwise engender.

Cultural worldviews assuage terror by providing answers to basic and universal cosmological questions (e.g., How did I get here? What do I do while I'm here? What happens after I die?) and structuring human perceptions (e.g., clocks, calendars) in ways that imbue the universe with meaning, order, and permanence. Cultures also provide prescriptions for valued behavior that when fulfilled, promise protection and ultimately death transcendence, either literally through such beliefs as heaven or reincarnation or symbolically through an identification with entities beyond one's self. It is important to note, therefore, that although religion is often a major component of a cultural worldview, this analysis views many other types of identifications, such as belief in one's family, country, or even basketball team, as ultimately fictional conceptions of reality that make it possible for people to be valued and significant members of a meaningful universe, in other words (following Becker, 1962, 1971), for them to have self-esteem. For example, the capitalistic patriot may find order in the laws of society, value in closing the big business deal, and permanence in contributing to his or her company or nation.

Thus, a cultural worldview need not have overtly religious overtones to serve the functions we are proposing. Indeed, one could also view the rigidity with which scientists often cling to their theories as an example of the trenchant need to maintain and defend faith in a system of beliefs that provides the basis for an individual's self-worth. In summary, terror management theory posits that these two structures, faith in a cultural worldview and self-esteem, result from living up to the standards of value associated with that worldview and are essential to sustain psychological equanimity; consequently, people are strongly motivated to maintain them and defend them against threats.

However, each person enters the world unadorned by a cultural worldview, and it is only in time that the repression of mortality concerns become a fundamental motivating force that instigates, directs, and regulates a substantial proportion of human activity.[3] Following a range of theorists (e.g., Becker, 1962, 1971; Bowlby, 1969; Horney, 1937; Mead, 1934/1968; Sullivan, 1953; Yalom, 1980), we propose that the foundation for this repression is acquired early in life, given the child's profound immaturity and consequent helplessness, and in the context of the socialization process. Unable to

[3]Although terror management research focuses on defensive motivation, such concerns are clearly not the only forces that impinge on human behavior. The human animal is also driven, for example, by the pursuit of pleasure and growth. A consideration of how these motives interact, however, is beyond the scope of this chapter (for an extended discussion of this issue, see Greenberg, Pyszczynski, & Solomon, 1995).

provide for themselves, children are totally dependent on their parents or caregivers for protection and fulfillment of their basic needs. Eventually, however, children must enter into the cultural world and act according to the values of their society. For example, the physical body and its natural functions become aspects of children's experience that must be controlled and regulated.

Defecation, previously a totally unregulated activity, is now expected to be performed in an elaborate and specific porcelain structure. Successful performance generally yields children immediate and massive doses of parental praise, whereas less successful efforts ("That's a Ming Dynasty vase, not a toilet!") result in a range of much less desirable outcomes, from verbal or physical punishment to silent rebuke or just a noticeable absence of overt affection. Thus children's sense of security becomes increasingly contingent on meeting parental standards of value, which ultimately reflect the parents' sense of the prevailing cultural worldview. Children learn that meeting these standards leads to feelings of significance and security and that failing to do so leads to feelings of inferiority, insecurity, and anxiety. In this fashion, self-esteem acquires its anxiety-buffering properties.

Children continue to function this way until the gradually dawning awareness of both their own mortality and the dwindling capacity of their caregivers to protect them from their anxieties becomes evident. Specifically, children begin to learn about and become concerned with the problem of death, culminating with the realization that their own death is inevitable (see Yalom, 1980, for an extensive discussion of childhood concerns about death).

> There is a time in the life of every boy when he for the first time takes a backward view of life. Perhaps that is the moment when he crosses the line into manhood. The boy is walking through the streets of his town. He is thinking of the future and of the figure he will cut in the world. Ambitions and regrets awake within him. Suddenly something happens; he stops under a tree and waits as for a voice calling his name. Ghosts of old things creep into his consciousness; the voices outside of himself whisper a message concerning the limitations of life. From being quite sure of himself and his future he becomes not at all sure. If he be an imaginative boy a door is torn open, and for the first

> time he looks out upon the world, seeing, as though they marched in procession before him, the countless figures of men who before his time have come out of nothingness into the world, lived their lives and again disappeared into nothingness. The sadness of sophistication has come to the boy. With a little gasp he sees himself as merely a leaf blown by the wind through the streets of his village. He knows that in spite of all the stout talk of his fellows, he must live and die in uncertainty, a thing blown by the winds, a thing destined like corn to wilt in the sun. He shivers and looks eagerly about. . . . Already he hears death calling. (Anderson, 1919/1992, pp. 234–235)

Concurrently, the parents, previously perceived to be ever present and all powerful, are now seen to be the humans that they are, fallible and mortal. Thus the need for the critical repression of death to maintain psychological equanimity arises and is accomplished by the transference (see Becker, 1973, for a detailed discussion of transference processes in light of this analysis) of the primary security base from the parents to the culture at large. Consistent with this analysis, research suggests that an individual's self-concept is strongly affected first by his or her parents and then later by the social institutions that impinge on the individual (Rosenberg, 1981). A range of teachings, from fairy tales to myths, schooling and entertainment, and religious deities and instruction, facilitate this transference by reinforcing the association between living up to certain values and experiencing feelings of goodness and security (cf. Lerner, 1980). The more that the individual meets these standards of value, the more the individual acquires feelings of personal significance (self-esteem).

According to this analysis then, self-esteem arises out of the context of childhood interactions with parents and significant others and culminates as a culturally constructed anxiety buffer that renders secure adult functioning possible. Note that self-esteem is based not on the absolute value of a particular trait or behavior but rather on social designation of the particular trait or behavior as valuable. In other words, as anthropologists have pointed out (e.g., Erchak, 1992; Goldschmidt, 1990), the standards on which self-esteem is based are culturally relative. For example, male adolescents of the Sambia in New Guinea engage in a ritual that demands them to perform fellatio on the older men of the village to achieve the most valued characteristic of *jergundu* (strength; Herdt, 1987). Although this behavior confers prestige and self-esteem to members of this culture, it is not likely to be warmly embraced by people in Western societies. Similarly, many behaviors in Western culture (e.g., having the most highly rewarded and regarded members of one's society be those who can toss round rubber balls through metal hoops) would be viewed with bewilderment or disdain by people from cultures unfamiliar with this practice.

Because self-esteem is ultimately based on standards of value espoused by one's culture, its anxiety-buffering function can be served only to the extent that faith in the cultural worldview is sustained. As the foregoing examples illustrate, because all cultural worldviews are relative, somewhat arbitrary social fictions (full of customs, myths, and beliefs that are based as much on superstition and historical happenstance as on pragmatic concerns), their perceived validity depends on continuous consensual validation from others (e.g., Berger & Luckmann, 1967; Festinger, 1954). Thus those who share or agree with one's beliefs reinforce, validate, and sustain one's notions of what is good and valuable. However, those who adhere to different belief systems threaten faith in one's worldview and undermine its capacity to buffer anxiety.

Accordingly, the mere existence of divergent beliefs is unsettling because either implicitly or explicitly alternative conceptions of reality threaten the confidence with which one's own cultural worldview can be asserted as absolutely true. Without such confidence, faith that the cultural prescriptions of appropriate conduct constitute the right way to do things, the foundation of one's sense of self-esteem, is undermined. This intolerable, anxiety-provoking threat must then be responded to with compensatory responses generally directed at restoring faith in that view (Berger & Luckmann, 1967). From this perspective, human beings' lurid and longstanding traditions of hostility and disdain toward anyone different than themselves can best be understood as egregious manifestations of the defenses marshaled against the threats different others pose to the self-esteem-producing, anxiety-reducing, death-denying properties of one's cultural worldview.

Figure 6.1 provides a brief summary of terror management theory. Human beings' sophisticated cognitive capabilities, instrumen-

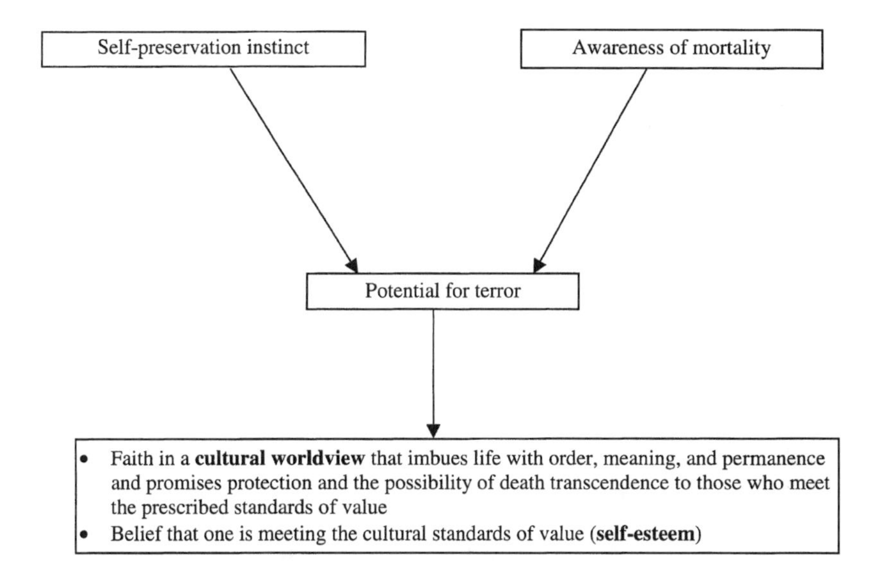

Figure 6.1. Overview of the terror management theory.

tal to their survival, also render all individuals aware that they will inevitably die, resulting in the ever-present potential for terrifying and enervating anxiety. We believe that repression evolved as a means to manage such crippling anxiety and, as Freud cogently argued, that efforts to provide an account of the motivational underpinnings of human behavior (and the history of humans on earth, for that matter) without recourse to the concept of repression are unlikely to succeed. Following those who drew from Freud, specifically, Rank (e.g., 1932/1989), Zilboorg (1943), Brown (1959), Becker (e.g., 1973), Yalom (1980), and Lifton (1983), we based our work on the premise that cultural worldviews evolved, at least in large measure, as shared beliefs about the nature of reality to facilitate the repression of death by providing a sense that one is a person of value in a world of meaning and hence qualified for safety and security while alive and for symbolic immortality, literal immortality, or both after death. Therefore, for human beings, mental health and physical well-being require ongoing faith in a meaningful conception of reality and the belief that one is meeting or exceeding the standards of value prescribed by that conception.

Empirical Assessment of the Terror Management Hypotheses

> Fear is felt not only lest something terrible occur within the personality but also lest there be a loss of certain pleasurable feelings, such as well-being, protection, and security, which were hitherto present. This feared loss may be characterized as a loss of self-esteem, the most extreme degree of which is a feeling of annihilation. (Fenichel, 1945, p. 134)

Initial research to assess the merits of terror management theory was directed toward two general hypotheses.

Mortality Salience Hypothesis

Because an individual's affiliation with the cultural worldview is believed to be motivated by the potential for terror engendered by the knowledge of one's own mortality, the theory predicts that reminding participants of their death (mortality salience) will provoke increased allegiance to their worldview. This proposition, termed the mortality salience hypothesis, has received considerable support from a paradigm in which participants answer two open-ended questions about their death and then evaluate targets who either threaten or support their worldview.[4]

In many of these studies (e.g., Greenberg, Simon, Pyszczynski, Solomon, & Chatel, 1992), American participants are asked to briefly think about their death and then to evaluate a target who attacks beliefs associated with the United States and a target who supports such beliefs. Results indicate that mortality salience par-

[4]Specifically, a typical experiment contains two short ostensibly unrelated studies, the first concerned with the relationship between personality traits and the second with impression formation. Within the first few personality questionnaires that participants complete is a form that contains either of the two following requests: (a) "Please briefly describe the emotions that the thought of your own death arouses in you" and "Jot down, as specifically as you can, what you think will happen to you physically as you die and once you are physically dead" or (b) parallel questions with respect to a non-death-related aversive event. The second study then presents participants with worldview relevant targets whom they are to evaluate.

ticipants engaged in worldview defense, specifically, becoming more positive in their evaluations of those who supported their worldview and more negative in their evaluations of those who challenged it. Greenberg et al. (1990) demonstrated another example of worldview defense. In Study 1, Christian participants engaged in worldview defense following a mortality salience induction by reporting enhanced regard for a Christian target and exaggerated disdain for a Jewish target (relative to control conditions). Research also demonstrates that after undergoing a mortality salience induction, participants are more reluctant to handle culturally valued artifacts in sacrilegious ways, such as a crucifix for Catholic participants or an American flag for American participants (Greenberg, Porteus, Simon, Pyszczynski, & Solomon, 1995). The participants also showed more physical aggression against a person who threatens their political orientation (McGregor et al., 1998), thus providing important evidence that mortality salience effects are not confined to paper-and-pencil measures.

Moreover, mortality salience effects have been obtained in other laboratories in the United States (e.g., Nelson, Moore, Olivetti, & Scott, 1997), Canada (e.g., Baldwin & Wesley, 1996), Israel (e.g., Florian & Mikulincer, 1997), Germany (e.g., Ochsmann & Mathay, 1996), and the Netherlands (Dechesne, Greenberg, Arndt, & Schimel, 1999),[5] from the use of various operationalizations of mortality salience, such as a fear of death scale (Greenberg, Simon, et al., 1995), fatal accident footage (Nelson et al., 1997), proximity to a funeral home (Pyszczynski et al., 1996), and subliminal death primes (Arndt, Greenberg, Pyszczynski, & Solomon, 1997), with various participants, from fifth graders (Florian & Mikulincer, 1998) to college students (e.g., Greenberg et al., 1990), Israeli soldiers (e.g., Taubman Ben-Ari, Florian, & Mikulincer, 1999), municipal court judges (Rosenblatt, Greenberg, Solomon, Pyszczynski, & Lyon, 1989), and pedestrians in Colorado and Germany (Pyszczynski et al., 1996).

[5]Although studies have not been conducted in highly collectivistic cultures, given their negative reactions to outsiders (Triandis, 1990), we strongly suspect that similar effects of mortality salience would be obtained in these cultures as well.

Mortality salience effects also appear to be unique to thoughts of mortality (e.g., Baldwin & Wesley, 1996; Greenberg, Simon, et al., 1995; Rosenblatt et al., 1989); thoughts of intense physical pain, social exclusion, meaninglessness, the failing of an important exam, dental pain, an actual failure experience, or even someone else's dying do not reproduce these effects. Indeed, the fatal accident footage only led to increased worldview defense when the footage reminded participants of their own mortality (Nelson et al., 1997). Additionally, a typical mortality salience manipulation does not produce physiological arousal (as measured by pulse rate, peripheral blood volume, and skin conductance) or self-reports of anxiety or negative affect (see Arndt, Allen, & Greenberg, 1999; and Greenberg et al., 1997, for a detailed review of this research).

Florian and Mikulincer (1998) obtained evidence that worldview defense following mortality salience does not appear in children at age 7 but is evident by age 11, which is consistent with Yalom's (1980) claim that death increasingly becomes a problem as children approach adolescence and with the developmental analysis presented above regarding how the repression of death is facilitated by adherence to cultural worldviews in the context of the socialization process. The presumed explanation for this difference is that the 11-year-old has developed the cognitive mechanisms to conceptualize death as an absolute annihilation, whereas the 7-year-old has not. However, it could also be the case that at age 7, the child's conceptualization of death is sufficiently developed, but his or her basis for security has not yet been transferred to the culture, so the parents remain as the child's primary base of security.

Anxiety-Buffer Hypothesis

Because self-esteem qualifies the individual for the protection and death transcendence afforded by the accepted worldview, a second general hypothesis derived from the theory is that self-esteem serves an anxiety-buffering function. Consequently, according to the anxiety-buffer hypothesis, when self-esteem is experimentally increased or dispositionally high, participants exposed to threatening stimuli exhibit less self-reported anxiety, physiological arousal, and anxiety-related defensiveness.[6]

Greenberg, Solomon, et al. (1992, Study 1) momentarily elevated participants' self-esteem by giving them each very flattering (albeit identical and contrived) feedback about their personalities; control participants received neutral feedback. Half of the participants then watched several minutes of a gory video, depicting scenes from an autopsy and an electrocution; the others watched a benign video of comparable length. All participants then completed a self-report anxiety scale. In accordance with the notion that self-esteem serves an anxiety-buffering function, participants given neutral personality feedback reported significantly higher anxiety after watching the gory video than did those whose self-esteem had been momentarily augmented.

Greenberg, Solomon, et al. (1992, Study 2 & 3) then replicated this effect using the anticipation of electrical shocks to induce threat and measures of electrodermal activity to assess anxiety. Momentarily raising self-esteem resulted in lower skin conductance scores for those anticipating electrical shocks, relative to the neutral self-esteem condition (and to nonthreat control conditions). Thus the anxiety-buffering capacity of self-esteem not only functions with regard to threats of mortality but also extends to other more general anxiety-provoking situations. Greenberg et al. (1993) then demonstrated that participants' momentarily elevated and dispositionally high self-esteem resulted in less vulnerability-denying defensive distortions. Specifically, these researchers found that heightened self-esteem reduced participants' tendency to skew

---

[6]In these experiments, dispositional self-esteem was measured by a self-report inventory, namely, the Rosenberg (1965) Self-Esteem Scale. To experimentally manipulate self-esteem, we used one of two well-established strategies in the social psychology literature. The first technique is to give participants bogus personality feedback, which for some is very flattering. Capitalizing on the Barnum effect (Forer, 1949), the feedback broadly extols the virtues of the participant's personality on the basis of the standards of value derived from the culture. The second technique is to give participants feedback on their performance on a bogus test. The test is generally described in a way that conveys its importance and value (e.g., a test of social sensitivity that predicts career and relationship success). Thus both techniques inform participants that they possess traits and skills commonly valued by their culture.

self-reports of emotionality when they were told that certain emotional characteristics are associated with a short life expectancy. Whereas in control conditions participants denied being emotional when told that emotional people die young (or denied being unemotional when told unemotional people die young), heightened self-esteem reduced this bias.

Self-Esteem and Mortality Salience

Recently researchers have also examined whether self-esteem reduces worldview defense in response to mortality salience. In one study, participants received generalized personality feedback intended to raise their self-esteem or to be neutral in this respect, responded to open-ended questions concerning their death or a control topic, and then evaluated a target that criticized the United States and a target that praised it (Harmon-Jones et al., 1997). In a second study, participants underwent a similar procedure but were instead divided on the basis of dispositional assessments of self-esteem. In both studies, after contemplating a control topic, high self-esteem participants showed more worldview defense; however, following mortality salience, high self-esteem participants responded with less worldview defense. Presumably this pattern emerged because people high in self-esteem were more invested in their worldview and thus responded more sensitively to that which impinged on it. However, to the extent that high self-esteem provided such individuals with protection from mortality concerns, they had less need to defend their worldview after these concerns were made salient. Finally, as we argued earlier, for elevated self-esteem to provide protection from mortality concerns, the standards or beliefs from which the feelings of self-esteem are derived must be consensually validated. Arndt and Greenberg (1999) recently demonstrated that when the target attacks the basis of the self-esteem boost following mortality salience and thus threatens the anxiety-buffering capacity of the boost participants respond by derogating the target.

Summary

Taken together, these studies provide powerful convergent support for the central tenets of terror management theory. Asking people to ponder their own demise reliably produces attitudinal and behavioral responses to defend important aspects of their cultural worldviews; these effects appear to be unique to thoughts of death. Other studies demonstrate that participants' high state or trait self-esteem attenuates their anxiety in response to stress. Finally, worldview defense following mortality salience is reduced if self-esteem, based on consensually validated standards, is elevated or is dispositionally high prior to the mortality salience induction, providing important evidence supporting the theoretically prescribed connection between feelings of self-worth and concerns about mortality.

Theoretical Refinements

Temporal and Cognitive Underpinnings of Mortality Salience Effects

Although terror management theory makes clear and direct predictions that have been repeatedly confirmed regarding the attitudinal and behavioral reactions to mortality salience, which we call "worldview defense," it does not precisely specify the psychological processes that underlie these effects. Recently, however, researchers have begun to elucidate the cognitive processes and temporal sequence through which mortality salience effects occur. Our desire to understand the psychological underpinnings of mortality salience effects originated when other researchers were unable to replicate our finding that thoughts of death engender exaggerated responses to similar and different others. We later learned that they had used mortality salience inductions exponentially more salient and impactful (e.g., asking people to consider their own death for 20 minutes) than the two relatively innocuous open-ended questions previously described. Because this was the only obvious difference between the studies in which mortality salience effects were obtained and those in which they were not, Greenberg, Pyszczynski, Solomon, Simon, and Breus (1994, Study 1) compared an impactful mortality salience induction with the typical subtle one and found the somewhat counterintuitive but nevertheless predicted result: Worldview defense was greater following a subtle mortality salience induction than following a more impactful procedure.

Having determined (rather ironically) that mortality salience effects do not occur if mortality is too salient, we decided to examine the interesting possibility that worldview defense following mortality salience can only occur to the extent that people are not consciously thinking about death. In Study 2 (Greenberg et al., 1994), following a typical subtle mortality salience (or control) induction, participants spent 3 minutes engaged in a word search exercise. They were given a list of words and asked to find as many of them as they could from a matrix of letters. They then evaluated pro- and anti-American targets to provide a measure of worldview defense. For half of the participants, the words were death related (e.g., *blood, murder, control*); the other half of participants received benign words of comparable length. Because worldview defense after mortality salience occurs only when thoughts of death are not currently conscious, the researchers obtained exaggerated reactions to the targets after participants thought about death and were subsequently distracted by having to search for benign words. However, when the mortality salience induction was followed by a task that required that participants' thoughts of death be kept in their consciousness, the researchers did not observe these exaggerated reactions.

Perhaps, then, when people are made aware of death, the first thing that must happen before worldview defense can occur is active suppression or the removal of conscious death thoughts from a person's awareness or focal attention (research reviewed later more explicitly addresses the question of why). Greenberg et al. (1994, Study 4) examined this possibility by measuring the accessibility of death-related thoughts either directly following a mortality salience induction or a few minutes after mortality was made salient, during which time participants read a 7-page descriptive passage from a novel. To measure the accessibility of death thoughts, they asked participants to engage in a word-fragment completion task; specifically, participants saw the parts of words, such as *sk___* and *coff__*, which could be completed as *skill* and *coffee* or as *skull* and *coffin*. On the basis of other research (e.g., Bassili & Smith, 1986), Greenberg et al. presumed that the accessibility of death-related thoughts could be inferred by the number of death-related word-fragment completions provided by each participant. Consistent with their claim that the conscious confrontation with death momentarily engendered by the mortality salience induction instigates active efforts to suppress death-related thoughts, higher levels of death accessibility following a distraction than immediately after the mortality salience induction were found. This effect presumably reflects initial efforts to suppress thoughts of death immediately after mortality is made salient, resulting in lower death-thought accessibility. After the suppression is relaxed over time (the 3-minute distraction period), higher death-thought accessibility results.

Arndt, Greenberg, Solomon, Pyszczynski, and Simon (1997) obtained more direct evidence for this process in a series of studies. Presuming that this suppression process would require the allocation of mental resources to sustain it, Arndt et al. denied such resources to some of their participants by introducing a cognitive load task found to impair suppression efforts (e.g., Wegner, 1992). Specifically, Arndt et al. asked participants during and after a mortality salience induction to keep 11 digits in mind until they were asked to recall them. The researchers found immediate increases in death-thought accessibility. The finding that death-thought accessibility was high immediately after mortality was made salient if people were denied the cognitive resources necessary to engage in suppression (the cognitive load) but was low if they were not similarly encumbered provides especially strong support for the claim that the explicit awareness of mortality engenders active efforts to suppress a person's thinking about death.

These findings seem to converge on the notion that worldview defense following mortality salience is of necessity a nonconscious process because such effects do not occur in response to blatant reminders of death or whenever death thoughts are explicitly conscious. Presumably, the more blatant reminders evoke more powerful thoughts of mortality that remain in consciousness longer than do thoughts evoked by more subtle treatments. Arndt, Greenberg, Pyszczynski, et al. (1997) obtained direct evidence that unconscious mortality concerns motivate worldview defense in three studies in which participants were exposed to subliminal reminders of death (specifically, having masked presentations of the word *death* flashed for 28 ms on a computer screen; control participants saw the word *field* or *pain* for the same length of time). Participants did not report seeing anything, could not pick out the subliminal stimulus they had been exposed to when asked to select it from a list of five options, and in a supplemental study were unable to identify the prime beyond chance when informed that it would be one of two possible words. Despite being unaware of what had happened to them, participants exposed to the death prime had increased death-thought accessibility and worldview defense.

We believe these studies provide the most compelling evidence to date in support of Freud's idea that unconscious drives and defenses play a significant role in human thought and behavior. Research supports the existence of subliminal perception (see Bornstein, Leone, & Galley, 1987). In addition, Silverman's (e.g., 1983) work suggests that nonconscious stimuli of symbiotic fantasies can affect thoughts relevant to clinical disorders, although some researchers continue to doubt whether the complex stimuli (sentences) Silverman used can be perceived in the absence of conscious awareness (e.g., Greenwald, 1992). Arndt, Greenberg, Pyszczynski, et al.'s (1997) work shows that a single word prime presented outside of a person's awareness can alter his or her judgments of stimuli semantically unrelated to the prime. Specifically, it shows that without awareness, concerns about death activate defense of a person's worldview.

Additional studies subsequently demonstrate that the same conditions leading to increased accessibility of death-related thoughts lead to elevated worldview defense (Harmon-Jones et al., 1997; Simon et al., 1997) and that worldview defense following mortality salience serves to reduce death accessibility (Arndt, Greenberg, Pyszczynski, et al., 1997). Taken together then, these research findings indicate that worldview defense in response to a consideration of mortality is a nonconscious process that occurs only when death thoughts are out of focal attention but are highly accessible. Moreover, the terror management function of high state or trait self-esteem and worldview defense (buttressing faith in the cultural worldview by derogating different others and exaggerated appreciation of those who share similar beliefs) are reflected by the decrease in accessibility of death thoughts found under these conditions.

Intimations of Mortality: Dual Defenses

The types of defensive reactions obtained in the mortality salience studies bear no clear logical or semantic relation to the problem of death. Prescribing harsher punishment for moral transgressors (e.g., Florian & Mikulincer, 1997; Rosenblatt et al., 1989), becoming more hostile toward outgroup members and those who challenge one's beliefs (e.g., Greenberg et al., 1990), exaggerating the extent of social consensus for one's attitudes (Pyszczynski et al., 1996), or increasing one's conformity to cultural standards (Greenberg, Simon, et al., 1992; Greenberg, Porteus, et al., 1995) has little or no bearing on one's belief regarding the ultimate reality that one will die someday. From a terror management theory perspective, such defensive reactions help shield individuals from fears surrounding their death by enabling them to view themselves as valuable members of a cultural reality that persists beyond the point of their own physical demise.

There is clear evidence, however, that people use a variety of cognitive distortions and biases to deny rationally their vulnerability to an early death when they are consciously confronted with information that reminds them of their vulnerability (e.g., Croyle & Sande, 1988; Croyle & Williams, 1991; Ditto, Jemmott, & Darley, 1988; Kunda, 1987; Quattrone & Tversky, 1984).[7] For example, Quattrone and Tversky told half of their participants that people with a high tolerance for cold live longer and the other half that people with a low tolerance for cold live longer. The former group then displayed a very high tolerance for having their hand in ice cold water, whereas the latter group showed little tolerance for this activity.

---

[7]Proximal defenses are rational in the sense that they entail seemingly logical analyses of available information to support the belief that death is not an immediate problem. In Epstein's (1995) terms, they involve processing within the rational system and operate according to the rules of logic and evidence. For these biases to serve their vulnerability-denying function effectively, individuals must maintain an illusion of objectivity concerning their beliefs by controlling the information that is accessed and how it is processed, so that it appears that the inference of a long life expectancy is derived in an entirely rational manner (Pyszczynski & Greenberg, 1987).

It appears then that people sometimes cope with the problem of death by denying their vulnerability to life-threatening conditions rationally and, at other times, cope in a way that serves the unconscious need for ultimate death transcendence by increasing their efforts to find meaning in life and value in themselves. We propose that these distinctly different modes of defense emerge in response to conscious and unconscious death-related thought, respectively.

Conscious thoughts of death instigate what we refer to as "proximal defenses," rational threat-focused attempts to remove conscious death-related thoughts from current focal attention by either suppressing such thoughts, often through the use of distraction, or pushing the problem of death into the distant future by biasing inferential processes to deny one's vulnerability. In contrast, unconscious thoughts of death instigate what we call "distal defenses," which use the symbolic conception of self and reality specified by one's culture as a way of responding to the unconscious knowledge (vs. current conscious awareness) of the inevitability of one's death (for an extended discussion of proximal and distal defenses, see Pyszczynski, Greenberg, & Solomon, 1999). This analysis is, of course, compatible with Freud's (1920/1989) view of the unconscious as unbounded by rationality and logic and Epstein's (1995) more recent suggestion that unconscious thought is largely experiential (rather than rational).

Research is consistent with this view. Simon et al. (1997) found worldview defense (a distal defense) after mortality salience when individuals were in an experiential mode of processing, induced by asking participants to respond quickly in a gut level and intuitive fashion but not when they were in a rational mode in which participants were asked to think carefully and rationally. Moreover, worldview defense is greater in response to subtle than to more blatant reminders of one's mortality, occurs when participants are distracted from death-related thoughts as opposed to keeping such thoughts in their current focal attention, and occurs robustly in response to subliminal death primes (Arndt, Greenberg, Pyszczynski, et al., 1997; Greenberg et al., 1994).

Conversely, conscious thoughts of death are posited to provoke proximal, "rational" efforts to minimize the threat posed by the awareness of mortality. As such, these defenses would be unnecessary after the problem of death is no longer conscious. If this is indeed the case, then proximal defenses should occur immediately following mortality salience but not after a delay and distraction, whereas distal defenses should appear following a delay and distraction but not immediately following mortality salience. This is precisely what Greenberg, Arndt, Simon, Pyszczynski, and Solomon (2000) found in a more recent study in which they directly compared the effects of distraction after reminders of one's mortality on proximal and distal defenses. In this study, researchers induced participants to think about their own mortality or a neutral topic and then gave them the opportunity to either deny their vulnerability to an early death and defend their cultural worldview (proximal defense followed by distal defense) or defend their cultural worldview and deny their vulnerability to an early death (distal defense followed by proximal defense).

Greenberg et al. (2000) assessed proximal defenses using the procedure developed by Greenberg et al. (1993) in which participants are led to believe that high levels of emotionality are associated with either a long or a short life expectancy and are then asked to report on their emotionality. Proximal defense is reflected by a bias toward reporting whatever level of emotionality is thought to be associated with a long life expectancy. The researchers assessed distal terror management defense, as in many other studies (e.g., Greenberg, Simon, et al., 1992), by having their participants read and evaluate essays written by foreign students who either praised or criticized the United States.

As predicted, more proximal direct denial of one's vulnerability to an early death emerged immediately after the mortality salience induction but not after a delay and distraction (Greenberg et al., 2000). Conversely, increases in distal worldview defense occurred after a delay and distraction between the mortality salience induction and the assessment of worldview defense (provided either by filling out the vulnerability-denying measure or by completing a distracting word search puzzle) but not when an assessment of worldview defense immediately followed mortality salience. These findings support the hypothesized sequence of proximal defense occurring when death-related thoughts are in conscious attention and of distal defense occurring when death-related thoughts are highly accessible but not in current conscious attention.

Summary

We established that worldview defense in response to mortality salience occurs only when thoughts of death are highly accessible but not explicitly conscious and that explicit reminders of death instigate an active suppression process to remove such thoughts from awareness. This led us to propose a basic distinction between conscious and nonconscious defensive responses to intimations of mortality. Conscious confrontations with death initiate proximal defenses directed at the elimination of such thoughts from explicit awareness. Distal defenses are initiated in response to death thoughts that are highly accessible but not conscious. Figure 6.2 summarizes these two types of defenses. We feel that this dual defense conception provides a useful means to consider the implications of terror management concerns for mental health and physical well-being. To these matters we now turn.

Body and Soul: Implications for Mental Health and Physical Well-Being

Using proximal and distal defenses to address the problem of mortality can positively affect mental and physical health by promoting healthy behaviors and helping people control their anxieties. Our research documents some of these effects. It is unfortunate and ironic that whereas proximal and distal defenses protect people from their terror of death, they may also actually accelerate people's own demise. Some of our most recent research also documents these effects.

Proximal Defenses

The purpose of proximal defenses is to remove death-related thoughts from consciousness. As our research shows, this goal is generally accomplished by two complementary processes. The first is an active suppression process in which the presence of death-

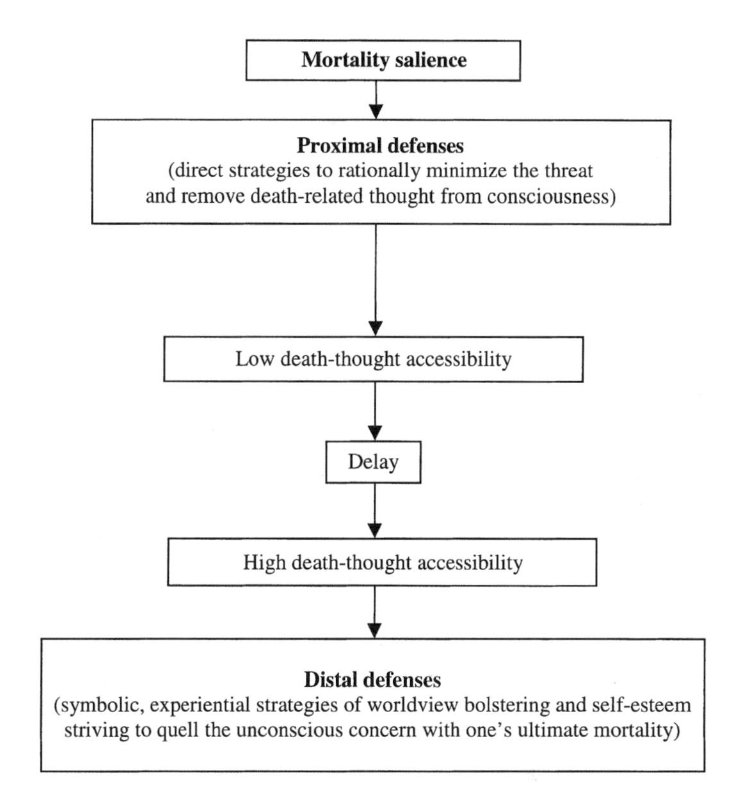

Figure 6.2. Overview of the sequence of defenses activated by mortality salience.

related thought is monitored and, if detected, removed as quickly as possible with the help of alternative thoughts to replace the threatening thoughts in consciousness. Death-related thoughts, of course, tend to draw attention because they often signal a need for decisions and action. For consciousness to let go of such thoughts, it may be necessary to minimize the potential threat. These strategies, described briefly in our overview of the research, help the individual consciously construe death not as a pressing problem but as something not worthy of current concern. As Steven Chaplin (in press) concisely put it, the individual attempts to draw the conclusion "not me, not now" and move on to other things. These defensive strategies can have both adaptive and ironic maladaptive consequences.

Adaptive consequences. Conscious reminders of mortality can be useful to the extent that they motivate people to engage in rational actions that actually serve to forestall death. Sometimes these reminders can awaken people to their vulnerabilities and to their life-threatening behavior patterns. For example, a visit to a lung cancer ward may motivate an individual to try to quit smoking. A high cholesterol report and stern talk from a physician may motivate someone to begin exercising and eating the right kinds of foods. A near-death experience may spur someone to drive more carefully, use seatbelts, wear a motorcycle helmet, or quit using a dangerous drug. In short, there are many ways in which reminders of mortality may sometimes help prolong someone's life.

However, no researchers have yet specifically assessed this type of response to thoughts of mortality, although public service advertisements to combat unsafe sex, drunk driving, and drug use sometimes attempt to use mortality salience to promote such responses. For example, a clever advertisement against drunk driving features a picture of a corpse in a morgue with a toe tag and advises that if one drinks and drives, a traffic ticket may be the least of one's worries. Research does indicate, however, that such advertisements must present an avenue toward protection or prevention in addition to the fear-eliciting imagery to be effective (Leventhal, 1970; Rogers & Mewborn, 1976) because grim reminders generally arouse other less adaptive responses, which we refer to as "ironic consequences."

Ironic consequences. Unfortunately, research suggests that the proactive responses to reminders of mortality are probably less common than purely intrapsychic adjustments that only minimize and avoid the matter of mortality. For example, due to their threatening content, mortality-focused advertisements often foster avoidance rather than behavior change (Leventhal, 1970). As Festinger (1957) noted with regard to smokers, it is much more difficult to change long-standing behavior patterns than it is simply to use cognitive strategies to avoid or rationalize away threats. These psychological defenses, while reducing conscious contemplation of the idea of death, do so at considerable cost because they require cognitive energy and lead to misperceptions and inactions that contribute to the actual occurrence of death. For example, when a lump is detected on the body where a lump should not be, a person may not rush to the doctor's office but may dismiss it, try to forget about it, and hope that it will just go away.

Suppression. For many, the initial response to being reminded of mortality is simply to try to suppress such thoughts. The extent to which suppression of mortality concerns from conscious awareness adversely affects physical health is an important question for future research. However, dire predictions may be in order, given the substantial literature (for a review, see Pennebaker, 1989; Smyth, 1994; and Smyth & Greenberg, chap. 4, this volume) documenting the unfortunate consequences of suppressing emotionally laden knowledge on a variety of physical and psychological outcomes. For example, people who have disclosed traumatic experiences may be less likely to contract cancer, hypertension, ulcers, and influenza than are those who have not had traumas or who have not confided in others about them (Pennebaker & Susman, 1988; Pennebaker & O'Heeron, 1984). Researchers using experimental manipulations of disclosure have found parallel effects with various measures of autonomic arousal (e.g., Pennebaker, Hughes, & O'Heeron, 1987). In addition, explicit instructions to suppress emotions in response to evocative stimuli typically lead to increased sympathetic nervous system activity (e.g., Gross & Levenson, 1993), which has, in turn, been linked to an increased risk of disease (e.g., Krantz & Manuck, 1984).

Distraction. Suppression of death-related concerns can be facilitated by distraction. Following mortality salience inductions, participants in studies (e.g., Arndt et al., 1997) are typically distracted (e.g., by reading a mundane passage or filling out an innocuous questionnaire) before distal defense effects emerge. In more natural settings then, perhaps after passing a gruesome accident scene, a person might turn up the radio or intensify attention directed at plans for the evening. Thus it appears that people may adopt an external focus of attention to avoid the implications of being self-aware and hence cognizant of their mortality (cf. Duval & Wicklund, 1972; see Pyszczynski, Greenberg, Solomon, & Hamilton, 1990, for a more detailed discussion of this issue). More recent research suggests this is indeed the case.

Arndt, Greenberg, Simon, Pyszczynski, and Solomon (1998) found that when mortality is salient, people avoid stimuli that increase self-awareness. In one study, participants in cubicles that either did or did not contain a large mirror (see Gibbons, 1990, for a review) wrote about their death or an important examination. In a second study, participants completed either a death anxiety scale or a future concerns scale and then wrote a story fostering either an internal or external focus of attention.

As predicted, in Study 1, the self-focusing stimulus reduced the time participants spent in the cubicles contemplating their mortality; in Study 2, mortality salient participants wrote less when the task prompted an internal focus of attention than when it prompted an external focus (Arndt et al., 1998). Moreover, in Study 2, the researchers also found higher accessibility of death thoughts for participants in the mortality salient external focus condition. An external focus of attention following mortality salience thus appears to facilitate a relaxation of suppression, leading in turn to increased death-thought accessibility (similar to effects found with distraction tasks used by Arndt, Greenberg, Solomon, et al., 1997; and Greenberg et al., 1994). However, when participants were internally focused following mortality salience, death accessibility was similar to that of control conditions, suggesting that death thoughts were actively suppressed under those conditions.

Thus mortality salience inclines people to avoid self-focused attention. Avoidance of self-awareness, in turn, is often accomplished by the use of alcohol and drugs. For example, alcohol consumption reduces self-awareness (Hull, Levenson, Young, & Sher, 1983), people recovering from alcohol abuse who obtained high scores on a dispositional assessment of self-awareness are more likely to relapse following failure experiences (Hull & Young, 1984), and experimental manipulations of failure under conditions of self-awareness lead to increased alcohol consumption (Hull & Young, 1983). To the extent that conscious thoughts about mortality motivate people to avoid self-awareness, they may also promote high levels of alcohol and drug use, which can adversely affect both physical and mental health.

Vulnerability denial. Immediately after being reminded of one's mortality, people bias their perceptions by disavowing those characteristics presumably associated with a short life expectancy (Greenberg et al., 2000). When encountering reminders of death over the course of a day, people may comfort themselves by noting that they get a lot of exercise, do not smoke, have relatively low levels of serum cholesterol, have little family history of cancer or heart disease, and so on. But if such soothing thoughts about fitness and nutrition are biased so that they obscure clear evidence to the contrary (i.e., if people actually do indeed possess risk factors of these sorts), they may lead to maladaptive courses of action. For example, by denying the extent of risk that such behaviors or characteristics entail, focusing their attention on whatever evidence might be available to support belief in long life expectancy or promising themselves to do what they can in the future to increase their life expectancy (e.g., "I'm going on a diet next week, quitting smoking, and starting an exercise program"), people may fail to seek medical help or effect important changes in diet, exercise, and life style. This may contribute to the failure to seek needed medical attention promptly and to the widespread problem of noncompliance with the recommendations of health professionals.

Summary. Proximal defenses against the awareness of death are those reactions designed to address the threats associated with conscious thoughts of mortality. Such reactions include active suppression of death-related cognition, often with the aid of a distraction, and engagement in biased reasoning to deny vulnerability to those factors associated with an early demise. These processes may then, in turn, have a variety of ramifications for health behavior. The suppression of emotional knowledge is linked to adverse physiological and physical health symptoms. The distraction from mortality thoughts may contribute to the failure to seek and use medical attention or changes in life style. Excessive use of drugs and alcohol may occur in part to avoid self-awareness —a condition that we posit facilitates the experience of existential terror and thereby indirectly contributes to morbidity. Finally, vulnerability denial in response to thoughts of mortality may lead people to risky activities and the avoidance of medical attention.

Distal Defenses

> The fear of death plays a major role in our internal experience; it haunts us as does nothing else; it rumbles continuously under the surface; it is a dark, unsettling presence at the rim of consciousness. . . . To cope with these fears, we erect defenses against death awareness, defenses that are based on denial, that shape

> character structure, and that if maladaptive, result in clinical syndromes. In other words, psychopathology is the result of ineffective modes of death transcendence. (Yalom, 1980, p. 28)

The distal defenses consist of bolstering the two components of the cultural anxiety buffer: faith in one's worldview and belief in one's value within the context of that worldview. As we noted earlier, these defenses contribute greatly to the inability of people to get along with different others, often leading to negative effects. Although these defenses benefit the mental and physical well-being of the individuals who use them, they may also have ironic and maladaptive consequence for health. As with the proximal defenses, the distal defenses also have ironic, maladaptive consequences for health.

Adaptive consequences. One of the core implications of terror management theory is that effective distal defense is tremendously beneficial because it helps people sustain their equanimity in the face of their vulnerability and ultimate mortality. Indeed, we argue that these defenses keep people from spending most of their waking moments preoccupied with death and engaging in the proximal defenses described above. As Yalom (1980) put it, the ongoing implicit knowledge of mortality, "the dark unsettling presence" continuously rumbling at the "rim of consciousness," is prevented from cascading over the rim into consciousness and causing debilitating anxiety to the extent that individuals perceive themselves to be valuable members of a meaningful universe. In other words, sharing a humanly created cultural worldview and successfully adhering to the standards of value prescribed by that worldview provide psychological equanimity by maintaining the repression of the implicit awareness of mortality. The exaggerated responses to similar and different others and strivings to meet cultural standards of value that consistently result from mortality salience reflect people's need to preserve their investment in cultural conceptions of meaning and self-worth to protect them from the terror potentiated by an awareness of death.

Following an existential perspective on psychopathology advanced by such clinicians and theorists as Rank (e.g., 1936/1978) and Yalom (1980), we suggest that psychopathological conditions may occur when individuals lack these psychological defenses necessary to "transcend" death. Of course, many other views outline factors that may contribute to forms of psychopathology. However, one element that is noticeably absent from many contemporary perspectives, such as the behaviorally oriented *Diagnostic and Statistical Manual of Mental Disorders* (American Psychiatric Association, 1994), is a consideration of the role of existential concerns. From a terror management perspective, because people either do not believe they are living up to the standards of value espoused by the cultural worldview to which they adhere or because they cannot accept the conception of reality offered by their cultural worldview, they consequently become vulnerable to psychological disorders and the physical health problems that go along with them. Unable to acquire a suitable replacement "blueprint of reality" (Wheelis, 1980) to confer meaning, people become demoralized, paralyzed in an ethical vacuum in the absence of socially prescribed standards of valued attributes and conduct from which assessments of self-worth can be obtained.

The inability to sustain a sense that one is a valuable member of a meaningful universe, which we suggest contributes to many forms of psychopathology, is in turn determined by a complex interaction between an individual's genetically acquired temperament, the specific beliefs and values of a particular cultural worldview, and specific events of a historical moment. Some people may have trouble acquiring meaning and self-esteem, regardless of the standards by which they are determined (i.e., in all times and places). For example, both genetic constitutions and environmental factors may make it difficult for some people to sustain a faith in the prevailing worldview or meet the standards necessary to derive self-worth from it (e.g., Kramer, 1993). For others, self-esteem is hard to come by because the culturally derived and parentally transmitted standards of value they have internalized are too difficult or impossible for them to attain (e.g., that physical attractiveness and material wealth is necessary to be considered beautiful and successful for American women and men respectively).[8]

[8]Note that this perspective is focused more on the family as an agent of culture rather than on the consequences of particular family dynamics. Other perspectives consider more explicitly the role of family in the etiology of psychopathological disorders, but a consideration of these perspectives is beyond the scope of this chapter.

Finally, people may be unable or unwilling to accept a prevailing worldview because historical or personal events render the view too discrepant with their experience of reality for them to be able to sustain faith in it. This could occur not only for isolated individuals within a culture but for societies as a whole. Indeed, Nietzsche (1887/1974) anticipated that Darwin's theory of evolution would have a devastating effect on the collective psychological equanimity of cultures previously united by 2,000 years of confident and collective adherence to the Judeo Christian tradition and therefore proclaimed a century ago that "God is dead. Christianity has become unbelievable." In the late 20th century, the highly publicized sexual escapades of U.S. President William Clinton in combination with the protracted efforts of Special Prosecutor Kenneth Starr and the U.S. Congress to dispose of him have similarly undermined the cherished belief (albeit already tarnished and uncertain) held by many Americans that the democratic political process consists of reasonable people behaving reasonably for the common good.

In summary, we suggest that psychological disorders emerge under circumstances in which people cannot sustain the belief that they are significantly and securely embedded in a cultural world of shared meaning. When people are "deprived of this shield ... [they are] exposed, alone, to the onslaught of [a] nightmare" (Berger & Luckmann, 1967, p. 102). On the basis of this analysis, Cozzarelli and Karafa (1998) reported research that is consistent with this claim. Specifically, these researchers found that American participants who scored high on the Misfit subscale of their Cultural Estrangement Inventory, by virtue of subscribing to the belief "that they do not fit in with mainstream American culture" (p. 253), were more alienated, anxious, depressed, and lower in self-esteem and life satisfaction, compared with participants who felt that they were part of and fit into the American way of life.

In general, a large literature documents the beneficial effects of high self-esteem. High self-esteem is associated with low anxiety (e.g., Rosenberg & Simmons, 1972; Strauss, Frame, & Forehand, 1987), less depression (e.g., Brown, Andrews, Harris, & Adler, 1986; Mollon & Parry, 1984), and fewer physical ailments following stressful circumstances (e.g., Delongis, Folkman, & Lazarus, 1988).

It is also associated with better functioning in stressful situations among police officers (Lester, 1986), firemen (Petrie & Rotherman, 1982), recently widowed older people (Johnson, Lund, & Dimond, 1986), spouses of soldiers sent to war (Hobfoll & London, 1986), recently unemployed individuals (Pearlin, Lieberman, Menaghan, & Mullan, 1981), medical students completing surgical internships (Linn & Zeppa, 1984), abused children (Zimrin, 1986), and new parents (Osofsky, 1985).

Whereas this evidence is correlational and therefore cannot definitively establish that self-esteem causes these associated psychological benefits, research (e.g., Greenberg, Solomon, et al., 1992) shows that self-esteem buffers anxiety under stressful conditions. As noted earlier, we showed that bolstering self-esteem leads to reduced self-reported anxiety, physiological arousal, and defensive responses in response to a gory video about death, threat of electric shock, and the usual mortality salience induction. Overall, then, research supports the terror management proposition that self-esteem in the context of a meaningful worldview buffers anxiety and thereby confers both psychological and physical benefits.

Terror management and specific psychological difficulties. We have also begun to examine the role of inadequate terror management in specific psychological problems. Our general strategy has been to compare defensive reactions to mortality salience by those with and without mild disorders. If the conditions we are studying involve inadequate terror management structures, we should see intensified and atypical reactions to mortality salience in samples of individuals with disorders.

Depression. We have found these reactions in studies examining the idea that depression occurs when the cultural anxiety-buffer fails to protect the individual effectively from existential concerns.[9]

---

[9]Due to ethical considerations, this research was limited to those participants who showed many symptoms of depression but who had not been clinically diagnosed with a major depressive disorder. For discussions of issues associated with mildly depressed versus clinically depressed samples, see, for example, Flett, Vredenburg, and Krames (1997); Tennen, Hall, and Affleck (1995); and Weary, Edwards, and Jacobson (1995).

Perhaps because of losses or other stressful life events, some individuals begin to lose faith in their conception of life as meaningful (see Pyszczynski & Greenberg, 1992, chap. 8, for a discussion of how this might occur). This notion that depressed individuals are more vulnerable to questions of meaning is shared by clinicians (e.g., Beck, 1967; Frankl, 1969; Yalom, 1980) and is also supported by empirical research. For example, Crumbaugh (1968), Emmons (1992), and Kunzendorf and Maguire (1995) have all reported negative correlations between level of depression and various measures of the extent to which life is regarded as meaningful and purposeful; Simon, Arndt, Greenberg, Solomon, and Pyszczynski (1998) found similar relationships in their research. In related research, a belief in the "just" world (specifically, the belief that one lives in a world where justice prevails and therefore good things happen to good people and bad things happen to bad people; Lerner, 1980), which may be construed as a component of the individual's cultural worldview (see Greenberg et al., 1997), is also associated with lower levels of depression (Lipkus, Dalbert, & Siegler, 1996). Finally, many depressed individuals report morbid thoughts and appear less able to repress the dismal cognitions associated with thoughts of death (Kunzendorf & McLaughlin, 1988). Taken together, these studies suggest that depressed individuals do indeed suffer from a lack of perceived meaning in life as well as from a preoccupation with death.[10]

If the cultural worldview is what imbues life with meaning, then this deficit in meaning among mildly depressed individuals may indicate a tenuous or fragile faith in their cultural worldview. Therefore, when confronted with thoughts of mortality, mildly de-

[10]Of course some depressed individuals may not consciously focus on issues of meaning, and certainly some do not report death-related thoughts. However, even in such cases, this does not mean that these issues are peripheral to the depressed person's problems. As explained in Pyszczynski and Greenberg (1992), the depressed individual's conscious focus of attention may be on subordinate concerns and goals rather than the underlying superordinate concerns that guide the more concrete issues pervading consciousness. For example, the depressed person may think "I'm a terrible mother" or "I'm a total failure as an artist," but the function of these (failed) aspirations is to provide the meaning and value necessary to sustain equanimity.

pressed individuals should be especially vulnerable and thus have a particularly great need to strengthen their investment in their own worldview. To test this hypothesis, Simon, Harmon-Jones, Greenberg, Solomon, and Pyszczynski (1996) conducted two studies in which mildly depressed participants wrote about their mortality or a control topic and then evaluated worldview impinging targets. In the first study, participants evaluated targets that threatened and supported beliefs about the United States. In the second study, they preselected participants who either favored or opposed the legalization of flag burning and assessed their reactions to targets who both supported and opposed their view.

The results of both studies (Simon et al., 1996) support the hypothesis. In the absence of mortality salience, mildly depressed participants exhibited especially low defense of their worldview. However, when exposed to mortality salience, mildly depressed participants showed greater levels of worldview defense than either nondepressed participants exposed to mortality salience or mildly depressed participants not exposed to mortality salience. Presumably this occurred because mildly depressed participants are less well protected by their worldview, so a reminder of mortality was particularly threatening for them, provoking intensified efforts to bolster faith in their worldview.

Simon et al. (1998) then reasoned that because mildly depressed participants initially have a tenuous faith in their worldview, their intensified reactions to those who impinge on their cultural worldview following mortality salience should reinvest them in their belief system and therefore increase their perception that life is meaningful, which the worldview is posited to provide. To test this hypothesis, Simon et al. induced mildly depressed and nondepressed American college students to think about either their own mortality or a control topic and then read essays that either supported or threatened the United States. After reading the essays, the participants were asked to evaluate them in a manner that either enabled them to defend their worldviews or did not provide such an opportunity. All participants then completed a scale designed to measure the perception of meaning in life (Kunzendorf & Maguire, 1995). As expected, mildly depressed participants reported less meaning in life than their nondepressed counterparts, except when they defended their worldviews in response to mortality salience; in this latter condition only, the mildly depressed participants' perceptions of meaning in life were just as high as those of nondepressed participants.

These results provocatively suggest that behaving defensively to bolster the integrity of one's worldview in response to mortality salience may remind mildly depressed individuals that indeed life can be meaningful and worthwhile. Feeling animosity for the person who criticized the United States or admiration for the person who praised the United States may remind participants that they do, in fact, care about their culture. It may be that this sense of caring is, at least in part, what makes life meaningful and worth living. Although it would be premature to generalize these findings to those diagnosed with clinical depression, the findings are consistent with the perspective advanced by existential psychotherapists (e.g., Yalom, 1980) and support the possibility that confrontation with one's mortality may stimulate depressed people to find that they care about something significant in their lives. This in turn may give these people the sense of meaning they previously lacked and encourage re-engagement in the business of living. Whereas this was accomplished in our research by reminding people of their mortality and then giving them the opportunity to defend their sense of national pride after it had been attacked or supported, no doubt many other aspects of the cultural worldview (i.e., besides derogating a different other) could be used similarly. For example, perhaps such reminders could be used to stimulate investment in family, close relationships, or even creative hobbies.

Neurosis. Whereas we view depression as largely a time-limited response to events that undermine an individual's sense of the meaningfulness of life and the value of self, our general perspective on neurosis is that it is a more entrenched problem that arises out of difficulties with a child's transition during socialization from being a mere physical creature to being a cultural entity, a person with a symbolic identity. Because of the tenuous embedding in the cultural worldview (which offers the possibility of transcendence over the physical realities of existence) of people high in neuroticism, we explored the idea that these people are therefore especially troubled with physical types of activities, which can remind people of their own mortality. As Becker (e.g., 1973), Brown (1959),

Freud (e.g., 1920/1989), and others have argued, one such activity is physical sex.

For Freud (see, e.g., 1920/1989), neurosis is inextricably linked to sexual conflicts that originate during socialization when children learn to repress their core animal instincts, most notably, the sex instincts. These repressed sexual instincts conflict first with the demands of the external environment and later with those of the internalized environment (superego). Anxiety resulting from this conflict produces defensive reactions in the form of neurotic symptoms. From this perspective, people high in neuroticism are those for whom the sex instincts are in constant battle with the repressing factors; there are numerous clinical examples of this sexual ambivalence in the literature (e.g., Breuer & Freud, 1893/1957). People low in neuroticism, on the other hand, are able to transform (sublimate) repressed sexual desires into consciously expressible thoughts, feelings, and behaviors and are thus spared the anxiety associated with those desires.

Eysenck (1976) suggested that people high in neuroticism have an approach–avoidance conflict concerning their sexuality from experiencing a high sexual drive and worries that complicate the consummation of their desires. This of course is consistent with Freud's general point of view. Eysenck (1971) found that neuroticism scale scores are positively correlated with sexual drive, guilty feelings about sex, worry about sex, problems controlling thoughts about sex, and the view that sexual behavior is disgusting. It is not surprising that Eysenck also reported a negative association between neuroticism and sexual satisfaction. Similarly, Mosher (1968) suggested that some individuals chronically respond to sexual arousal by feeling guilty. In addition, religious and parental condemnation of sex is found to contribute to sexual disorders (Masters, Johnson, & Kolodny, 1992; McCabe, 1994; Simpson & Ramberg, 1992), and high scores on neuroticism inventories are found to contribute to disorders of impotence and premature ejaculation (Cooper, 1968; Johnson, 1965).

All these findings are consistent with Freud's (1927/1957) proposition that neurosis complicates sexual life. However, we also feel that the relationship between neurosis and sex can be clarified by considering how such people are affected by existential concerns.

Death, neurosis, and sex. Both Rank (1932/1989) and Becker (1973) examined neurosis from a different vantage point than

Freud did, asserting that the individual high in neuroticism is unable to subscribe to a cultural worldview and to obtain the resulting psychological equanimity:

> If man is the more normal, healthy and happy, the more he can . . . successfully . . . repress, displace, deny, rationalize, dramatize himself and deceive others, then it follows that the suffering of the neurotic comes . . . from painful truth. . . . Spiritually the neurotic has been long since where psychoanalysis wants to bring him without being able to, namely at the point of seeing through the deception of the world of sense, the falsity of reality. He suffers, not from all the pathological mechanisms which are psychically necessary for wholesome living but in the refusal of these mechanisms which is just what robs him of the illusions important for living . . . [; he] is much nearer to the actual truth psychologically than the others and it is just that from which he suffers. (Rank, 1936/1978, pp. 251–252)

From a terror management perspective, the chronic anxiety and low self-esteem associated with neuroticism (Lester, 1990; Loo, 1979) occurs because such individuals lack the soothing balm of culture from which to obtain the "golden elixir" of self-esteem. They see themselves as material beings, not properly dressed in the symbolic attire of cultural identity. With respect to sexuality, people high in neuroticism therefore are less successful at sublimating concerns about sex into love, romance, or both because such sublimation requires a cultural context to provide guidance and direction. Individuals high in neuroticism should therefore be especially concerned about the physical or creature aspects of sex in general, and reminders of death should make physical aspects of the sexual experience especially aversive.

We believe that sex is especially problematic for people high in neuroticism because it is connected to the human need to deny mortality. Sex is inextricably bound to mortality concerns because it is an activity that represents humans' core animal nature and hence their ultimate mortality. In Becker's (1973) trenchant words,

> sex and death are twins. . . . Animals who procreate, die. . . . Nature conquers death not by creating eternal organisms but by making it possible for ephemeral ones to procreate. . . . But now the rub for man: If sex is a fulfillment of his role as an animal

> in the species, it reminds him that he is nothing himself but a link in the chain of being, exchangeable with any other and completely expendable in himself. Sex represents, then, species consciousness and, as such, the defeat of individuality. . . . But it is just this personality that man wants to develop . . . a special cosmic hero with special gifts for the universe. He doesn't want to be a mere fornicating animal like any other. (p. 163)

Following Becker, we argue that just as people manage the terror of death by investing in a cultural worldview, sex is managed in much the same way. Romantic love transforms sex from an animal act to a human "experience" by making it a highly meaningful part of one's cultural worldview. By associating sex with love and superimposing a culturally prescribed set of acceptable sexual rituals and practices (who can do what and how, with whom, and under what circumstances), sex becomes a uniquely human, transcendent spiritual experience different than (i.e., desexualized) and superior to (i.e., sublimated; Brown, 1959) the hormonally regulated, solely procreational copulations of mere mortal animals.

Research supports this view. For example, just as inducing levels of sexual arousal in men causes them to express greater love for their romantic partner (Dermer & Pyszczynski, 1978), so too may reminders of mortality. Greenberg, Arndt, Pyszczynski, and Solomon (1999) asked men and women in romantic relationships how in love and how committed they were to their relationship partner after they contemplated either their own mortality or an aversive control topic. In the control conditions, consistent with popular conceptions regarding sex differences in emotional expressivity, women reported greater love and commitment than did men. However, after mortality salience, men increased their reports of love and commitment to the equivalent levels of women.

The problem for people high in neuroticism is that having a tenuous grasp on the symbolic transformation of the physical world, they may not readily conceptualize sex within the meaningful cultural framework of love; therefore, for them, the connection between sex and death is not sufficiently mitigated. In three recent studies, Goldenberg, Pyszczynski, McCoy, Greenberg, and Solomon (in press) tested the hypothesis that sex is especially threatening to people high in neuroticism because it is connected to death. In the first study, all participants completed a neuroticism inventory (Eysenck & Eysenck, 1967) and responded to questions about the physical (e.g., feeling my partner's sweat on my body) and romantic (e.g., expressing love for my partner) aspects of a sexual experience. Half of the participants were reminded of their death using the standard paradigm. The researchers predicted that the similarity of physical sex to animal sex would make it especially threatening and hence unappealing for people high in neuroticism when asked to think about death. It was not expected that the romantic aspects of sex would be threatening under conditions of mortality salience because such a framing should not lead the participants to think of sex as creaturely but as a uniquely human contrivance (i.e., love, romance). The results support this prediction. Specifically, whereas in the control condition, participants scoring high in neuroticism found the physical aspects of sex more appealing than did those with low scores (which is consistent with Freud's, 1908/1959, and Eysenck's, 1976, findings; they both suggested that whereas people high in neuroticism are conflicted about sex, they do have a high level of general physical arousal), individuals with high scores on neuroticism responded to reminders of their mortality with a decreased interest in the physical aspects of the sexual experience.

More direct evidence that physical sex is threatening to people high in neuroticism because it is connected to death was then obtained in a second study (Goldenberg et al., 1999). Whereas in the previous study Goldenberg et al. assessed the impact of mortality salience on the appeal of physical sex, in Study 2 they examined the impact of thinking about the physical nature of sex on the accessibility of thoughts of death. Specifically, the researchers manipulated the salience of physical sex by having participants either describe the appeal of physical sex or complete the romantic sex subscale from Study 1. Goldenberg et al. then assessed the accessibility of death-related thoughts with the word-fragment completion task described earlier. Goldenberg et al. reasoned that if physical sex, but not romantic sex, is threatening to people high in neuroticism because it is connected with death, then reminders of physical sex should make thoughts of death more accessible than should reminders of romantic sex. Sure enough, participants who obtained high neuroticism scores (but not those who obtained low scores) responded to the physical sex prime with greater death accessibility than did their counterparts exposed to the romantic sex prime. This provides direct evidence that sex and death are indeed twins, as Becker proposed.

To clarify the nature of the sex problem of a person high in neuroticism, in their third study Goldenberg et al. (in press) reasoned that if the problem with physical sex of the person high in neuroticism results from an inability to imbue sex with meaning, then explicitly connecting sex with love should reduce the threat and be reflected by a reduction in the accessibility of death thoughts found in Study 2. To test this notion, the researchers replicated Study 2 and added a condition in which some of the participants were reminded of love. Specifically, after thinking about physical or romantic sex, participants were asked to complete an open-ended question that asked them to describe the feelings associated with either being in love or eating a good meal, followed by the word-fragment completion measure. As expected, participants who scored high in neuroticism and were asked to ponder the eating of a good meal had higher death accessibility after the physical sex questionnaire than after the romantic sex questionnaire (replicating the previous study). But those who thought about love after the physical sex questionnaire did not show a corresponding increase in death accessibility.

To summarize this research, individuals who scored high on a neuroticism scale and were asked to think about their mortality found the physical aspects of sex less appealing, presumably because people high in neuroticism are not thoroughly embedded in a cultural worldview from which they can derive self-esteem or sublimate their sexual desires. Such individuals also show elevated accessibility of death thoughts after thinking about sex, establishing a direct link between sex and concerns about mortality. Finally, when individuals scoring high in neuroticism were given an opportunity to supplement thoughts of physical sex with a conscious consideration of love, death accessibility decreased accordingly. Love apparently made sex tolerable by divesting it of its creaturely connotations.

These initial explorations of the relationship between neuroticism and mortality salience support the idea that people high in neuroticism are indeed deficient in their terror management structures. Among participants high in neuroticism, thoughts of mortality reduced the appeal of physical sex, and the mere reminder of physical sex made death thoughts highly accessible. Of course, the specific nature of the deficits in faith in their worldview and self-esteem of the person high in neuroticism should be examined, and the consequences of these deficits in other domains should be explored. But as with the research in depression, it appears that at least some of the problems of psychologically disturbed people concern their deficits in the distal defenses that effectively protect most people from their concerns about mortality.

Summary. The distal defenses of sustaining faith in a meaningful worldview and a sense of one's self-worth contribute greatly to mental and physical well-being by helping people function securely. Those lacking such defenses may be vulnerable to anxiety and, because of that anxiety, may be more susceptible to physical illnesses, such as heart disease. They may also be more vulnerable to depression or may suffer from neurosis and consequent problems with physical activities, such as sex. However, even when functioning effectively, these defenses may also have ironic, maladaptive consequences for physical health.

Ironic consequences. We suggested that proximal defenses, by encouraging false beliefs about one's vulnerability to death, may lead people to risky, imprudent decisions. Distal defenses can also contribute to such unhealthy decisions because symbolic investments in worldviews and self-esteem often lead people to decisions that are similarly hazardous to their health.

Worldview. On the worldview side, faith in a spiritual belief system, which helps defend against ultimate mortality concerns, may often lead people to rely on spiritual protection from death in lieu of modern medical routes to forestalling it. An extreme example of this in U.S. culture is the Christian Scientists, who because of their religious beliefs routinely refuse needed medical treatment for themselves and, more disturbingly, for their ailing children. Another tragic example was the great reggae artist Bob Marley who because of his Rastafarian beliefs refused treatment for cancer in his toe, only to have it spread and lead to his death while he was in the prime of his life. Systematic research adds further support for the existence of this phenomenon. Morgan and Layne (1999) found evidence that people particularly highly invested in spiritual meaning systems are especially likely to fail to comply with medical recommendations. Thus the very worldviews that give humans a sense of death transcendence may accelerate their rendezvous with death.

Of course, cultural worldviews do not have to include beliefs that discourage standard medical practices. In fact, worldviews that value good nutrition and fitness may enhance actual health while providing certain levels of meaning and value for those who subscribe to them (see, e.g., Koenig et al., 1997; and Levin, 1994). The difficult aspect of this is that strictly science-based worldviews, although promoting the possibility of forestalling death, may not be particularly compelling at providing a sense that one can actually transcend mortality. As Freud (1927/1957) noted in the conclusion of his brilliant book about religion, *The Future of an Illusion*, "no, science is no illusion. But it would be an illusion to suppose that we could get anywhere else what it cannot give" (p. 102). Of course, it cannot give people what they really want and what spiritual beliefs can: The hope that death is something other than absolute annihilation and that life is more than an absurd and pointless accident.

Self-esteem. The striving for self-esteem, driven by the need to feel secure and in some sense immortal, also may ironically hasten one's own demise. Many of the cultural standards by which self-esteem is attained and sustained may lead people toward life-threatening actions. Among examples of such behavior are acts of physical heroism, displays of athletic ability, sexual prowess, ability to handle large doses of alcohol or other drugs, and defense of one's honor and possessions. Thus to bolster a death-denying sense of self-worth, people sometimes increase their actual likelihood of death. Extreme examples of this are suicidal actions to establish one's heroism, such as the kamikaze Japanese pilots of World War II and the suicide bomber and Islamic holy warrior terrorists of the 1990s. In these cases, the individuals secure their heroism and qualification for immortality by dying.

Recent research supports a more mundane example of this ironic phenomenon. Taubman Ben-Ari et al. (1999) found that after mortality salience, participants who perceived driving as relevant to their self-esteem drove more recklessly on a simulated driving exercise and reported more reckless driving habits. Presumably, this occurred because mortality salience motivated these individuals to try to enhance their self-esteem; reckless driving was the unfortunate result. Similarly, in a study manipulating mortality salience and assessing participants' interest in a variety of high-risk activities including bungee jumping and trying heroin, Hirschberger, Florian, Mikulincer, Goldenberg, and Pyszczynski (1999) found that for men but not women, mortality salience increased an interest in such activities. We are investigating this sex difference with further research, but given male and female sex roles in American culture, we think it most likely occurs because risk-taking behavior is probably more self-esteem bolstering for men than for women.

Along with encouraging risk taking, cultural standards of value may also promote other unhealthy behaviors by promoting unnatural and unrealistic requirements for self-esteem. Perhaps the most pervasive example of this in American culture is the valuing of thinness and particular bodily features, which have become such an important basis of self-worth for so many American women. Largely because of these rigid and excessive standards of value, female Americans, especially in adolescence, experience stress, suffer low self-esteem, diet again and again, develop maladaptive eating habits, binge and purge, and, in extreme cases, suffer from clinically significant conditions of bulimia and anorexia nervosa (e.g., Brumberg, 1997; Chernin, 1981; Fredrickson & Roberts, 1997; Garner, Garfinkel, Schwartz, & Thompson, 1980). It is interesting to note that these eating disorders are rare or nonexistent in non-Western cultures (Nasser, 1988).

A few research examples illustrate the link between these standards of attractiveness and difficulties with self-esteem and eating habits. Cash and colleagues have shown that distress is common among individuals who feel they are not living up to internalized cultural standards of attractiveness (Cash & Pruzinsky, 1990; Cash & Szymanski, 1995; Szymanski & Cash, 1995). This in turn plays a role in the etiology of eating disorders. Indeed, not only are body image disturbances a leading cause of eating disorders (Cash & Brown, 1989; Cash & Deagle, 1997), but Cash and Szymanski also found that body image dissatisfaction significantly predicted disturbed eating patterns. Negative correlations have also been reported between body esteem and shame (McKinley & Hyde, 1996), and people who are prone to shame are more likely to develop eating disorders (Andrews, 1997). Finally, families of patients with anorexia tend to be preoccupied with weight and physical appearance and rely on external standards to demonstrate self-worth (Garfinkel & Garner, 1992).

To the extent that knowledge of personal mortality drives the desire to meet cultural standards of value, these concerns may contribute to the maladaptive efforts commonly used to meet the narrow and idealized standards of bodily attractiveness promoted in the United States. Goldenberg, McCoy, Pyszczynski, Greenberg, and Solomon (1999) recently conducted preliminary research to examine the role of mortality concerns in these phenomena. In these studies, they manipulated mortality salience in people high and low in body self-esteem. They found that mortality salience increased body identification and interest in physical aspects of sex in those who were happy with their bodies but led to avoidance of thinking about physical appearance in those who valued physical appearance but had low body self-esteem. Thus, there is preliminary support for a role of mortality concerns in how people view and react to their own bodies.

Summary. All of these examples suggest that as long as cultures prescribe worldviews that support ideas that run counter to sound health practices, mortality thoughts, by intensifying investment in such worldviews, will have maladaptive consequences. Similarly, as long as cultures prescribe ways to attain self-esteem that can encourage health risks, mortality concerns will contribute to risky behaviors that increase the likelihood of confirming one's mortality sooner rather than later.

Conclusion

A summary of the adaptive and ironic consequences of proximal and distal defenses in response to death thought is displayed in Table 6.1. We believe there is a sound theoretical basis for arguing that these defenses have substantial effects on both physical and mental well-being. We think that the existing evidence makes a strong case for the adaptive consequences of a secure faith in one's worldview and self-worth.

Table 6.1

Overview of Consequences of Defenses Against Mortality Concerns

	Consequences	
Defenses	Adaptive	Ironic
Proximal	Realization of vulnerabilities, leading to healthy life-style changes	Long-term suppression, leading to health problems; distraction from and denial of vulnerability, leading to avoidance of proper medical care and engagement in risky behaviors
Distal	Buffering of anxiety, contributing to physical and mental health	Worldviews interfering with sound medical care, self-esteem striving, encouraging risky and unhealthy behaviors

There is also solid empirical support for the ironic consequences of these defensive structures, although more research on these phenomena is certainly needed. The direct evidence regarding the adaptive and ironic consequences of the proximal defenses is more limited at this point. However, given the likely role of these defenses in widespread problems of avoidance of medical exams and treatments, noncompliance with treatment regimens, and self-focus avoidance strategies such as alcohol and other drug use, we believe this is a particularly important avenue for future research.

At a more theoretical level, we believe that terror management research has firmly established that death concerns constitute a central motivating force in human thought, feeling, and behavior. In addition, this research has increased the understanding of the psychological defenses that serve conscious and unconscious concerns. In so doing, this body of work supports Freud's view that unconscious concerns greatly influence human thought and behavior. Finally, terror management theory and research reveals the importance of attending to the nature of people's individualized worldviews and bases of self-worth as a way to help people both in the context of individual psychotherapy and in the context of broad social policies.

> If you are a psychiatrist or social worker, and want to understand directly what is driving your patient, ask yourself simply how he thinks of himself as a hero, what constitutes the frame of reference for his heroic strivings—or better, for the clinical case, why he does not feel heroic in his life. (Becker, 1971, p. 77)

References

American Psychiatric Association. (1994). *Diagnostic and statistical manual of mental disorders* (4th ed.). Washington, DC: Author.

Anderson, S. (1992). *Winesburg, Ohio.* New York: Penguin Books. (Original work published 1919)

Andrews, B. (1997). Bodily shame in relation to abuse in childhood and bulimia: A preliminary investigation. *British Journal of Clinical Psychology, 36,* 41–49.

Arndt, J., Allen, J. J. B., & Greenberg, J. (1999). *Traces of terror: Mortality salience and physiological indices of arousal and affect.* Manuscript submitted for publication, University of Missouri—Columbia.

Arndt, J., & Greenberg, J. (1999). The effects of a self-esteem boost and mortality salience on responses to boost relevant and irrelevant worldview threats. *Personality and Social Psychology Bulletin, 25,* 1331–1341.

Arndt, J., Greenberg, J., Pyszczynski, T., & Solomon, S. (1997). Subliminal exposure to death-related stimuli increases defense of the cultural worldview. *Psychological Science, 8,* 379–385.

Arndt, J., Greenberg, J., Simon, L., Pyszczynski, T., & Solomon, S. (1998). Terror management and self-awareness: Evidence that mortality salience provokes avoidance of the self-focused state. *Personality and Social Psychology Bulletin, 24,* 1216–1227.

Arndt, J., Greenberg, J., Solomon, S., Pyszczynski, T., & Simon, L. (1997). Suppression, accessibility of death-related thoughts, and cultural worldview defense: Exploring the psychodynamics of terror management. *Journal of Personality and Social Psychology, 73,* 5–18.

Baldwin, M. W., & Wesley, R. (1996). Effects of existential anxiety and self-esteem on the perception of others. *Basic and Applied Social Psychology, 10,* 75–95.

Bassili, J. N., & Smith, M. C. (1986). On the spontaneity of trait attribution. *Journal of Personality and Social Psychology, 50,* 239–245.

Beck, A. T. (1967). *Depression: Clinical, experimental, and theoretical aspects.* New York: Harper & Row.
Becker, E. (1962). *The birth and death of meaning.* New York: Free Press.
Becker, E. (1971). *The birth and death of meaning* (2nd ed.). New York: Free Press.
Becker, E. (1973). *The denial of death.* New York: Free Press.
Becker, E. (1975). *Escape from evil.* New York: Free Press.
Berger, P. L., & Luckmann, T. (1967). *The social construction of reality.* Garden City, NY: Anchor.
Bornstein, R., Leone, D. R., & Galley, D. J. (1987). The generalizability of subliminal mere exposure effects: Influence of stimuli perceived without awareness on social behavior. *Journal of Personality and Social Psychology, 53,* 1070–1079.
Bowlby, J. (1969). *Attachment and loss. Vol. 1. Attachment.* New York: Basic Books.
Breuer, J., & Freud, S. (1957). *Studies on hysteria* (J. Strachey, A. Freud, A. Strachey, & A. Tyson, Trans.). New York: Basic Books. (Original work published 1893)
Brown, G., Andrews, B., Harris, T., & Adler, Z. (1986). Social support, self-esteem, and depression. *Psychological Medicine, 16,* 13–31.
Brown, N. O. (1959). *Life against death: The psychoanalytical meaning of history.* Middletown, CT: Wesleyan Press.
Brumberg, J. J. (1997). *The body project: An intimate history of American girls.* New York: Random House.
Cash, T. F., & Brown, T. A. (1989). Gender and body images: Stereotypes and realities. *Sex Roles, 21,* 361–373.
Cash, T. F., & Deagle, E. A. (1997). The nature and extent of body-image disturbances in anorexia nervosa and bulimia nervosa: A meta-analysis. *International Journal of Eating Disorders, 22,* 107–125.
Cash, T. F., & Pruzinsky, T. (Eds.). (1990). *Body images: Development, deviance, and change.* New York: Guilford Press.
Cash, T. F., & Szymanski, M. L. (1995). The development and validation of the Body-Image Ideals Questionnaire. *Journal of Personality Assessment, 64,* 466–477.
Chaplin, S. (in press). *The psychology of time and death.* New York: Sonnet Press.
Chernin, K. (1981). *The obsession: Reflections on the tyranny of slenderness.* New York: Harper & Row.
Cooper, A. J. (1968). Neurosis and disorders of sexual potency in the male. *Journal of Psychosomatic Research, 12,* 141–144.
Cozzarelli, C., & Karafa, J. A. (1998). Cultural estrangement and terror management theory. *Personality and Social Psychology Bulletin, 24,* 253–267.
Croyle, R. T., & Sande, G. N. (1988). Denial and confirmatory search: Paradoxical consequences of medical diagnosis. *Journal of Applied Social Psychology, 18,* 473–490.

Croyle, R. T., & Williams, K. D. (1991). Reactions to medical diagnosis: The role of illness stereotypes. *Basic and Applied Social Psychology, 12,* 227–241.

Crumbaugh, J. C. (1968). Cross-validation of Purpose-in-Life Test based on Frankl's concepts. *Journal of Individual Psychology, 24,* 78–81.

Dechesne, M., Greenberg, J., Arndt, J., & Schimel, J. (1999). *Terror management and sports fan affiliation: The effects of mortality salience on fan identification and optimism.* Manuscript submitted for publication, University of Nijmegen, Nijmegen, The Netherlands.

Delongis, A., Folkman, S., & Lazarus, R. (1988). The impact of daily stress on health and mood: Psychological and social resources as mediators. *Journal of Personality and Social Psychology, 54,* 486–495.

Dermer, M., & Pyszczynski, T. (1978). Effects of erotica upon men's loving and liking responses for women they love. *Journal of Personality and Social Psychology, 36,* 1302–1309.

Ditto, P. H., Jemmott, J. B., III, & Darley, J. M. (1988). Appraising the threat of illness: A mental representational approach. *Health Psychology, 7,* 183–200.

Duval, S., & Wicklund, R. A. (1972). *A theory of objective self-awareness.* New York: Academic Press.

Emmons, R. A. (1992). Abstract versus concrete goals: Personal striving level, physical illness, and psychological well-being. *Journal of Personality and Social Psychology, 62,* 292–300.

Epstein, S. (1995). Integration of the cognitive and psychodynamic unconscious. *American Psychologist, 49,* 709–724.

Erchak, G. M. (1992). *The anthropology of self and behavior.* New Brunswick, NJ: Rutgers University Press.

Eysenck, H. J. (1971). Personality and sexual adjustment. *British Journal of Psychiatry, 118,* 593–608.

Eysenck, H. J. (1976). *Sex and personality.* Austin: University of Texas Press.

Eysenck, H. J., & Eysenck, S. B. G. (1967). *Personality structure and measurement.* London: Routledge & Kegan Paul.

Fenichel, O. (1945). *The psychoanalytic theory of neurosis.* New York: Norton.

Festinger, L. (1954). A theory of social comparison processes. *Human Relationships, 1,* 117–140.

Festinger, L. (1957). *A theory of cognitive dissonance.* Stanford, CA: Stanford University Press.

Flett, G. L., Vredenburg, K., & Krames, L. (1997). The continuity of depression in clinical and nonclinical samples. *Psychological Bulletin, 121,* 395–416.

Florian, V., & Mikulincer, M. (1997). Fear of death and the judgment of social transgressions: A multidimensional of terror management theory. *Journal of Personality and Social Psychology, 73,* 369–380.

Florian, V., & Mikulincer, M. (1998). Terror management in childhood: Does death conceptualization moderate the effects of mortality sali-

ence on acceptance of similar and different others. *Personality and Social Psychology Bulletin, 24,* 1104–1112.
Forer, B. R. (1949). The fallacy of personal validation: A classroom demonstration of gullibility. *Journal of Abnormal and Social Psychology, 44,* 118–123.
Frankl, V. E. (1969). *The will to meaning.* New York: Times Mirror.
Fredrickson, B. L., & Roberts, T. (1997). Objectification theory: Towards understanding women's lived experiences and mental health risks. *Psychology of Women Quarterly, 21,* 173–206.
Freud, S. (1938). *The basic writings of Sigmund Freud* (A. A. Brill, Ed. & Trans.). New York: Modern Library.
Freud, S. (1939). Thoughts for the times on war and death. In E. Jones (Ed.), *Collected papers of Sigmund Freud* (Vol. 4, pp. 288–317). London: Hogarth Press. (Original work published 1915)
Freud, S. (1957). *The future of an illusion.* New York: Norton. (Original work published 1927)
Freud, S. (1959). Civilized sexual morality and modern nervousness. In E. Jones (Ed.), *Collected papers of Sigmund Freud* (Vol. 2, pp. 76–99). London: Hogarth Press. (Original work published 1908)
Freud, S. (1966). *On the history of the psychoanalytic movement* (J. Riviere, Trans.). New York: Norton. (Original work published 1938)
Freud, S. (1989). *Introductory lectures on psycho-analysis.* New York: Norton. (Original work published 1920)
Garfinkel, P. E., & Garner, D. M. (1992). *Anorexia nervosa: A multidimensional perspective.* New York: Brunner/Mazel.
Garner, D. M., Garfinkel, P. E., Schwartz, D., & Thompson, M. (1980). Cultural expectation of thinness in women. *Psychological Reports, 47,* 483–491.
Gibbons, F. X. (1990). Self-attention and behavior: A review and theoretical update. *Advances in Experimental Social Psychology, 23,* 249–303.
Goldenberg, J. L., McCoy, S. K., Pyszczynski, T., Greenberg, J., & Solomon, S. (1999). *The body as a source of self-esteem: The effects of mortality salience on appearance monitoring and identification with the body.* Manuscript in preparation, University of Colorado, Colorado Springs.
Goldenberg, J. L., Pyszczynski, T., McCoy, S. K., Greenberg, J., & Solomon, S. (in press). Death, sex, love, and neuroticism: Why is sex such a problem? *Journal of Personality and Social Psychology.*
Goldschmidt, W. (1990). *The human career: The self in the symbolic world.* Cambridge, MA: Blackwell.
Greenberg, J., Arndt, J., Pyszczynski, T., & Solomon, S. (1999). *The romantic solution to terror management: The effect of mortality salience on feelings of love in heterosexual romantic relationships.* Manuscript in progress, University of Arizona, Tucson.
Greenberg, J., Arndt, J., Simon, L., Pyszczynski, T., & Solomon, S. (2000). Proximal and distal defenses in response to reminders of one's mor-

tality: Evidence of a temporal sequence. *Personality and Social Psychology Bulletin, 26,* 91–99.

Greenberg, J., Porteus, J., Simon, L., Pyszczynski, T., & Solomon, S. (1995). Evidence of a terror management function of cultural icons: The effects of mortality salience on the inappropriate use of cherished cultural symbols. *Personality and Social Psychology Bulletin, 21,* 1221–1228.

Greenberg, J., Pyszczynski, T., & Solomon, S. (1986). The causes and consequences of a need for self-esteem: A terror management theory. In R. F. Baumeister (Ed.), *Public self and private self* (pp. 189–212). New York: Springer-Verlag.

Greenberg, J., Pyszczynski, T., & Solomon, S. (1995). Toward a dual-motive depth psychology of self and human behavior. In M. H. Kernis (Ed.), *Efficacy, agency, and self-esteem* (pp. 73–99). New York: Plenum Press.

Greenberg, J., Pyszczynski, T., Solomon, S., Pinel, E., Simon, L., & Jordan, K. (1993). Effects of self-esteem on vulnerability-denying defensive distortions: Further evidence of an anxiety-buffering function of self-esteem. *Journal of Experimental Social Psychology, 29,* 229–251.

Greenberg, J., Pyszczynski, T., Solomon, S., Rosenblatt, A., Veeder, M., Kirkland, S., & Lyon, D. (1990). Evidence for terror management II: The effects of mortality salience on reactions to those who threaten or bolster the cultural worldview. *Journal of Personality and Social Psychology, 58,* 308–318.

Greenberg, J., Pyszczynski, T., Solomon, S., Simon, L., & Breus, M. (1994). Role of consciousness and accessibility of death-related thoughts in mortality salience effects. *Journal of Personality and Social Psychology, 67,* 627–637.

Greenberg, J., Simon, L., Harmon-Jones, E., Solomon, S., Pyszczynski, T., & Chatel, D. (1995). Testing alternative explanations for mortality effects: Terror management, value accessibility, or worrisome thoughts? *European Journal of Social Psychology, 12,* 417–433.

Greenberg, J., Simon, L., Pyszczynski, T., Solomon, S., & Chatel, D. (1992). Terror management and tolerance: Does mortality salience always intensify negative reactions to others who threaten one's worldview? *Journal of Personality and Social Psychology, 63,* 212–220.

Greenberg, J., Solomon, S., & Pyszczynski, T. (1997). Terror management theory of self-esteem and social behavior: Empirical assessments and conceptual refinements. *Advances in Experimental Social Psychology, 29,* 61–139.

Greenberg, J., Solomon, S., Pyszczynski, T., Rosenblatt, A., Burling, J., Lyon, D., Pinel, E., & Simon, L. (1992). Assessing the terror management analysis of self-esteem: Converging evidence of an anxiety-buffering function. *Journal of Personality and Social Psychology, 63,* 913–922.

Greenberg, J., Solomon, S., Pyszczynski, T., & Steinberg, L. (1988). A reaction to Greenwald, Pratkanis, and Baumgardner (1986): Under what conditions does research obstruct theory progress? *Psychological Review, 95,* 566–571.

Greenwald, A. G. (1992). New Look 3: Unconscious cognition reclaimed. *American Psychologist, 47,* 766–779.

Gross, J. J., & Levenson, R. W. (1993). Emotional suppression: Physiology, self-report, and expressive behavior. *Journal of Personality and Social Psychology, 64,* 970–986.

Harmon-Jones, E., Simon, L., Greenberg, J., Pyszczynski, T., Solomon, S., & McGregor, H. (1997). Terror management theory and self-esteem: Evidence that increased self-esteem reduces mortality salience effects. *Journal of Personality and Social Psychology, 72,* 24–36.

Herdt, G. (1987). *The Sambia: Ritual and culture in New Guinea.* New York: Holt, Rinehart, & Winston.

Hirschberger, G., Florian, V., Mikulincer, M., Goldenberg, J. L., & Pyszczynski, T. (1999). *A terror management perspective on risky behavior: The moderating role of gender and self-esteem.* Manuscript submitted for publication, Bar-Ilan University, Ramat Gan, Israel, and University of Colorado, Colorado Springs.

Hobfoll, S., & London, P. (1986). The relationship of self-concept and social support to emotional distress among women during war. *Journal of Social and Clinical Psychology, 52,* 18–26.

Horney, K. (1937). *The neurotic personality of our time.* New York: Norton.

Hull, J. G., Levenson, R. W., Young, R. D., & Sher, K. J. (1983). The self-awareness reducing effects of alcohol consumption. *Journal of Personality and Social Psychology, 44,* 461–473.

Hull, J. G., & Young, R. D. (1983). Self-consciousness, self-esteem and success–failure as determinants of alcohol consumption in male social drinkers. *Journal of Personality and Social Psychology, 44,* 1097–1109.

Hull, J. G., & Young, R. D. (1984). The self-awareness reducing effects of alcohol consumption: Evidence and implications. In J. Suls & A. G. Greenwald (Eds.), *Psychological perspectives on the self* (Vol. 2, pp. 159–190). Hillsdale, NJ: Erlbaum.

James, W. (1978). *The varieties of religious experience.* Garden City, NY: Image Books. (Original work published 1910)

Johnson, J. (1965). Prognosis of disorders of sexual potency in the male. *Journal of Psychosomatic Research, 9,* 195–200.

Johnson, R., Lund, D., & Dimond, M. (1986). Stress, self-esteem, and coping during bereavement among the elderly. *Social Psychology Quarterly, 49,* 273–279.

Kierkegaard, S. (1957). *The concept of dread* (W. Lowrie, Trans.). Princeton, NJ: Princeton University Press. (Original work published 1844)

Koenig, H. G., Hays, J. C., George, L. K., Blazer, D. G., Larson, D. B., & Landerman, L. R. (1997). Modeling the cross-sectional relationships between religion, physical health, social support, and depressive symptoms. *American Journal of Geriatric Psychiatry, 5,* 131–144.

Kramer, P. D. (1993). *Listening to Prozac.* New York: Viking.

Krantz, D. S., & Manuck, S. B. (1984). Acute psychophysiologic reactivity and risk of cardiovascular disease: A review and methodologic critique. *Psychological Bulletin, 96,* 435–464.

Kunda, Z. (1987). Motivated inference: Self-serving generation and evaluation of causal theories. *Journal of Personality and Social Psychology, 53,* 636–647.

Kunzendorf, R. G., & Maguire, D. (1995). *Depression: The reality of "no meaning" versus the delusion of negative meaning.* Unpublished manuscript, University of Massachusetts, Lowell.

Kunzendorf, R. G., & McLaughlin, S. (1988). Depression: A failure to suppress the self-conscious "monitoring" of dismal cognitions. *Imagination, Cognition, and Personality, 8,* 3–17.

Laudan, L. (1977). *Progress and its problems: Towards a theory of scientific growth.* Berkeley: University of California Press.

Laudan, L. (1984). *Science and values: An essay on the aims of science and their role in scientific debate.* Berkeley: University of California Press.

Lerner, M. J. (1980). *The belief in a just world: A fundamental delusion.* New York: Plenum Press.

Lester, D. (1986). Subjective stress and self-esteem of police officers. *Perceptual and Motor Skills, 63,* 1334.

Lester, D. (1990). Maslow's hierarchy of needs and personality. *Personality and Individual Differences, 11,* 1187–1188.

Leventhal, H. (1970). Findings and theory in the study of fear communications. *Advances in Experimental Social Psychology, 5,* 120–186.

Levin, J. S. (1994). Religion and health: Is there an association, is it valid, and is it causal? *Social Science and Medicine, 38,* 1475–1482.

Liberman, E. J. (1993). *Acts of will: The life and work of Otto Rank* (2nd ed.). Amherst: University of Massachusetts Press.

Lifton, R. J. (1983). *The broken connection: On death and the continuity of life.* New York: Basic Books.

Linn, B., & Zeppa, R. (1984). Stress in junior medical students: Relationship to personality and performance. *Journal of Medical Education, 59,* 7–12.

Lipkus, I. M., Dalbert, C., & Siegler, I. C. (1996). The importance of distinguishing the belief in a just world for self versus others: Implications for psychological well-being. *Personality and Social Psychology Bulletin, 22,* 666–677.

Loo, R. (1979). Note on the relationship between trait anxiety and the Eysenck Personality Questionnaire. *Journal of Clinical Psychology, 35,* 110.

Masters, W. H., Johnson, V., & Kolodny, R. C. (1992). *Human sexuality* (3rd ed.). New York: HarperCollins.

May, R. (1953). *Man's search for himself.* New York: Norton.

McCabe, M. (1994). Childhood, adolescence and current psychological factors associated with sexual dysfunction. *Sexual and Marriage Therapy, 9,* 267–276.

McGregor, H., Lieberman, J. D., Solomon, S., Greenberg, J., Arndt, J., Simon, L., & Pyszczynski, T. (1998). Terror management and aggression: Evidence that mortality salience motivates aggression against worldview threatening others. *Journal of Personality and Social Psychology, 74,* 590–605.

McKinley, N. M., & Hyde, J. S. (1996). The Objectified Body Consciousness Scale: Development and validation. *Psychology of Women Quarterly, 20,* 181–215.

McMendree, M. (Producer), & Cassavetes, J. (Director). (1960). *Shadows* [Film]. (Available from Metro Goldwyn Mayer Studies, Inc., Santa Monica, CA)

Mead, G. H. (1968). *Mind, self, and society.* Chicago: University of Chicago Press. (Original work published 1934)

Mollon, P., & Parry, G. (1984). The fragile self: Narcissistic disturbance and the protective function of depression. *British Journal of Medical Psychology, 57,* 137–145.

Morgan, S. E., & Layne, W. (1999). *The underlying mechanisms motivating medical noncompliance: From terror management to threat reactance theory.* Unpublished manuscript, University of Kentucky, Lexington.

Mosher, D. L. (1968). Measurement of guilt in females by self-report inventories. *Journal of Consulting and Clinical Psychology, 32,* 690–695.

Nasser, M. (1988). Culture and weight consciousness. *Journal of Psychosomatic Research, 32,* 573–577.

Nelson, L. J., Moore, D. L., Olivetti, J., & Scott, T. (1997). General and personal mortality salience and nationalistic bias. *Personality and Social Psychology Bulletin, 23,* 884–892.

Nietzsche, F. (1974). *The gay science* (W. Kaufman, Trans.). New York: Random House. (Original work published 1887)

Ochsmann, R., & Mathay, M. (1996). *Depreciating of and distancing from foreigners: Effects of mortality salience.* Unpublished manuscript, Universitat Mainz, Mainz, Germany.

Osofsky, H. (1985). Transition to parenthood: Risk factors for parents and infants. *Journal of Psychosomatic Obstetrics and Gynecology, 4,* 303–315.

Pearlin, L., Lieberman, M., Menaghan, E., & Mullan, J. (1981). The stress process. *Journal of Health and Social Behavior, 22,* 337–356.

Pennebaker, J. W. (1989). Confession, inhibition, and disease. *Advances in Experimental Social Psychology, 22,* 211–244.

Pennebaker, J. W., Hughes, C. F., & O'Heeron, R. C. (1987). The psychophysiology of confession: Linking inhibitory and psychosomatic processes. *Journal of Personality and Social Psychology, 52,* 781–793.

Pennebaker, J. W., & O'Heeron, R. C. (1984). Confiding in others and illness rate among spouses of suicide and accidental-death victims. *Journal of Abnormal Psychology, 93,* 473–476.

Pennebaker, J. W., & Susman, J. R. (1988). Disclosure of traumas and psychosomatic processes [Special issue]. *Social Science and Medicine, 26,* 327–332.

Petrie, K., & Rotherman, M. (1982). Insulators against stress: Self-esteem and assertiveness. *Psychological Reports, 50,* 963–966.

Pyszczynski, T., & Greenberg, J. (1987). Toward an integration of cognitive and motivational perspectives on social inference: A biased hypothesis-testing model. *Advances in Experimental Social Psychology, 20,* 297–340.

Pyszczynski, T., & Greenberg, J. (1992). *Hanging on and letting go: Understanding the onset, progression, and remission of depression.* New York: Springer-Verlag.

Pyszczynski, T., Greenberg, J., & Solomon, S. (1999). A dual-process model of defense against conscious and unconscious death-related thoughts: An extension of terror management theory. *Psychological Review, 106,* 835–845.

Pyszczynski, T., Greenberg, J., Solomon, S., & Hamilton, J. (1990). A terror management analysis of self-awareness and anxiety: The hierarchy of terror. *Anxiety Research, 2,* 177–195.

Pyszczynski, T., Wicklund, R. A., Floresky, S., Gauch, G., Koch, S., Solomon, S., & Greenberg, J. (1996). Whistling in the dark: Exaggerated estimates of social consensus in response to incidental reminders of mortality. *Psychological Science, 7,* 332–336.

Quattrone, G. A., & Tversky, A. (1984). Casual versus diagnostic contingencies: On self-deception and the voter's illusion. *Journal of Personality and Social Psychology, 46,* 237–248.

Rank, O. (1958). *Beyond psychology.* New York: Dover. (Original work published 1941)

Rank, O. (1978). *Truth and reality.* New York: Knopf. (Original work published 1929)

Rank, O. (1978). *Will therapy.* New York: Norton. (Original work published 1936)

Rank, O. (1989). *Art and artist: Creative urge and personality development.* New York: Knopf. (Original work published 1932)

Rogers, R. W., & Mewborn, C. R. (1976). Fear appeals and attitude change: Effects of a threat's noxiousness, probability of occurrence, and the efficacy of the coping response. *Journal of Personality and Social Psychology, 34,* 54–61.

Roheim, G. (1943). The origin and function of culture. *Nervous and Mental Disease Monograph Series, 69*(4), 107.

Rosenberg, M. (1965). *Society and the adolescent self-image.* Princeton, NJ: Princeton University Press.

Rosenberg, M. (1981). The self-concept: Social product and social force. In M. Rosenberg & R. H. Turner (Eds.), *Social psychology: Sociological perspectives* (pp. 591–624). New York: Basic Books.

Rosenberg, M., & Simmons, R. G. (1972). *Black and White self-esteem: The urban school child.* Washington, DC: American Sociological Association.

Rosenblatt, A., Greenberg, J., Solomon, S., Pyszczynski, T., & Lyon, D. (1989). Evidence for terror management theory I: The effects of mortality salience on reactions to those who violate or uphold cultural values. *Journal of Personality and Social Psychology, 57,* 681–690.

Silverman, L. H. (1983). The subliminal psychodynamic activation method: Overview and comprehensive listing of studies. In J. Masling (Ed.), *Empirical studies of psychoanalytic theory* (pp. 69–100). Mahwah, NJ: Erlbaum.

Simon, L., Arndt, J., Greenberg, J., Solomon, S., & Pyszczynski, T. (1998). Terror management and meaning: Evidence that the opportunity to defend the worldview in response to mortality salience increases the meaningfulness of life in the mildly depressed. *Journal of Personality, 66,* 359–382.

Simon, L., Greenberg, J., Harmon-Jones, E., Solomon, S., Pyszczynski, T., Arndt, J., & Abend, T. (1997). Cognitive–experiential self-theory and terror management theory: Evidence that terror management occurs in the experiential system. *Journal of Personality and Social Psychology, 72,* 1132–1146.

Simon, L., Harmon-Jones, E., Greenberg, J., Solomon, S., & Pyszczynski, T. (1996). The effects of mortality salience on depressed and nondepressed individuals to those who violate or uphold cultural values. *Personality and Social Psychology Bulletin, 22,* 81–90.

Simpson, W. S., & Ramberg, J. A. (1992). Sexual dysfunction in married female patients with anorexia and bulimia nervosa. *Journal of Sex and Marital Therapy, 18,* 44–54.

Smyth, J. M. (1998). Written emotional expression: Effect sizes, outcome types, and moderating variables. *Journal of Consulting and Clinical Psychology, 66,* 174–184.

Solomon, S., Greenberg, J., & Pyszczynski, T. (1991). A terror management theory of social behavior: The psychological functions of self-esteem and cultural worldviews. In M. P. Zanna (Ed.), *Advances in experimental social psychology* (Vol. 24, pp. 93–159). New York: Academic Press.

Strauss, C., Frame, C., & Forehand, R. (1987). Psychosocial impairment associated with anxiety in children. *Journal of Clinical Child Psychology, 16,* 235–239.

Sullivan, H. S. (1953). *The interpersonal theory of psychiatry.* New York: Norton.

Szymanski, M. L., & Cash, T. F. (1995). Body-image disturbances and self-discrepancy theory: Expansion of the Body-Image Ideals Questionnaire. *Journal of Social and Clinical Psychology, 14,* 134–146.

Taubman Ben-Ari, O., Florian, V., & Mikulincer, M. (1999). The impact of mortality salience on reckless driving: A test of terror management mechanisms. *Journal of Personality and Social Psychology, 76,* 35–45.

Tennen, H., Hall, J. A., & Affleck, G. (1995). Depression research methodologies in the *Journal of Personality and Social Psychology:* A review and critique. *Journal of Personality and Social Psychology, 68,* 870–884.

Triandis, H. C. (1990). Cross-cultural studies of individualism and collectivism. In J. J. Berman (Ed.), *Nebraska Symposium of Motivation, 1989* (pp. 41–133). Lincoln: University of Nebraska Press.

Weary, G., Edwards, J. A., & Jacobson, J. A. (1995). Depression research methodologies in the *Journal of Personality and Social Psychology*: A reply. *Journal of Personality and Social Psychology, 68,* 885–891.

Wegner, D. M. (1992). You can't always think what you want: Problems in the suppression of unwanted thoughts. *Advances in Experimental Social Psychology, 25,* 193–225.

Wheelis, A. (1980). *The scheme of things.* New York: Harcourt Brace Jovanovich.

Yalom, I. D. (1980). *Existential psychotherapy.* New York: Basic Books.

Zilboorg, G. (1943). Fear of death. *Psychoanalytic Quarterly, 12,* 465–475.

Zimrin, H. (1986). A profile of survival. *Child Abuse and Neglect, 10,* 339–349.

Chapter

7

Death Cannot Keep Us Apart: Mortality Following Bereavement

Paul Raphael Duberstein

Mrs. A. died at home 3 months before her 50th wedding anniversary. Eleven months later, on a brisk June morning, Mr. A. made his weekly pilgrimage to his wife's grave. When leaving, he whispered, "I'll be seeing you soon." He went home and shot himself to death.[1]

I thank the U.S. Public Health Service for its financial support (Grant K07-MH01135), my colleagues in the Center for the Study and Prevention of Suicide (Rochester, NY) and the Center for Psychoneuroimmunology (Rochester, NY) for their intellectual support, and Nancy Talbot for her comments on a draft of this chapter.

[1]As part of a retrospective study of completed suicide (Conwell, Duberstein, Cox, Herrmann, Forbes, & Caine, 1996), my colleague, Yeates Conwell, conducted a postmortem interview with Mr. A.'s son.

Tales of spouses or lovers dying in rapid succession have long been told and may even constitute a timeless theme in literature. Although stories of suicide may be the most dramatic and romantic of the genre, tales of natural deaths have been told too. Engel (1961) remarked that "the newspapers repeatedly report persons collapsing and dying soon after learning of the death of a loved person. Literature and folklore are replete with the notion that people fall ill and die of grief" (p. 19). For ease of communication, I refer to this phenomenon as bereavement-related mortality (BRM). Not only has BRM been a theme in arts and letters, it has also long been known to medicine and science. Benjamin Rush (1812/1962), a signer of the Declaration of Independence who is often thought of as the "father of American psychiatry," observed that grief "sometimes brings on sudden death, without any signs of previous disease, either acute or chronic. Dissections of persons who have died of grief show congestion in, and inflammation of, the heart, with a rupture of its auricles and ventricles" (p. 315).

It may seem surprising that Sigmund Freud, whose originality was rivaled only by his range, paid little attention to BRM. He did not avoid the topic completely. In a rarely cited article intended for a mass audience, Freud (1905/1953) asserted that a "sudden bereavement" could cause "a peculiar alteration in the tone of an organism which may have a favorable influence on some well-established pathological condition or may even bring it to an end" (p. 287). In other words, he argued that bereavement has a potentially positive effect on health, a notion that has been confirmed by research (Potter & Zautra, 1997). But just a few sentences later, Freud (1905/1953) noted that "the duration of life can be appreciably shortened by depressive affects" (p. 288), another idea that is empirically supported (Wulsin, Vaillant, & Wells, 1999).

In reporting the case of Elisabeth Von R., Freud (Breuer & Freud, 1893/1955) argued that decrements in physical health during caregiving (he used the phrase "sick nursing") arise from sleep disturbances, self-neglect, and "the effect of constant worry on vegetative functions" (p. 161). Here he correctly anticipated modern research on caregiving (Kiecolt-Glaser, Dura, Speicher, Trask, & Glaser, 1991; Vitaliano, Scanlan, Krenz, Schwartz, & Marcovina, 1996). Whereas modern literature emphasizes the role of stress,

Freud invoked a construct that was, well, Freudian, namely, emotional suppression.

> Anyone whose mind is taken up by the hundred and one tasks of sick nursing which follow one another in endless succession over a period of weeks and months will, on the one hand, adopt a habit of suppressing every sign of his emotion, and on the other, will soon divert his attention away from his own impressions, since he has neither the time nor strength to do justice to them. (pp. 161–162)

Freud could have easily taken this scenario one step further and argued that the decline in physical health portended a premature death (which it does; Schulz & Beach, 1999). Despite his medical training, he was more intrigued by emotional suppression and how it could lead to psychogenic symptoms in his patients. Freud circled around the issue of BRM, referring instead to the health consequences of caregiving, speculating about a link between depression and mortality, and commenting on the effect of bereavement on the "tone of the organism." But he left the field itself open to be explored by others.

Indeed, it lay fallow for decades. Although it had been known since the end of the 19th century that widowed people commit suicide at higher rates than do married people (Durkheim, 1897/1951) and there had been scattered reports of excess mortality in widowed people in the early decades of the 20th century (Ciocco, 1940; March, 1912), there had been few systematic, rigorous examinations of BRM. In his presidential address to the American Psychosomatic Society, Engel (1961) noted that "no one has ever studied the bodily changes occurring during grief" (p. 19) and indicated that he was not aware of any empirical substantiation of the notion that grief can kill. Just a couple of decades later, Bowlby (1980) declared somewhat hyperbolically that after the death of a spouse, "almost always health suffers . . . even fatal illness is more common" (p. 100) in bereaved people.

One might say that the field of BRM sprang to life between Engel (1961) and Bowlby (1980). The 1960s and 1970s saw a dramatic increase in research on the mortality of bereavement (Cox & Ford, 1964; Ekblom, 1963; Rees & Lutkins, 1967; Young, Benjamin, & Wallis, 1963), including an important study by Parkes (Parkes, Benjamin, & Fitzgerald, 1969), whom Bowlby recruited to Tavistock. During this period, Averill (1968) published a seminal article proposing a biosocial theory of grief and Kastenbaum and Kalish founded a newsletter (later the journal *Omega*) concerned with death and bereavement.[2] These developments were accompanied by the gradual ascendance of the stress paradigm in health psychology and other branches of psychological science. Buoyed by Hans Selye's (1951) discoveries, early epidemiological research (Hinkle & Wolff, 1958), Holmes and Rahe's (1967) attempt to operationalize Adolf Meyer's ideas, and experiments demonstrating that animals subjected to stress show neuroendocrine and immune changes and greater susceptibility to infection (e.g., Friedman, Ader, & Glasgow, 1965), the stress paradigm insinuated itself into psychology, physiology, and psychiatry. Premised on the assumption that life events, such as the death of a spouse, affect psychological equilibrium and could even lead to destabilization or a "reorganization . . . of the person's personality" (Epstein, 1993, p. 118), stress theories of bereavement emphasize situational variables and postloss cognitive processes (Epstein, 1993; Janoff-Bulman, 1992; Parkes, 1987; Taylor, 1983; Wortman, Silver, & Kessler, 1993). Although most stress theories acknowledge the significance of pre-event characteristics, their emphasis is unmistakably on postevent psychological processes.

With few recent exceptions (e.g., McEwen & Stellar, 1993), physiological theorists have also emphasized postevent processes, not pre-event vulnerability. Whereas psychologists have alternately conceived of stress as stimulus, response, or emotional state, physiological theorists literally equated stress with physiological activity (Selye, 1951). From decades of research, it is assumed that stress increases the activity of the hypothalamic–pituitary–adrenal (HPA) axis, which in turn leads to immune downregulation and

[2]Research on bereavement had implications for other areas of clinical psychology and psychiatry during this period. For example, Jackson (1986) observed that Aaron Beck's first book on cognitive theory and therapy, published in 1967, "hardly takes into account" (p. 241) the role of loss and bereavement in depression. In Beck's 1976 book, "the role of loss had acquired a considerable prominence in his thought on both predisposing and precipitating factors" (Jackson, 1986, p. 241).

perhaps increased morbidity and mortality (see Sapolsky, 1994). The following quotations illustrate the extent to which the stress paradigm has held sway in research on the physical morbidity and mortality of bereavement: "Typically, it is assumed that . . . grief following the loss alters immunologic effectiveness and leaves the bereaved less resistant to infection and pathological organisms" (Norris & Murrell, 1987, p. 606). "The loss experience is likely to be accompanied by alterations of immune function, which, in turn, lower resistance to infectious diseases and increase risk of morbidity and mortality from these causes" (W. Stroebe & Stroebe, 1987, p. 106). "Although not always explicitly stated . . . the consequences of bereavement for risk of mortality have generally been attributed to . . . the stress of bereavement" (Schaefer, Quesenberry, & Wi, 1995, p. 1143).

Stress theories may be contrasted with life-course theories, which emphasize preloss characteristics, such as long-standing personality traits, reactions to early life events, and physiological vulnerabilities mediated by genetic inheritance or exposure to unexpected conditions early in development (Ader, 1983; Haracz, 1984; Hofer, 1984, 1996; Kagan, 1994). Unlike the stress paradigm, a life-course approach is premised on the assumption that stable patterns of responding to life's disappointments must be considered to understand the relationship between bereavement and health. Ignoring these stable patterns yields an incorrect understanding of that relationship. Freud (1917/1957) noted that people who become depressed following a loss have a "pathological disposition" (p. 243). He labeled this disposition "ambivalence, which sometimes arises more from real experiences, sometimes more from constitutional factors [but] must not be overlooked among the preconditions of melancholia" (p. 251). Psychoanalytic theory, with its emphasis on long-standing traits and psychological context, views bereavement through a "life-course" lens. It is not a stress theory. Following Freud's lead, psychoanalytic theory and other life-course theories have essentially ignored BRM. Stress theories have gone virtually unchallenged.

In this chapter, I strive to stimulate psychodynamically oriented theory and research on BRM. Whereas other chapters in this series begin with psychoanalytic theory as their starting points and seek to determine how well the data fit the theory (e.g., Duberstein,

Seidlitz, & Conwell, 1996; Masling, 1986), this chapter takes a different approach. I start with the data, conclude that the stress paradigm is heuristic but inadequate, and argue that life-course concepts ought to be used in BRM research as well. The chapter focuses primarily on bereavement following the death of a spouse, but references are made to studies conducted on bereavement following other types of loss.

First, I discuss some of the major findings in research on the psychological sequelae of loss. Just as it is impossible to understand the psychological consequences of a disease without knowing the biology of the disease, a proper understanding of BRM requires knowledge of the psychological effects of bereavement. In the next two sections, I review both the epidemiological literature on BRM and psychoneuroimmunological research on bereavement and immune function. In both instances, I conclude that methodological difficulties preclude unambiguous interpretation. There is little evidence to support the widely held notion that the stress of a loss decreases immune function, which in turn increases mortality. Then, I recommend replacing the stress paradigm with a life-course approach, one that recognizes the influences of psychoanalytic concepts, particularly dependency and help seeking, early loss, ambivalence, and identification symptoms. I offer suggestions for research. Finally, I conclude by emphasizing the need for creative psychodynamic formulations and theorizing on mortality following bereavement.

Psychological Effects of Bereavement

In this section, I discuss some of the major findings and tensions in the literature on the psychological sequelae of loss: Reactions following the death of a spouse follow a reasonably predictable course; there are sex differences in adjustment to widowhood, with women typically faring better than men; bereavement following violent causes of death (accidents, homicides, suicides) may differ from responses following natural deaths; there is a need for a broad conceptualization of bereavement "outcome"; and whereas Freud distinguished mourning (or uncomplicated grief) from melancholia, recent research shows that traumatic grief can be distinguished from both depression and uncomplicated grief.[3] All these issues have implications for the conduct and interpretation of research on health consequences of bereavement.

Reactions Follow a Reasonably Predictable Course

Most bereaved people experience acute effects that abate in due course. Still, efforts to validate stage models of uncomplicated grief have generally been unsuccessful (Bowlby, 1980; Lund, Caserta, & Dimond, 1993; Parkes, 1987; Wortman et al., 1993). Precisely what is meant by due course is a matter of controversy, one that is not easily resolved because it is influenced by so many other variables (e.g., cause of death, psychiatric history). Prigerson et al. (1997) provided an interesting example of how timeline issues can affect the interpretation of research findings. Traumatic grief measured at 6 months was associated with health outcomes at 13- and 25-months postloss. Associations between traumatic grief at 2 months and subsequent health outcomes were nonsignificant. Had the authors relied solely on data collected at 2 months, the association between traumatic grief and health would not have been detected. These findings are consistent with the notion that acute effects subside by 6 months for most people. Consequently, there is greater heterogeneity among the bereaved at 6-months postloss than at 2 months; people who remain symptomatic at 6 months are probably not representative of a bereaved population. Still, these numbers (2 months, 6 months) should not be taken too seriously because course is influenced by so many variables.

Thompson, Gallagher-Thompson, Futterman, Gilewski, and Peterson (1991) showed that depressive symptoms are usually resolved 1 year after the loss but grief persists for at least 30 months.

---

[3]Confusion about the use of certain terms has led me to adopt a standard nomenclature for this chapter. I use the terms *uncomplicated grief* and *grief* to refer to "normal," uncomplicated, nonpathological, or expectable grief or mourning. The term *traumatic grief* is reserved for mourning or grief that is considered "abnormal," complicated, or pathological. I do not distinguish grief from mourning. For articles and chapters of historical significance, I preserve the terms used in the original. I do not retitle the alliterative "Mourning and Melancholia" (Freud, 1917/1957) as "Uncomplicated Grief and Major Depression."

Specific components of the grief response, such as yearning, may persist unabated for years (Wortman & Silver, 1989). Yet the psychological meaning of these findings is elusive. Gorer (1965) wondered whether prolonged yearning is the product of an unbidden sense of obligation to the deceased person or a genuine affect.

Sex Differences

In their review of the literature on the effects of bereavement on physical and mental health, W. Stroebe and Stroebe (1987) stated that "there is still a lack of reliable information on sex differences. In the majority of studies only widows have been included" (p. 178). They tentatively concluded that "bereavement appears to have more extreme effects on mental health of men than of women" (p. 182, also see M. Stroebe & Stroebe, 1983). MacMahon and Pugh (1965) commented that especially in men, "suicide clustering in the shorter intervals [after conjugal loss] is more marked in the older age groups" (p. 28), and Bock and Webber (1972) speculated that older men may be particularly vulnerable to suicide after a loss of "perhaps . . . the most significant person through whom [they] related to others in the community" (p. 29). One must be prudent, however, about drawing a sweeping conclusion about such a broad criterion (mental health) because women may fare worse than men using other outcome measures. For example, a recent prospective investigation suggests that women have higher levels of traumatic grief, depression, and anxiety, but symptoms of traumatic grief tend to have a stronger influence on the health of widowers (Chen et al., 1999; cf. Pearlin, 1989).

Violent Causes of Death

Wortman (1997) estimated that annually 900,000 people in the United States fail to seek needed mental health treatment for a psychiatric disorder related to the traumatic death of a friend or relative (unexpected and sudden accident, homicide, or suicide). Bereavement following a violent death of a family member is more likely to be complicated and perhaps even categorically distinct from bereavements following a natural death (Ness & Pfeffer, 1990; Parkes, 1993; Rynearson, 1995). Lindemann's (1944) description of people bereaved as a result of the Coconut Grove fire, which broke out on the evening of the Harvard–Yale football game on November 28, 1942, and killed 491 people (Cobb & Lindemann, 1943; Cope, 1943), is relevant here. He described a patient whose daughter died in the fire who visualized her desperately calling for his assistance from a telephone booth. So troubled was he by this image that he "became oblivious of his surroundings" (Lindemann, 1944, p. 142).

Severe re-enactment imagery, posttraumatic symptoms, intense rage, and undermined trust in others and "the system" may characterize those people bereaved by homicide and manslaughter (L. Miller, 1998; Parkes, 1993; Rynearson, 1995). People who seek treatment following the homicide of a family member frequently report experiencing re-enactments of the murder scene. They may also fantasize about what the deceased was feeling and experiencing in the final moments of life (Rynearson, 1995). Given that most of the studies conducted in this area have been poorly controlled, limited to treatment seekers, or both, no firm conclusion can be drawn.

Some people report feeling relieved after the death of a spouse. Rarely do these feelings reflect the psychology of the widowed person independent of the circumstances of the death. Spouses of Alzheimer's patients apparently mourn the loss prior to the death while still under considerable caregiving strain. After the death, many report relief and a renewed sense of mastery (Bass & Bowman, 1990; Mullan, 1992).

A favorable bereavement course has also been observed in partners of some people who kill themselves, presumably because they were relieved of the burden of living in an intolerable and volatile household (Shepherd & Barraclough, 1974). My own experience conducting postmortem interviews with partners of younger, male suicide victims who had histories of alcoholism (e.g., Duberstein, Conwell, & Caine, 1993) suggests that the old adage about not speaking ill of the dead is not universally endorsed. Domestic violence is relatively common among younger men who kill themselves (Conner, Duberstein, & Conwell, in press). Women who had been beaten by a man who suicides may feel relieved because they do not have to worry about being attacked again. It is important to emphasize that these reactions are specific both to the circumstances of the death and to the nature of the relationship between the deceased person and the surviving partner. Wives of older men who kill themselves in the midst of their first depressive episode rarely report feeling relieved.

Research on bereavement following specific causes of death is complicated by assortative mating and psychological merging. The former refers to the tendency of like to marry like; the latter refers to the tendency of a couple to become more similar over time. These concepts are discussed later in greater detail. For now, consider two groups of younger women: those whose husbands died of cancer and those whose husbands committed suicide. The bereavement course for the two groups is likely to be distinct. Some of these differences may be ascribed to the cause of death and to the extent to which the death was forewarned (e.g., Carnelley, Wortman, & Kessler, 1999). But some of the differences may stem from differences between the two groups of women prior to the loss, ascribed in turn to assortative mating. Women who marry men who eventually commit suicide may differ from women who marry men who eventually die of cancer.

The Need for a Broad Conceptualization of Bereavement Outcome

Spousal bereavement increases a person's risk for depression (Bruce, Kim, Leaf, & Jacobs, 1990; Harlow, Goldberg, & Comstock, 1991; Hays, Kasl, & Jacobs, 1994; Mendes De Leon, Kasl, & Jacobs, 1994; Turvey, Carney, Arndt, Wallace, & Herzog, 1999), especially in people with histories of dysphoria (Hays et al., 1994) and other psychopathology (Nuss & Zubenko, 1992; but also see Turvey et al., 1999). Longitudinal research shows that depressive symptoms increase prior to a loss during the spouse's final illness (Carnelley et al., 1999; Harlow et al., 1991; Lichtenstein, Gatz, Pedersen, Berg, & McClearn, 1996; Mendes De Leon et al., 1994). What happens after the death is somewhat surprising: a relatively sharp increase in loneliness, a decrease in life satisfaction, and little change in depression (Carnelley et al., 1999; Lichtenstein et al., 1996).

Loneliness continues to be a problem for many, even a decade or more after the loss (Lichtenstein et al., 1996; Lopata, 1980). Anxiety is also common. In a comparison of widowers and married men, age 65 years and older, Byrne and Raphael (1997) found that widowers reported more anxiety, sleep disturbance, and thoughts of death and suicide, despite comparable levels of self-reported depression. Subsyndromal depression, sleep disturbances, alcohol consumption, use and iatrogenic abuse of sedatives and sleep medications, and health care negligence should also be considered. These problems may not be as obvious as depression, yet they may insidiously contribute to long-term maladjustment, physical health consequences, and excess mortality.

The need to move beyond depressive disorders is especially important in research conducted with older adults. In his comparison of younger and older widows, Parkes (1987) noted that the former experienced more psychological problems, whereas the older widows had numerous physical problems. It is possible that older people may mistakenly ascribe their grief to "normal" age-related health problems (W. Stroebe & Stroebe, 1987), an explanation consistent with the finding of age differences in the symptoms associated with affective disorders. Older people are less likely than younger people to report dysphoria, sadness, or suicidal ideation (Duberstein et al., 1999; Gallo, Anthony, & Muthen, 1994; Lyness et al., 1995).

These findings may also be ascribed to birth cohort differences in symptom reporting. People born in the first decades of the 20th century are less likely than those born in the middle decades to discuss their feelings. Bereaved older people who do not report sadness or suicidal ideation may still be considered at risk for the pathogenic effects of loss if they exhibit vegetative symptoms, excessive alcohol consumption, abuse of sedatives–hypnotics, and health care negligence. Mr. A., discussed at the beginning of this chapter, did not appear to have any clinically significant signs or symptoms of major depression or any other psychiatric disorder in the days and weeks prior to his suicide.

Spousal loss can have other social, biological, and existential consequences that may ultimately have negative effects on health. The loss of a confidante and the potential loss of a spouse's friends, family, and acquaintances may decrease "social support." This is unfortunate because social support may confer health benefits and may even decrease the risk for premature mortality (Berkman, 1995; House, Landis, & Umberson, 1988). But social support is a complicated construct. Indeed, it is impossible to disentangle the psychological characteristics of bereaved people from their social support. Bonanno and Keltner (1997) commented on emotional expression following a loss and its potential implications for the recruitment and retention of social support. Excessive neediness and hostile demandingness can alienate friends, family, and health care professionals (Parkes, 1987), leading to a cycle of loneliness and anger. Anger scares away friends and family. At the other end of the spectrum are those who remain at home for fear of showing distress in public and making others uncomfortable (Parkes, 1987).

It is also difficult to disentangle social support from longstanding personality traits and patterns of interpersonal relatedness. Westen (1998) argued that social support reflects object relations; prospective research shows that stable personality traits predict social support scores several decades later (Newman, Caspi, Moffitt, & Silva, 1997; Von Dras & Siegler, 1997). Social support is related to heart rate variability (Horsten et al., 1999), which may be an indicator of temperament, especially shyness and behavioral inhibition (Kagan, 1994). Shy men who relied on their wives to maintain their social calendar may be especially vulnerable to disruptions in their social network (Bock & Webber, 1972). In one study, older people were asked to indicate the extent to which widowhood, retirement, and other events had disrupted their social network. Shy people reported more frequent disruptions (Hansson, 1986).

Decreased tactile stimulation (touching, hugging, fondling) may also mediate negative health consequences, given the empirically documented salutary effects of touch (Field, 1998). Unmet sexual needs in widowed people have not been empirically documented. It is hardly surprising (Efron, 1985) that few studies have been conducted on sexual behavior following the death of a spouse. Parkes's (1987) anecdotal reports "suggest that sexual activity is low" (p. 116). He speculated that some widows may avoid sex and remarriage for fear of being unfaithful to their dead husband. Lopata (1980) similarly observed that some widows tend to "idealize their late husbands to the point of sanctification, making mere mortal men unable and unwilling to compete with them" (p. 238). Still, the possibility of sexual acting out has also been noted (Swigar, Bowers, & Fleck, 1976).

Bereaved people are "surprised to find how large a part of [their] customary activities [were] done in some meaningful relationship to the deceased" (Lindemann, 1944, p. 142). These routines may have had implications for biocircadian physiological rhythms (sleep, neuroendocrine function), which are frequently synchronized in cohabiting adults (Hofer, 1984; McClintock, 1978). The death of a spouse may lead to disturbed routines and may therefore disrupt biocircadian rhythms (Ehlers, Frank, & Kupfer, 1988) and cause adverse health consequences. For example, recently widowed people may find it difficult to sleep alone in a bed that they had shared for decades with their spouse. This may contribute to sleep disturbance, which can have adverse effects on immune function (Irwin et al., 1994) and, ultimately, physical health. Mealtime represents another social routine affected by bereavement. After decades of preparing meals for their husbands, many recently widowed women cannot imagine eating alone. Nutritional status suffers as a result. Other routines are similarly affected. Spousal bereavement forces widowers to attend to household tasks, whereas widows find themselves worrying about changing the oil in their car and managing their own finances (Umberson, Wortman, & Kessler, 1992).

Few would dispute the implications the death of a spouse has for a bereaved person's sense of identity, self-definition, and plans and dreams for the future. These are not inevitably bad outcomes because the death could precipitate a period of personal growth (Yalom & Lieberman, 1991).[4] In one study, women were more likely than men to report that they felt stronger and more self-confident following the death of their spouse (Umberson et al., 1992). However, men who were unable to find meaning in the death of their partner or close friend to AIDS showed faster rates of HIV progression, as indexed by CD4 (T-helper lymphocytes; these cells release substances that promote the activation of other immune cells and thereby "enhance" immune response) counts, than did those who found meaning. They also had a higher rate of AIDS-related mortality over a 4- to 9-year follow-up period (Bower, Kemeny, Taylor, & Fahey, 1998).

---

[4]Although he never wrote on the positive consequences of loss, Freud seemed to subscribe to this view. Shortly after his father died, Freud confided to Fliess that "I now have a quite uprooted feeling" (cited in Gay, 1988, p. 89). In recalling this experience 24 years later after the death of Ernest Jones's father, Freud tried to console his young disciple by saying "you will soon find out what it means to you. . . . I was about your age when my father died, and it revolutioned my soul" (p. 390).

Existential struggles with meaning, identity, and self-definition are probably exacerbated by a lack of clear, consensually valid norms prescribing both proper mourning rituals and the place of the widowed person in society (Gorer, 1965; Parkes, 1987). The latter in particular may lead the widowed person to ask "Who am I?" and "How do I fit in?" In an article integrating existential and sociological concepts, Kuypers and Bengston (1973) speculated that ambiguity about identity may force people to become dependent on external (societal) labels. This important formulation ignores individual differences in the extent to which older people are vulnerable to the effects of labeling. Psychodynamic theory (Fenichel, 1945; Fromm, 1947/1990; Rado, 1956) and research (Bornstein, 1992, 1993; Masling, 1986) suggests that depressed and dependent people may tend to look outside themselves for validation and are more likely to be disappointed when validation is not forthcoming.

Distinguishing Grief From Depression

When Freud set forth to compare and contrast grief and depression, he was indeed "treading in the footsteps of many predecessors over the centuries" (Jackson, 1986, p. 234). In 1691, a diarist named Timothy Rogers published *A Discourse Concerning Trouble of Mind, and the Disease of Melancholy* (cited in Jackson, 1986). Reflecting on the age-old concern with distinguishing depression "with cause" from depression "without cause," Rogers differentiated depression from grief and sorrow in response to "the loss of Children, by some sudden and unlooked for disappointment that ruines all their former Projects and Designs" (cited in Jackson, 1986, p. 136).[5]

Freud's "Mourning and Melancholia" was published in 1917, 2 years after he completed it. For an article that has become so influential, the tone is rather tentative. Freud (1917/1957) began with

---

[5]Freud himself had played with the comparison for decades. In Draft G of the Fliess papers, believed to be written in 1895, he asserted that the "affect corresponding to melancholia is that of mourning, that is longing for something lost" (Freud, 1950/1966, pp. 200–201), by which he meant "loss of libido." In a recorded discussion of a Vienna Psychoanalytic Society meeting on suicide in schoolchildren, he stated that a "comparison between [melancholia] and the affect of mourning" (1910/1957, p. 232) is warranted.

a "warning against any overestimation of the value of our conclusions" (p. 243), which are based on "a small number of cases whose psychogenic nature was indisputable" (p. 243). Throughout the article, he struggled with the somatic versus psychogenic tension, making reference to the problem of diurnal variation, sleeplessness, and tendency of some "melancholic" people to become manic. After listing the characteristic symptoms of melancholia, he concluded that "with one exception, the same traits are met with in mourning. The disturbance of self-regard is absent in mourning; but otherwise the features are the same" (p. 244). By disturbance in self-regard, Freud did not mean low self-esteem. His formulation was more specific and subtle. Manifestations of this self-disturbance (in translation, at least) include "self-reproaches and self-revilings" (p. 244), a "delusional expectation of punishment" (p. 244), an "impoverishment of [the] ego on a grand scale" (p. 246), and a sense of being "morally despicable" (p. 246). For Freud, this latter self-disturbance was paramount: "Dissatisfaction with the ego on *moral grounds* is the most outstanding feature" (p. 248, emphasis added) of melancholia.

Freud's (1917/1957) hypothesis that normal mourning and psychogenic depression could be distinguished in this manner has, to my knowledge, not been subject to any rigorous investigation. Although many psychoanalysts have been skeptical of Freud's hypothesis (e.g., Bibring, 1953; Siggins, 1966), data from a number of studies are suggestive (Bruce et al., 1990; Mendes De Leon et al., 1994; Parkes, 1987; Prigerson et al., 1996). Most impressive are investigations conducted with community, not clinical, samples. Bruce et al. showed that married depressed people are more likely than widowed depressed people to report feelings of worthlessness and guilt. Mendes De Leon et al. reported that acutely bereaved people reported sadness and dysphoria but were less likely to endorse symptoms related to negative appraisals, such as "I felt that people disliked me" or "people were unfriendly."

Freud (1917/1957) was interested in differentiating grief from depression. He made no effort to distinguish uncomplicated grief from traumatic grief, musing that "it is really only because we know so well how to explain [mourning] that this attitude to us does not seem pathological" (p. 244). However, more recently researchers have attempted to identify symptoms of traumatic grief that are distinct from those of major depression and are also maladaptive (Horowitz et al., 1997; Prigerson et al., 1995, 1996). Because these studies are likely to have a significant impact on the way traumatic grief is conceptualized in the clinical setting, they are discussed here in detail.

Prigerson et al. (1995) collected data on a sample of 82 widowed participants, age 60 years and older, in a study on sleep physiology in bereavement. Exclusion criteria included use of medications with known psychotropic effects, psychiatric history, dementia, and current psychiatric disorder other than depression. Slightly less than half of the volunteers screened were eligible to participate. The investigators administered a battery of self-report measures and conducted an in-depth, structured clinical interview designed to establish psychiatric diagnoses and severity of depressive symptoms. They administered measures at baseline (3- to 6-months postloss) and at an 18-month follow-up. They factor analyzed items from the Hamilton Depression Rating Scale (HDRS; Hamilton, 1960), a self-esteem scale, and several grief scales.

A principal components analysis yielded two factors, labeled "bereavement depression" (26.2% of variance) and "complicated grief" (20.0% of variance; Prigerson et al., 1995). Symptoms of bereavement depression were hypochondriasis, apathy, insomnia, anxiety, suicidal ideation, guilt, loneliness, depressed mood, psychomotor retardation, hostility, and low self-esteem. Symptoms of traumatic grief were preoccupation with thoughts of the deceased spouse, crying, yearning, searching for the deceased spouse, disbelief about the death, being stunned by the death, and acceptance of the death. Self-esteem loaded on the depression factor, not the grief factor, which some may interpret as providing additional support for Freud's formulation. A regression analysis showed that high levels of traumatic grief at baseline were significantly associated with worse global functioning, worse self-perceived sleep quality, lower self-esteem, and a greater probability of having a depressed mood at the 18-month follow-up. Bereavement depression was associated only with more physical illness burden at the 18-month follow-up.

This study, an important first step in the establishment of a core set of grief symptoms, was conducted with a small sample of patients who sought and received treatment from a major tertiary care facility. Prigerson et al. (1996) conducted a second study with a community sample. Participants were spouses of medical patients who had died within 6 months of hospitalization. The authors subjected items from several self-report measures of depression, anxiety, and grief to principal axis factoring with varimax rotation. A grief factor emerged, defined mainly by the following symptoms, each of which had a loading of greater than .7: has mental images of spouse, feels spouse's presence, hears things associated with spouse, has pain in the same area as spouse, needs to call spouse's name, and is drawn to associations with spouse. Other symptoms had smaller but still significant, loadings. Two other factors emerged: depression and anxiety. A subsequent study shows that traumatic grief was associated with physical morbidity and mortality (Prigerson et al., 1997).

Horowitz et al. (1997) studied 70 recently bereaved spouses to identify a core set of grief symptoms that could be distinguished from the diagnostic criteria for major depressive disorder. Using latent class models and signal detection theory, the authors identified a cluster of symptoms distinct from those that constitute major depression. These symptoms, which the authors believe may comprise a syndrome, include intense intrusive thoughts, pangs of severe emotion, distressing yearnings, feeling excessively alone and empty, excessively avoiding tasks for fear that they would stimulate memories of the deceased, unusual sleep disturbances, and loss of interest in personal activities.

The distinction between complicated grief and major depression has potentially important implications for research and treatment. Researchers interested in the effects of bereavement on health outcomes rarely distinguish among uncomplicated grief, traumatic grief, and depression, but these constructs may have different physiological correlates and implications for health and social outcomes. With respect to treatment, few contemporary clinicians would agree with Benjamin Rush (1812/1962), who recommended opium, administered "in liberal doses" during the first "paroxysm" of grief and "repeated afterwards . . . to obviate wakefulness" (pp. 319–320). Still, authorities (Parkes, 1987; W. Stroebe & Stroebe, 1987; Worden, 1991) believe that inappropriate medication for the bereaved person is common, although I am unaware of any hard data on this issue. Sedatives and hypnotics may be transiently useful, but they may "muffle reactions and hinder realization of the loss" (W. Stroebe & Stroebe, 1987, p. 244). However, they may make it easier for people to manage their fear and anger and thereby help them recruit functional support. Antidepressants may be effective in treating some symptoms of depression following a bereavement period, but no drug has been designed to relieve the pangs of yearning associated with complicated grief.

Mortality Risk

Analyzing census data from France, Prussia, and Sweden from 1886 to 1895, March (1912) identified a "classic pattern" (W. Stroebe & Stroebe, 1987) of findings: (a) Mortality rates are higher for widowed than married people, (b) the excess risk is greater for younger widowed than older widowed people, and (c) the excess risk is greater for men than for women. This pattern has subsequently been repeatedly confirmed cross-nationally and across historical period and birth cohort (Ciocco, 1940; Shurtleff, 1955; Kraus & Lilienfeld, 1959). These classic conclusions were based on comparisons of crude death rates. The numbers were obtained from official statistics (e.g., census bureaus) and were not statistically adjusted for potential confounds. Over the past 3 decades, numerous cohort (or longitudinal) studies have examined the relationship between bereavement and mortality.

Before discussing those investigations, I now turn to the methodological and conceptual issues that plagued the early studies and continue to pose challenges to interpretation. It is frequently assumed that BRM exists and, moreover, that this excess mortality can be ascribed to the stress of bereavement. Consider this typical sentence: "It thus seems that bereavement leads to an overall weakening of a person's ability to cope with disease" (Martikainen & Valkonen, 1996b, p. 1092). This interpretation rests on the assumption that alternative explanations have been ruled out (for an extensive discussion of some of these issues, see W. Stroebe & Stroebe, 1987).

Alternative Explanations

Widowed people who remarry are healthier than those who do not remarry. If this is true, then those who remain widowed may die at a higher rate than married people because they are in poorer health to begin with, not because of stress. It is still possible that the "stress of widowhood" exacerbates risk. Although the relationship between marital status and health remains controversial (e.g., Waldron, Hughes, & Brooks, 1996), some empirical research supports the notion that healthier widowed people are "selected back" into marriage, leaving those in the widowed category more vulnerable (Helsing, Szklo, & Comstock, 1981).

Widowed people are older than married people. Another potential confound is age. Their higher death rates may simply be ascribed to age, not the stress of widowhood. (Widowed people may also be underrepresented in the collection of census data and overrepresented on the mortality ledgers [W. Stroebe & Stroebe, 1987]. This would also exaggerate the difference in crude mortality rates.) It is true that age may have confounded the interpretation of earlier studies. However, recent investigations are based on data collected prospectively from cohorts (vs. census data). Also age has been controlled statistically.

Spouses share beliefs, traits, and behaviors. This may increase the likelihood of married couples developing similar diseases and dying in close temporal proximity to one another (Kreitman, 1964). Thus the death of the widowed spouse is not due to the stress of widowhood, but it simply reflects the fact that the survivor shared many mortality-relevant habits and traits with the deceased spouse. Three psychosocial mechanisms can account for these shared habits and traits: assortative mating, psychological merging, and joint unfavorable environment.

Assortative mating. The term assortative mating may have been first used in an anonymous article, which is believed to be written by Karl Pearson ("Assortative mating in man," 1903). Like marries like; spouses share similar attitudes, values, and religious beliefs and practices. One study reports husband–wife correlations of .27 and .38 for cigarette smoking and alcohol consumption, respectively (Schaefer et al., 1995), which may reflect shared anxiety or depression. Mates may select each other on the basis of a characteristic that has been implicated in mortality, such as depression or physical health–fitness. If this is true, the probability of BRM would increase, but the plausibility of the stress explanation would decrease.

Psychological merging. Even if they do not share similar features prior to marriage, spouses may grow to resemble each other. After all, if the timing of menstrual flow and other biocircadian rhythms can become synchronized in cohabiting women (McClintock, 1978), it is possible that husbands and wives who live together for decades may develop social routines that become biologically entrained and have implications for circadian physiology. But psychological merging may occur on other levels as well. Abraham's (1925/1955) clinical experience led him to conclude that often "both partners in a marriage have a harmful effect on each other, so that they both become increasingly neurotic" (p. 96). In a study of 317 married couples interviewed in 1982, 1985, and 1988, Tower and Kasl (1996) showed that changes in depressive symptoms in one spouse contributed to changes in depressive symptoms in the other. There is some evidence that wives might be more quickly influenced by their husband's symptoms than vice versa. Zajonc and colleagues have argued that spouses make similar facial expressions, which in turn permanently alter the physical features of the face (Zajonc, 1985; Zajonc, Adelmann, Murphy, & Niedenthal, 1987). In one study, undergraduates rated two sets of photographs of married couples, one photo taken shortly after marriage and one taken 25 years later. Results suggest an increase in similarity of physical appearance that is associated with marital satisfaction (Zajonc et al., 1987).

Joint unfavorable environment. Still another confound has been termed joint unfavorable environment by Kraus and Lilienfeld (1959). The argument here is similar to that of assortative mating–psychological merging, but the similarity refers to common exposure to an unhealthful social- or bioecology, such as poverty, limited access to health care, or environmental toxins. Spouses who drink the same contaminated water for decades would be expected to develop and die from similar diseases.

Confounds. Does bereavement increase risk for mortality independent of other established risk factors? There is not much evidence on this issue. Even though researchers' study designs have improved over the past decade, they have not controlled for established correlates of mortality risk, such as alcohol consumption, blood pressure, cigarette smoking, and objective disease burden. Nor are there adequate data on the psychological correlates of mortality, such as depression, personality, and self-perceived health. Perhaps widowed people smoke and drink more than married people. If this is so, their excess mortality risk would reflect the cumulative effect of these behaviors over a lifetime in addition to any change in these habits immediately preceding or following the loss.

Cause and timing of death. Other explanations must be ruled out before stress hypotheses can be seriously entertained. Consider deaths from motor vehicle accidents. The passenger may be killed instantly, but the driver may linger for 1 week before dying. The two deaths occur in close temporal proximity, but it is unlikely that the driver's death is associated with the stress of bereavement. A similar argument can be made for murder–suicide. Common infection is another problem. Analyzing data on causes of death between 1898 and 1938, Ciocco (1940) showed that 26.3% of the widowed people who died of tuberculosis were predeceased by a spouse who died of that disease. Writing shortly before the AIDS pandemic entered public consciousness, W. Stroebe and Stroebe (1987) noted that common infection is unlikely to explain the increased mortality risk in widowed people because "the control of infectious disease [has] increased dramatically during this century" (p. 156). Changing historical circumstances and cross-cultural differences admonish against generalizing conclusions beyond the specific historical and sociocultural context within which a study is conducted. M. S. Stroebe and Stroebe (1993) noted that the bereavement–mortality link has not been established in any "undeveloped country" (p. 178).

From the perspective of the stress paradigm, it is not sufficient to demonstrate that widowed people are at increased risk of death because of violence (suicide, homicide, accidents). If it is assumed that BRM is mediated by altered immune and neuroendocrine function (W. Stroebe & Stroebe, 1987), it must also be shown that widowed people die from diseases that are definitively immune mediated (admittedly a murky task, given recent evidence that independent of stress, the immune system may be involved in heart disease and other chronic illnesses; e.g., Kuo et al., 1993; Overmier

& Murison, 1997).[6] Furthermore, it must be demonstrated that mortality risk is relatively high at timepoints proximal to the loss but lower thereafter. Bowlby (1980) concluded that "even *fatal illness* is more common in the bereaved" (p. 100, emphasis added). Similarly, the image conjured by Engel (1961) and Bowlby is unmistakably that of the grieving spouse suddenly stricken or ravaged by disease, but this is not the picture emerging from the scientific canvas.

Recent Cohort Studies

In the decade or so between the publication of Engel's (1961) classic article and Bowlby's (1980) book, several reasonably well-designed studies revealed excess mortality in widowed people, an effect moderated by age and sex (Cox & Ford, 1964; Ekblom, 1963; Helsing, Comstock, & Szklo, 1982; Parkes et al., 1969; Rees & Lutkins, 1967; Young et al., 1963). More recently, most but not all investigations (e.g., Murrell, Himmelfarb, & Phifer, 1988) continue to find excess mortality following bereavement (Kaprio, Koskenvuo, & Rita, 1987; Korenman, Goldman, & Fu, 1997; Lichtenstein, Gatz, & Berg, 1998; Martikainen & Valkonen, 1996a; Mendes de Leon, Kasl, & Jacobs, 1993; Schaefer et al., 1995; Smith & Zick, 1996). Negative findings are typically ascribed to inadequate sample sizes (M. S. Stroebe & Stroebe, 1993). In one study, Lichtenstein et al. found a decrease in the risk of death among widowed women under age 70 if they survived 4-years postloss; the authors ascribed this odd finding to the possibility that for some women, widowhood is a "growth experience" (p. 641).

More than 1 decade ago, Osterweis, Solomon, and Green (1984) noted that the excess mortality in widowed people can be ascribed largely to suicide, cirrhosis, and cardiac arrest. Although it is still possible to point to design flaws that preclude unambiguous interpretation, recent studies' findings are generally consistent with this idea. But the mechanism—the explanation—for BRM contin-

---

[6]Hooper (1999) provided an accessible account of the idea that chronic diseases often have infectious etiologies. Ewald (1994) presented a novel perspective on the relationship between immunology and epidemiology.

ues to be elusive. A consensus is building that the stress of widowhood leads to BRM, but no investigation has been able to establish this. In analyses examining specific causes of death, researchers have not controlled for potential confounds. Those that have controlled for confounds have not examined specific causes of death. None has adjusted for all relevant confounds. To provide the reader with a sense of how these studies are conducted, I discuss three of them in detail.

In one of the better designed studies, Kaprio et al. (1987) examined specific causes of death but did not attempt to control for potential confounds. They analyzed all death certificates in Finland from 1972 to 1976 inclusive. These files were linked with the Central Population Registry records to determine if the deceased had been married and to obtain the personal identification data on the deceased's spouse. There were 95,647 widowed spouses whose identification data were then linked back to the death certificate records to determine whether they, too, died during the study period. Mortality from all causes was 6.5% higher than expected. This increase was not randomly distributed across causes of death. Natural deaths were elevated by 3.2%; violent deaths (motor vehicle accidents, suicide) were elevated by 93.0%. For women, deaths that were due to ischemic heart disease were remarkably elevated in the first week (249.0%) and month (50.0%). The pattern for men was somewhat distinct: elevated in the first month (130%), then moderately elevated (8.0–16.0%) through Year 4, and down to expected levels by 5-years postloss. The authors invoked stress theory when they concluded that excess mortality for heart disease "may be related to grief and emotional distress which induce disturbances of sleep and predispose to arrythmias leading to cardiac mortality" (Kaprio et al., 1987, p. 285).

In another well-designed study, Schaefer et al. (1995) attempted to control for confounds but did not examine specific causes of death. They studied 12,522 spouse pairs enrolled in the Kaiser Foundation Health Plan in the San Francisco (CA) area. All participants had had an extensive checkup at some point during the 10-year interval between 1964 and 1973 inclusive. To be eligible for study entry, both members of the couple were required to be over age 40. The checkup included a physical exam and a self-report battery, which inquired about 32 conditions and problems and 22 minor but potentially serious symptoms (e.g., shortness of breath with exertion). Other items inquired about depression and anxiety. Using record-linkage techniques, the authors obtained mortality data through 1987. Consistent with stress theory, mortality risk was greatest during the first year of widowhood and declined slightly thereafter. However, elevated mortality rates were observed throughout the lengthy follow-up period, a finding inconsistent with an acute stress hypothesis. Another finding was inconsistent with that hypothesis. Being remarried, rather than being in a first marriage, increased mortality risk following a spouse's death.

The multivariate analyses, the major strength of this study, show that the relative risk of mortality in women was not significantly elevated in the first 6 months after Schaefer et al. (1995) controlled for the effects of age, number of self-reported chronic conditions or health problems, education, alcohol use, smoking, and self-reported depression. However, mortality risk was elevated during Months 7–12 and declined to expected levels thereafter. In men, a similar analysis reveals an interaction between baseline health status and bereavement. Those with few health problems were at an increased risk for BRM throughout the study period, but the risk of death attributable to bereavement was significantly diminished in men with many health problems.

The major strength of Martikainen and Valkonen's (1996a) study is their use of data on specific causes of death. Beginning with a sample of over 1 million married people between ages 35 and 84, the authors linked 1985 Finnish census data with death certificates from 1986 to 1991. There were 83,980 widowed spouses identified in this manner, almost 10,000 of whom also died during the study period. In this latter group, death because of accidents and violence was elevated by 94% in men and 51% in women. For alcohol-related diseases (alcoholic psychosis, alcoholism, alcohol-related chronic liver disease, cirrhosis of the liver, and pancreatitis), the excess was substantial: 140% for men and 122% for women. For chronic ischemic heart disease, the numbers for men and women, respectively, were 36% and 30%. For acute myocardial infarction, the corresponding figures were 11% and 6%—the latter finding was not statistically significant. It is somewhat surprising that the risk of dying by lung cancer was elevated: 24% excess mortality for men and 21% for women, although again the latter finding was not significant.

When Martikainen and Valkonen (1996a) restricted the analyses to mortality prior to 6-months postloss, the relative risk of dying by acute myocardial infarction was 14% for men (ns) but 18% for women, a statistically significant difference. When the authors divided the sample into three age groups (35–64 years, 65–74 years, 75+ years), they detected a significant age gradient. Corresponding relative risks for all diseases in the three age groups were 1.56, 1.21, and 1.06, respectively, in men. This means, for example, that the excess mortality due to natural causes and attributable to bereavement was 56% among men ages 35–64. In women, the numbers were not as impressive for all three age groups: 1.19, 1.10, and 1.00, respectively. Further analyses reveal that BRM exists across socioeconomic strata, but people in the lower strata are at greater risk than those in the upper strata (Martikainen & Valkonen, 1998). In summary, the authors confirmed the classic pattern: Excess mortality following bereavement is (a) not a statistical artifact, (b) greater among men than women, (c) most evident shortly after loss with excess risk declining with the passage of time, and (d) greater among younger than older people.

Whereas substantiating the classic pattern, this careful study also represents a challenge to stress theory. First, the relative risks for violent deaths are extremely high. It is possible that suicide, accident, and homicide may each theoretically be related to physiological stress, but it is unlikely. Second, excess mortality was evident for major chronic diseases with relatively long latencies, such as lung cancer and chronic ischemic heart disease. In fact, the mortality risk for acute myocardial infarction was lower than the risk for chronic ischemic heart disease, and the risk for deaths because of respiratory infections was not elevated in the short term. Acute stress theory cannot parsimoniously explain these findings.

Summary and Critique

Epidemiological studies of mortality following bereavement have steadily improved in design over the past 3 decades. I tentatively conclude that there is an association between widowhood and mortality risk, but numerous methodological issues confound an interpretation of published findings. No study adequately addresses the alternative explanations discussed in the previous section. Thus, the jury is still out on acute stress theories of BRM. In addition, other methodological issues need to be considered when one is interpreting the literature on BRM.

The accuracy of certifications of cause of death can be questioned. People who are lost to follow-up because they moved out of the geographic region covered by the official statistics may not represent the sample as a whole. Moreover, relying on death certificate data—a postmortem snapshot—obscures causal processes. For example, suicide following the death of a spouse may be more common in those who experience a worsening of heart disease in widowhood; death by ischemic heart disease in recently widowed people might be precipitated or exacerbated by major depressive disorder. Studies using record-linkage techniques do not, and perhaps cannot, examine these possibilities.

Results published in the 1990s are based on data collected in the 1960s in particular geographic regions. Concern can be raised about their generalizability to contemporary birth cohorts and other geographical locales. Many epidemiological studies have been conducted in northern European countries (average population of Scandinavian countries in 1997: 5.6 million). Not only do these countries differ from each other ("Survey of the Nordic Countries," 1999), they contrast starkly with the United States in respect to ethnic makeup and socioeconomic disparities.

No study has gauged the effects of marital trajectories (Barrett, 1998) on BRM. Some married people have been divorced several times; others have been divorced and widowed; some have been continuously married to the same person. These distinctions have not yet been examined in research on mortality and bereavement. Few studies examine the effects of remarriage following widowhood, but this practice has probably served to underestimate mortality effects (Schaefer et al., 1995).

With respect to statistical analyses rather than using survival analyses to identify the intervals of greatest risk, most studies somewhat arbitrarily divide the follow-up periods into 6-month or annual intervals. This also makes it difficult to compare findings across investigations. Some analyses attempt to control for potential confounds, such as health status, using baseline values (at study entry), but these data were collected years or decades prior to widowhood and therefore may not accurately reflect the situation shortly prior to widowhood. Although attempts to control for physical health are laudable, assessment of physical health through self-report is complex and potentially confounded by depression and personality. Risk diminishes somewhat in multivariate analyses, even when one is adjusting for suboptimally measured covariates (Martikainen & Valkonen, 1996b; Schaefer et al., 1995). Presumably, using covariates that are measured more reliably and validly may further diminish the bereavement effect.

In summary, no study comprehensively controls for potential confounds, while examining specific causes of death. Such a design may not be feasible, given that few (if any) nations collect meaningful psychological data as part of the standard census procedure. Even relatively comprehensive prospective databases such as Kaiser's (Schaefer et al., 1995) appear to provide only limited coverage of key psychological constructs. Without prospective data on grief, depression, immune function, and neuroendocrine functioning, epidemiological research cannot substantiate the causal conclusion that bereavement "leads to an overall weakening of a person's ability to cope with disease" (Martikainen & Valkonen, 1996b, p. 1092). Nor can it adequately test the hypothesis that bereavement is accompanied by "alterations of immune function, which, in turn, lower resistance to infectious diseases and increase risk of morbidity and mortality from these causes" (W. Stroebe & Stroebe, 1987, p. 106). No single study is likely to be able to examine these hypotheses in all their complexity. Converging evidence, multiple studies using multiple designs, is required. In the next section, I review the studies that attempt to establish a connection between bereavement and immune function.

Immune Function

It is popularly assumed that stress increases the activity of the HPA axis, which in turn leads to immune downregulation or a decrease in immune function (e.g., Sapolsky, 1994), thereby conferring increased risk for morbidity and mortality.[7,8] W. Stroebe and Stroebe (1987) noted that "the loss experience is likely to be accompanied by alterations of immune function" (p. 106). Any review of the literature on BRM would thus be incomplete without an examination of the literature on immune function following bereavement.

There are numerous methodological and logistical issues involved in human psychoneuroimmunology research (for a review of the methods, see Kiecolt-Glaser & Glaser, 1988; for a succinct overview, see Maier, Watkins, & Fleshner, 1994; for an overview of the immune system, see Roitt, 1997). One of the biggest obstacles can be ascribed to the remarkable sensitivity of the immune system to exogenous stimuli. Caffeine, alcohol, tobacco, and some medications are known to affect immune function. Intake of these and other substances must be monitored, as must the presence of viral diseases or chronic disease. In women, menstrual and menopausal status should be measured, and in all people, biocircadian rhythms

---

[7]Admittedly, "immune function" is a vague term, and I suspect the phrase will be retired in coming decades. "Broad statements such as the 'immunosuppressive effects of stress' have little biological meaning and belie the true complexity of the immune system" (Coe, Rosenberg, Fischer, & Levine, 1987, p. 1426). Apparently, there are many examples of a stress-precipitated increase in one immune parameter accompanied by a decrease in another. However, for ease of communication, I use the phrase immune function in this chapter.

[8]Why would it be adaptive for immune function to be suppressed following stress? A number of speculative explanations have been offered (Maier, Watkins, & Fleshner, 1994; Sapolsky, 1994). On the basis of the notion that some physiological functions evolved as accidental byproducts of other processes, Sapolsky (1994) entertained the possibility that downregulation is a meaningless epiphenomenon. But he argued that "this is probably not the case" (p. 145), and "it is probably not just an accident" (p. 148) of evolution. Instead, he believes that immune downregulation following stress evolved because it inhibits the development of autoimmune diseases. Maier et al. believe that immune downregulation following stress evolves because it prepares the body to respond to injury or infection. Of course, neither of these hypotheses is directly testable. As Bakan (1968) put it, "Darwinian theory . . . provided a way of explaining evolution without any notion of telos, of explaining, as someone once said, how it might be possible to build a house just by throwing bricks. . . . Historical hypotheses are all intrinsically uncomfirmable" (p. 31).

require careful monitoring of time-of-day during which data (i.e., blood, saliva) are collected. Handedness may play a role in the lateralization of autoimmune diseases and the immune response (Geschwind & Galaburda, 1987); this may be especially important when one is interpreting the results of delayed hypersensitivity testing. Some authors have recommended controlling for handedness in such analyses (Jemmott & Locke, 1984), but the broader implications for human psychoneuroimmunology research of cerebral lateralization have not been pursued.

The following section is a more detailed description of two of the methods used to assess immune function, namely, mitogen stimulation and natural killer (NK) cell cytotoxicity. Each method is limited. Reflecting her dissatisfaction with mitogen stimulation, O'Leary (1990) predicted that it would soon be replaced, and Herbert and Cohen (1993) similarly commented on the availability of immune tests that are used too rarely in psychological research. Delayed hypersensitivity, activation of a latent virus, and responses to a vaccination have been infrequently used in bereavement research, so I do not discuss them in this section.

Assays

Mitogen stimulation. One of the most reliable ways to assess immune function is to separate the lymphocytes from the rest of the blood and measure their response to mitogen (*mito*sis *gen*erators) in vitro (outside the body). This is an artificial process, one that has no known analogue in nature. Mitogens are extracts of plant seeds, called lectins, that stimulate cellular division nonspecifically in T- or B-cell lymphocytes and other cells. These lymphocytes are critical to specific immunity, an acquired rather than innate capacity to recognize and destroy foreign substances, which are called "antigens" (*anti*body *gen*erators); these are typically disease-bearing microbes, infected cells, or tumors. (A specific type of T cell [helper or CD4+] is destroyed by the human immunodeficiency virus, which opens the door for opportunistic infections.) The most commonly used plant extracts are phytohemagglutinin (PHA) and concanavalin A (Con A), which stimulate T cells, and pokeweed mitogen (PWM), which stimulates B cells.

However, responsivity to these mitogens tends to be nonspecific and highly correlated.

When lymphocytes are incubated, or cultured, with mitogens in a medium that contains a radioactive protein (usually thymidine or idoxuridine), they divide—a process referred to as proliferation, replication, or blastogenesis. When the cells divide, they incorporate the radioactive protein into their newly synthesized DNA. This process of incorporation can indeed be quantified. It is assumed that the extent of proliferation, reflected by the radioactivity, is related to functional effectiveness. The greater the proliferation, the better the immune system is presumed to be functioning.

The advantages of the mitogen stimulation paradigm must be weighed against its disadvantages. It is relatively noninvasive, cheap and easy to perform reliably. It does have a degree of predictive validity; decreased proliferation is related to mortality (Murasko, Weiner, & Kaye, 1988). Individuals who test positive for HIV have lower proliferative response, and are at an increased risk for AIDS (Hofmann et al., 1987). It must be acknowledged that these assays are conducted in vitro; as Kagan (1998) said in another context, "artificial conditions can create artificial facts" (p. 107). Ader and Cohen (1993) argued that the health consequences of decreased proliferative responses are not obvious, and that changes in mitogen responsiveness may or may not reflect one's capacity to mount an effective response.

Cytotoxicity. The focus here is on NK cells. NK cells are large, granular lymphocytes that kill pathogen-infected cells and tumor cells in the absence of antigen priming. Although this is a theoretically important capacity, potentially allowing NK cells to contribute to cancer surveillance by killing tumor cells in the absence of antigen expression, the "relationship between NK cell activity and tumor progression has been difficult to establish" (Trinchieri, 1989, p. 297). NK cells play a role in the body's resistance to viral, and possibly bacterial and parasitic, infections (Trinchieri, 1989).

Turning to the assay itself, NK cells are cultured for several hours with commercially prepared foreign target cells, typically tumors, which are labeled with chromium^{51}. The destruction, or lysis, of the tumor (target) cell by the NK (effector) cell causes the chromium to be released into the surrounding fluid, or supernatant, where the chromium is counted. The amount of chromium released reflects the extent to which the targets were lysed. The assay is repeated several times at different effector:target ratios, commonly at 5:1, 10:1, 25:1, 50:1, and 100:1. The higher the ratio, the greater the likelihood that tumor cells will be lysed. The number of effector cells required to kill a certain percentage of target cells is referred to in terms of "lytic units," a quantity independent of the effector: target ratio used in any given study. Thus, results can be compared across studies with different effector:target ratios.

The Research: From Stress to Depression

Acknowledging Selye's (1951) contributions and encouraged by the findings of U.S. National Aeronautical and Space Administration Skylab scientists who documented decreases in lymphocyte proliferation on the day of their splashdown (Kimzey, 1975), Bartrop, Luckhust, Lazarus, Kiloh, and Penny (1977) decided to investigate immune function in bereaved people. They studied 26 widows and 26 race-, age-, and sex-matched controls at two timepoints, separated by 1 month. Data collection from widowed people corresponded roughly to 2- and 6-weeks postbereavement. The groups had remarkably similar hormone profiles; no differences were observed in serum thyroxine, triiodothyronine, prolactin, and growth hormone. Nor were there differences in the numbers of T cells and B cells. However, among widowed people, T-cell responses to Con A and PHA were lower at the 6-week timepoint. T-cell responses to PHA were also lower at the 2-week timepoint. These findings tentatively suggest that the stress of bereavement contributed to decreased lymphocyte proliferation. "For the first time we have shown prospectively that severe psychological stress can produce a measurable abnormality in immune function" (Bartrop et al., 1977, p. 835). Unfortunately, the absence of data on mood, personality, concurrent stressors, and psychiatric diagnoses precluded definitive, psychologically meaningful conclusions. The absence of prebereavement data makes it hard to know whether the apparent immune decrements predated or followed the death of the spouse.

More than 5 years passed before the scientific community had another opportunity to consider a study on bereavement and immune function. Schleifer, Keller, Camerino, Thornton, and Stein (1983) recruited a sample of 15 men whose wives eventually died of metastatic breast cancer following their treatment at Mount Sinai Hospital in New York City. The men ranged in age from 33 to 76 years and had been married for a median of 30 years (range: 5–43 years). Their wives had been diagnosed with cancer well before study entry (range: 1–5 years, median = 2.5 years). The men had their blood drawn, on average, three times prior to the deaths of their wives, and one (n = 8) or two (n = 7) times at unspecified points during the first 2-months postloss. Twelve of the men were studied during the follow-up period, defined as 4- to 14-months postloss. The number of blood samples obtained and analyzed during that period was not described. The researchers observed a decreased proliferation to Con A, PWM, and PHA at 1-month postloss, compared with prebereavement. It is interesting to note that follow-up beyond 2 months yielded no further decrements and, on average, prebereavement immune function appeared to recover. However, the authors carefully pointed out that this apparent recovery may have obscured the presence of subgroups. Some of the participants may have continued to manifest lower mitogen responses throughout the year after their bereavement. The finding of an apparent recovery to baseline is also difficult to interpret because the prebereavement levels did not reflect a stress-free baseline. At study entry, each participant's wife was dying from breast cancer. Moreover, the absence of psychological and social data again make it impossible to draw psychologically meaningful conclusions.

A study by Linn, Linn, and Jensen (1984) is frequently cited in support of the notion that bereavement suppresses immune function, but participants included those who "had experienced serious family illness or deaths" (p. 219). Although this was not a study of conjugal bereavement, it is significant because the authors were the first to examine the role of depression in the context of stress. Men, age 40–60 years, were divided into four groups, on the basis of life event status over the past 6 months (yes or no) and self-reported depression score (high or low, based on a median split). The authors observed a decreased lymphocyte proliferation in response to stimulation with PHA in individuals with high depression scores. There was no effect of bereavement status on immune function and no evidence that depression moderates the relationship between bereavement and immune function. This latter null finding may be real, or it can be ascribed to numerous methodological weaknesses, including the time frame used to assess life events (immune effects may disappear by 6 months) and the measurement of depression (self-report).

Subsequent research strongly supports the notion that depression, rather than bereavement status per se, is associated with immune downregulation. Irwin, Daniels, Smith, Bloom, and Weiner (1987) prospectively studied 10 women whose husbands had died of metastatic lung cancer 1–4 months before study entry and had been diagnosed 3–12 months prior. In comparison with a control sample of 8 women whose husbands were in good health, the recently widowed women had significantly lower NK cell function; there were no differences in the absolute number of lymphocytes. Six of the women, who entered into the study shortly after their husbands' diagnoses, were followed prospectively through the bereavement period. The authors did not observe a difference in NK cell activity from pre- to postbereavement. However, change in the severity of depressive symptoms, as measured by the Hamilton Depression Rating Scale, was associated with change in NK cell activity. The authors concluded that "change in depressive symptoms, not merely the death of the spouse, appears to be correlated with changes in NK activity" (Irwin et al., 1987, p. 102).

Zisook et al. (1994) delivered more bad news for stress theories. These investigators studied 21 widows and 21 controls matched for age and length of marriage. Inclusion criteria required that participants have no history of psychiatric disorder and no current or recent alcohol or drug abuse or use of psychotropic medications. All participants were between 45 and 65 years of age and had been married for at least 10 years. A comparison of widowed and nonwidowed participants revealed no difference on many of the immunological measures, including numbers and percentages of lymphocytes, NK cell activity, and proliferative responses to Con A. Further analyses showed, however, that the subgroup of widowed participants who met diagnostic criteria for major depressive disorder had lower NK cell function.

Is there any specific symptom of major depression "responsible" for immune downregulation? Some of the most provocative research in human psychoneuroimmunology focuses on sleep. Whereas some studies suggest that sleep deprivation is associated with decreased NK activity (e.g., Irwin, Smith, & Gillin, 1992), others show an increased NK activity following sleep deprivation (e.g., Dinges et al., 1994). Precisely how these differences can be reconciled is debatable, but few would dispute that there is some connection between sleep and immune function.

In one study, Hall et al. (1998) examined the relationship between electroencephalogram assessed sleep and NK cell number and function. The participants consisted of 29 treatment-seeking widows (n = 20) and widowers (n = 9) ranging in age from 40 to 78 years. The experimental hypothesis was based in part on the finding that total sleep time, sleep efficiency, and duration of nonrandom eye movement sleep were all positively correlated with NK cell activity in depressed inpatients and nondepressed controls (Irwin et al., 1992). On the basis of preliminary analyses of their data, the authors hypothesized that minutes spent awake would mediate the relationship between self-reported distress, measured by the Impact of Events Scale (IES; Horowitz, Wilner, & Alvarez, 1979), and NK cell number.

Consistent with their hypothesis, the relationship between IES score and NK cell number was no longer significant after the authors (Hall et al., 1998) controlled for minutes spent awake—a finding that dovetails with data from a study conducted on stress and immune function in people whose lives were affected by Hurricane Andrew (Ironson et al., 1997). In that investigation, subjective sleep complaints mediated the relationship between IES score and NK cell activity, although the effects were "not particularly strong" (Ironson et al., 1997, p. 137), suggesting that "at best, sleep problems were explaining only part of the picture" (p. 138). Still, it appears that depression-related sleep disturbances must be carefully considered when evaluating the relationship between bereavement and mortality. The suggestion that bereavement-related cardiac mortality "may be related to grief and emotional distress which induce disturbances of sleep" (Kaprio et al., 1987, p. 285) appears to have some validity. It is not known how sleep disturbances lead to arrhythmias.

Summary and Comment

Were Schleifer et al. (1983) correct when they argued that their findings are "consistent with a hypothesis that changes in the immune system following bereavement are related to the increased mortality of bereaved widowers" (p. 377)? More likely, it is an overly enthusiastic interpretation of limited data. Parkes (1987) is more circumspect: "The meaning of these changes in the lymphocytes and their connection with resistance to disease is still a matter for conjecture" (p. 56). Irwin et al. (1987) similarly admonished that "it may be too simple to suggest that bereavement-related decreases in one immune parameter may necessarily lead to an increase in disease susceptibility" (p. 103). Spurrell and Creed (1993) are more pessimistic. Noting that the magnitude of the relationship between depression and immune function is "trivial compared with [immune changes] associated with infection," Spurrell and Creed (1993) suggested that depression-related immune downregulation, if it exists at all, probably reflects "the biological changes that occur in depressive illness rather than providing a link between depression and overt physical disease" (p. 63).

The definitive study on immune downregulation following bereavement has yet to be conducted. This conclusion is based both on the methodological weaknesses in this area of research and the skepticism about the clinical meaning and predictive validity of the immune assays used. Even though there are obvious benefits in studying a sample at high risk for bereavement, such as spouses of cancer patients, it cannot be assumed that data collected prebereavement reflect baseline values. Unless data are collected from an unselected cohort (e.g., Lichtenstein et al., 1996), findings at study entry will likely reflect the anxiety, depression, and sleep disturbances frequently observed in spouses of seriously ill people. Prospective studies of unselected cohorts reveal that elevated levels of depressive symptoms prior to a spouse's death are relatively common (Harlow et al., 1991; Lichtenstein et al., 1996; Mendes De Leon et al., 1994). I am aware of no prospective studies on immune function following a stressful life event using data collected on an unselected cohort. Admittedly, the logistical barriers are significant. It took Schleifer et al. (1983) 3 years to obtain prebereavement and postbereavement blood samples on a selected cohort of 15 men.

With the exception of Irwin et al. (1987), it appears that no other research group has attempted to duplicate that feat.

Stress Theory Is Inadequate: The Need for Alternative Explanations

Pioneering epidemiological studies pose a challenge to theories that ascribe excess mortality following bereavement to acute physiological stress. People who "follow their spouses to the grave" have particular vulnerabilities. The highest relative risks are reported for deaths due to violence (Kaprio et al., 1987; Martikainen & Valkonen, 1996a), yet suicide following the death of a spouse is rare in the absence of a prior psychological vulnerability (Duberstein, Conwell, & Cox, 1998). Similarly, many bereaved individuals do not evidence immune suppression, and those who do are probably clinically depressed because of a prior vulnerability. Indeed, alterations in immunity may be most evident in older, clinically depressed people (Herbert & Cohen, 1993; Kiecolt-Glaser & Glaser, 1991). Those who feel helpless and hopeless, absent agitation and activation, may be most prone to immune downregulation. Katz, Beaston-Wimmer, Parmelee, Friedman, and Lawton (1993) believe that such patients are suffering from a form of failure to thrive, which may be mediated in part by an increased production of cytokines. Along similar lines, a meta-analysis shows that depression, but not stressors, leads to reactivation of latent herpes simplex virus (Zorrilla, McKay, Luborsky, & Schmidt, 1996). An analogous conclusion can be drawn from the literature on physical morbidity following bereavement. Whereas early studies seemed to show that bereavement resulted in an increased number of infections (Maddison & Viola, 1968), subsequent research suggests that bereavement itself has little impact on physical morbidity or health care use (Avis, Brambilla, Vass, & McKinlay, 1991; Wolinsky & Johnson, 1992). Instead, traumatic grief and depression appear to increase physical morbidity (Prigerson et al., 1997).

Irwin and Pike (1993) were on the right track when they speculated that depression, not stress or bereavement per se, drives down immune function: "To the degree that one becomes depressed over the loss of a loved one, alterations in various parameters of the immune system are likely to occur" (p. 167). But depression following a loss is not a random event: Vulnerable people become depressed in response to loss. "Every life is punctuated with disappointment; pathology develops in only a few. Hence, it is necessary to go beyond the event and ask about the stable psychological and biological characteristics of the person" (Kagan, 1994, p. 248). Freud (1917/1957) noted that those who become depressed following a loss have a "pathological disposition" (p. 243). He labeled this disposition "ambivalence, which sometimes arises more from real experiences, sometimes more from constitutional factors [but] must not be overlooked among the preconditions of melancholia" (p. 251). By focusing on psychological and physiological stress responses postloss, stable psychological and physiological vulnerabilities have been overlooked; the critical role of depression, in all its complexity, remains uncharted territory. Individuals who experience adverse health consequences following bereavement have prior vulnerabilities, conferred by nature and nurture. Stress theories do not offer a map of this potentially murky terrain, but life-course theories do.

Life-Course Theories

Several converging lines of evidence suggest that the relationship between bereavement and both immunity and mortality is not simply the product of stress but instead reflects specifically the effects of depression. The story could end here. But few clinicians and scientists would be satisfied with such an ending. As reviewed in the previous section, researchers have begun to examine whether the relationship between stress and immune function is mediated by sleep disturbance (Hall et al., 1998; Ironson et al., 1997). However, initial findings have been somewhat inconsistent and discouraging, and similar efforts will likely be disappointing.

Mixed (but interesting) findings are the rule, not the exception, in research using the stress paradigm. Animal research clearly shows that the relationship between stressor and outcome depends on the nature, timing, intensity, and duration of the stressor (Ader & Cohen, 1993). The developmental history of the animal is also important (Ader, 1983), and there is even some evidence that genetically mediated temperament moderates immune response (Pettito, Lysle, Gariepy, & Lewis, 1994). Too often, these and other contextual variables are ignored in research on stress and disease.

A product of interdisciplinary social science, the family of theories labeled "life course" (Caspi & Bem, 1990) ascribes central significance to contextual influences that vary with the level of analysis (Cacioppo & Bernston, 1992; Engel, 1980). There is no consensus on how these levels should be defined or conceptualized, but life-course theorists generally agree that science and practice are best served by attempts to integrate findings across levels (Cacioppo & Bernston, 1992; Engel, 1980). Engel identified 11 levels, ranging from the molecular through to what he termed "community" and "society/nation." From my perspective, important contextual influences at the individual level of analysis include maturation (age), sex, education, ethnicity, personality, early life history, birth order, and chronic patterns of physiological response to stress (e.g., sympathetic tone). Important influences at macro levels include historical era and membership in a particular birth cohort (Caspi & Bem, 1990; Elder, 1974; Kagan, 1998; Parkes, 1987). The level of analysis concept illustrates an important point: Conclusions regarding the relationship between stress and disease are constrained by context, which in turn can be operationally defined at multiple levels.

Two life-course theories, temperament and psychoanalytic, focus primarily, but not exclusively on the individual level of analysis. Unlike stress theories, life-course theories are premised on the assumption that stable patterns of responding to life's disappointments must be considered to understand the nature of the relationship between stress and health. Ignoring these stable patterns of behavior will yield an incorrect understanding of that relationship.

Life-course theories agree on certain basic premises that distinguish them from stress theories. All life-course theories are skeptical of attempts to interpret studies of the relationship between stress and health outcomes (e.g., morbidity, mortality, immune function) without carefully considering the influence of stable psychological features. But there is significant variability between life-course theories. For example, temperament theories of response to spousal loss might emphasize stable, physiologically mediated patterns of behavior (Kagan, 1994), whereas psychoanalysis emphasizes the roles of dependency, early loss, ambivalence, and identification.

Temperament theory and psychoanalytic theory are not mutually exclusive. Indeed, a major task for future research and theorizing is to consider the implications of one for the other. Each poses significant challenges to the now dominant stress paradigm. Whereas temperament theory attacks the stress and coping paradigm for paying insufficient attention to biologically mediated, stable patterns of behavior, psychoanalysis undermines the romanticism of the notion that forlorn people die of broken hearts (W. Stroebe & Stroebe, 1987) by pointing to the potentially pathogenic roles of dependency and ambivalence. In the following sections, I expand on these ideas and begin to outline several directions for research.

Temperament, Personality, and Immune Function

As G. E. Miller, Dopp, Myers, Stevens, and Fahey (1999) observed, "models of stress and immunity . . . have downplayed the contribution of dispositional variables" (p. 269). Nonrandom relations between immune function and temperament obscure efforts to interpret the relations between stress and immune-mediated disease. Some of the most provocative and rigorously controlled studies on temperament and immune function have been conducted on animals. For example, Petitto et al. (1994) compared mice bred to be highly aggressive with those bred to be socially inhibited. The latter had lower levels of mitogen-induced proliferation of T cells, lower NK cell activity, and even increased susceptibility to tumor development. Cohen, Kaplan, Cunnick, Manuck, and Rabin (1992) studied cynomolgus monkeys that had been classified as either socially affiliative or socially isolated, on the basis of 2 years of behavioral observation. Some of the animals were exposed to a social stressor. Only the isolated monkeys that had been exposed to stress showed lower levels of mitogen-stimulated T-cell proliferation. Studies conducted with humans reveal a similar pattern of findings. Manuck, Cohen, Rabin, Muldoon, and Bachen (1991) found that men with high cardiovascular reactivity, believed to be a component of temperament, showed a more compromised immune system following stress than those with low reactivity. Cacioppo (1994) reported that T-cell responses to influenza vaccine diminished in participants with high cardiovascular reactivity, compared with those low in reactivity. G. E. Miller et al. (1999) showed that men who obtained high scores on a measure of cynical hostility tended to have larger increases in NK cell cytotoxicity during a laboratory-based marital stressor. Those who obtained low scores on the hostility scale tended to show little or no change in NK cell cytotoxicity. It is possible that people who are dispositionally prone to anger may be more immunologically reactive to an interpersonal conflict than to an impersonal stressor. In general, it is not known whether people with particular personality traits show immune responses to certain classes of stressors but not to others.

Relations between personality and immune function have been obtained even in studies that are not predicated on the temperament theory assumption that personality is physiologically mediated. McClelland, Alexander, and Marks (1982) administered the Thematic Apperception Test to prison inmates. Men who reported high stress and told stories that betrayed their need for power had lower immune function than did those without this "stressed power motivation."[9] Although the assay used in that study has been criticized on methodological grounds (Stone, Cox, Valdimarsdottir, & Neale, 1987), the overall pattern of findings is consistent with the notion of nonrandom relations between behavior or personality and immune cell counts or function (McKay, 1991; McKay et al., 1997; Shea, Burton, & Girgis, 1993). Such an interpretation becomes more credible when one considers that these nonrandom relations have real world implications. For example, inhibited children and adults report more allergies than their extraverted counterparts (Bell, Jasnoski, Kagan, & King, 1990; Kagan, Snidman, Julia-Sellers, & Johnson, 1991).

Findings of a relationship between a personality trait such as inhibition and immune outcome are typically interpreted as fol-

---

[9]See McClelland (1989) and McClelland et al. (1989) for reviews of similar research on implicit versus self-attributed motives and their implications for health.

lows: The tendency to inhibit one's feelings has an adverse effect on an arm of the nervous or neuroendocrine system, which in turn increases disease risk. Omitted from this formulation is the possibility that both the tendency toward inhibition and the vulnerability to specific diseases or allergies share a common neurophysiological substrate. To some extent, the immune system and nervous system may develop in concert (Geschwind & Galaburda, 1987). Genetic, prenatal, and early postnatal factors that affect the development of the nervous system may also affect the development of the immune system, leading to nonrandom relations between neurophysiologically mediated behaviors (e.g., hand preference, components of temperament) and disease (Geschwind & Galaburda, 1987).[10] Geschwind and Galaburda's ideas remain underdeveloped and underinvestigated, but their implications for psychodynamic health psychology are profound. One's temperament may define (or serve as a marker for) the extent to which one is predisposed to experience a downturn in health as a result of a particular change in life circumstance; it may also define the particular disease to which one is susceptible. The notion of an inextricable relationship between temperament and health is at least 2,000 years old (Siegel, 1968). It attests to a remediable flaw in those investigations of stress and disease that do not consider life-course-defined contextual variables, such as temperament and personality.

Psychodynamic Perspective

Although Freud (1905/1953) speculated about the health consequences of depression and acknowledged that people who minister to dying others can experience physical problems during their period of bereavement (Breuer & Freud, 1893/1955), he did not comment on the possibility that caregiving or bereavement-related depression may place people at risk for physical disease or death. In fact, he appears to have believed precisely the opposite, that is, the stress of bereavement could have positive health effects. A "sudden

---

[10]Also suggestive in this regard are Eysenck's (1990) observations on the relationships between personality and both blood group polymorphism and body type and Kagan's (1994) discussion of the implications of prenatal events for outcomes as seemingly diverse as facial width, eye color, and autonomic tone.

bereavement" could cause "a peculiar alteration in the tone of an organism which may have a favorable influence on some well-established pathological condition or may even bring it to an end" (Freud, 1905/1953, p. 287). Although there may be scattered evidence for this (e.g., Potter & Zautra, 1997), findings of increased mortality following the death of a spouse have been more consistently documented. Neither Freud nor his followers predicted these findings a priori.[11]

Yet psychoanalytic theory goes far beyond stress theory by emphasizing that depression develops in the context of premorbid personality traits, early life experiences, and emotional ambivalence. However, as illustrated by Mr. A., whose suicide was briefly noted at the beginning of this chapter, the loss–mortality relationship need not be mediated by depression. This point is roughly consistent with the notion that an absence of sadness following a loss may signal risk (Bowlby, 1980; Deutsch, 1937; Lindemann, 1944). A pathogenic dependency and help-seeking dynamic, early loss, and ambivalence may each increase mortality risk, even in the absence of obvious depressive symptoms. It is unlikely that any of these psychological constructs directly increases mortality risk. More likely, the relationships are indirect. For example, dependent individuals may alienate their social support network, which in turn leads them to feel angry and to secrete pathogenic levels of stress hormones.

Dependency, helplessness, and help seeking. People who are interpersonally oriented may be more distressed by a loss than those who are oriented primarily toward personal achievement.

---

[11]Scholars have speculated about how Freud's own wishes, fears, and personal experiences may have colored his writings (e.g., Becker, 1973; Gay, 1988). Freud invited this scrutiny. In the preface to the second edition of *The Interpretation of Dreams,* Freud (1900/1965) wrote that the book represents "a portion of my own self-analysis, my reaction to my father's death—that is to say, to the most important event, the most poignant loss of a man's life" (p. xxvi). Following the death of his pregnant daughter, Freud wrote "I work as much as I can, and am grateful for the diversion" (cited in Gay, 1988, p. 393). Apparently, Freud believed that loss begets intellectual development. Acknowledging that "the entanglement of autobiography with science has bedevilled psychoanalysis from its beginnings" (Gay, 1988, p. 89), is it really surprising that Freud believed that loss could benefit physical health?

Those who have the Type A behavior pattern (see O'Neill, chap. 2, this volume) may be more distressed by an illness requiring sustained periods of immobilization or bedrest than those who do not have this behavior pattern. In the parlance of modern personality research, the vulnerability conferred by personality traits to specific classes of life events is termed "reactive interaction" (Caspi & Bem, 1990).

This general principle can be traced to psychoanalytic theorizing about bereavement. Fenichel (1945) noted that the person who "has been orally fixated and has had unconscious longings for sexualized 'eating' " (p. 396) would be especially vulnerable to depression following a loss. Those who viewed the deceased primarily as a "provider of narcissistic supplies" (p. 396) would also be at risk. Without invoking the concept of psychosexual stages, Bowlby (1980) made a similar point when he asserted that people exposed to disrupted interpersonal relations were more vulnerable to complicated grief. Bowlby (1980) identified three groups at risk: One is prone to "anxious attachments, suffused with overt or covert ambivalence" (p. 202); a second is "nervous, overdependent, clinging, or temperamental" (p. 202); and a third, counterdependent group makes "strenuous attempts to claim emotional self-sufficiency and independence of all affectional ties" (p. 202).

Reactive interaction is a valid and heuristic principle in the context of bereavement research. Although there have been negative findings, numerous empirical studies demonstrate that dependent people are more likely to become depressed following loss, interpersonal rejection, conflict, and disapproval; those less prone to dependency are more likely to become depressed following events that threaten their need for independence, achievement, mastery, and power (Blatt & Zuroff, 1992; Bornstein, 1993; Mazure, 1998; but also see Coyne & Whiffen, 1995).

Given that dependency increases one's risk for depression, it is reasonable to hypothesize that it also increases one's risk for BRM. Even in the absence of a life event, dependency increases risk for physical disease, perhaps more so than any other personality trait (Bornstein, chap. 1, this volume). A deeper understanding of the relationship between dependency and health should be pursued. Special emphasis ought to be placed on the interpersonal dynamics of help seeking (Bornstein, 1993; Masling, 1986; Nadler, 1997), especially as they pertain to bereavement.

Bornstein's (chap. 1, this volume) object relations/interactionist model of interpersonal dependency and his four-category model (Bornstein, 1998) may help frame such an endeavor. Drawing on McClelland's (McClelland, Koestner, & Weinberger, 1989) concept of self-attributed versus implicit motives, Bornstein (1998) described a four-category model of dependency. People in Category 1 are genuinely low in dependency; those in Category 2 have a dependent self-presentation; Category 3 includes those who are genuinely high in dependency; and people in Category 4 do not acknowledge their dependency needs. Counterdependent people (Category 4) may be at greatest risk following a loss in part because they are unwilling or unable to acknowledge their helplessness, possibly a key factor in the recovery from bereavement. After the death of his daughter, Freud wrote to his son-in-law indicating that "one must bow one's head under the blow, as a helpless, poor human being with whom higher powers are playing" (cited in Gay, 1988, p. 392).

A consideration of mode of death makes this story even more complex. There is probably greater social constraint (Lepore, Silver, Wortman, & Wayment, 1996) and stigma following an unexpected versus expected loss. In this case, those in Category 3 may be more adversely affected than those in 4. A woman whose husband died of prostate cancer may find it easier to talk to others and seek help than a woman whose husband hung himself in the garage. Stigma and social constraint impede help seeking and lead to worse outcomes, especially among those in Group 3 who are accustomed to recruiting social support. The person's style of emotional expression must also be considered. Bonanno and Keltner (1997) noted that minimizing the expression of negative affect may lead to enhanced social support. In an application of this reasoning to Bornstein's typology, those in Category 2 or 3 may undermine the recruitment of social support by alienating members of their social network.

The relationship between dependency and bereavement outcome also depends on the mode of data collection. People in Category 3 who alienate their social networks or do not seek help in the first place are likely to be at greatest risk in terms of *self-reported* physical and psychological symptoms. Morbidity among those in Category 4 is more evident on *objective or physiological* measures of health and behavior than on self-report measures. If Category 4 people are experiencing symptoms, they are as unlikely to mention them to their neighbors as they are to a bereavement researcher who asks them to complete a questionnaire. Bowlby (1980) commented that they "are least likely to volunteer to participate" (p. 211) in bereavement research and "it is easy to overlook such people" (p. 211) because they do not express their negative feelings. Similarly, Parkes (1987) noted that many people who need counseling will not seek such help on their own accord. Another potential wrinkle concerns the conceptualization of dependency. It is assumed that it is a trans-situational construct, but it is possible that dependency on one's spouse is not synonymous with dependency in other contexts. Parkes and Weiss (1983) argued that post-bereavement adjustment is a function, in part, of the degree of dependency in the marital relationship. In all likelihood, the correlation between widely used self-report measures of dependency and self-reported dependency in marriage is not impressive, even if it should prove to be statistically significant. It would be desirable to assess both constructs in research on spousal bereavement.[12]

Although it is not my intent to articulate the mechanisms whereby dependency confers risk for specific physical diseases, I briefly broach this topic. In all probability, there are several pathophysiological mechanisms. For example, people who are excessively dependent (Bornstein's, 1998, Category 3) or conflicted about their dependency (Category 4) may alienate their social networks. This may elicit strong emotions, especially anger, which in turn may lead to oversecretion of catecholamines. Emotional inhibition, which probably characterizes individuals in Bornstein's Category 4, has been associated with overactivation of the HPA axis (cf. Ka-

[12]Parkes (1987) wrote that "the situation is further confused by the ambiguity of the term 'dependent,' which is used sometimes to mean 'intolerance of separation' and sometimes to indicate 'reliance on someone for the performance of particular roles or function.' Thus, I may be dependent on my wife because I cannot bear to be parted from her or because I need her to get me up in the morning" (p. 138). Bowlby (1980) was more verbose, but the essence of his argument is the same: "Much confusion is caused by the ambiguity of the term 'dependent.' Often it is used to refer to the emotional quality of an attachment in which anxiety over the possibility of separation or loss, or of being held responsible for a separation or loss, are commonly dominant if covert features. Sometimes, it refers merely to reliance on someone else to provide certain goods and services, to fill certain social roles, perhaps without there being an attachment of any kind to the person in question" (p. 176).

gan, 1994). Chronic, dysregulated secretion of hormones and cytokines could lead to long-term health consequences (McEwen & Stellar, 1993).

It is remarkable that so little is known about the relationship between dependency and bereavement outcome. Although personality is among the most consistently discussed determinants of bereavement outcome (Horowitz, Bonanno, & Holen, 1993), its role, according to Raphael was "unclear" (p. 63) in 1983. W. Stroebe and Stroebe (1987) concluded that the data on personality and bereavement outcome are inconclusive, not because there have been negative findings but because "very few personality traits have as yet been examined in the context of bereavement" (p. 198). Now, more than 1 decade after the Stroebes and Parkes published their landmark texts, the paucity of data on dependency and bereavement-related morbidity is both unfortunate and truly puzzling, especially given the research that links dependent personality processes to psychophysiological disorders and impaired physical well-being (Bornstein, chap. 1, this volume; Greenberg & Bornstein, 1988). Research on personality and bereavement may lead to a greater understanding of the etiology of psychologically mediated physical disorders and symptoms. It also has practical import because it would aid in the identification of people who may be at high risk for morbidity or even mortality following the death of a spouse.

Early loss and separation. Spitz's (1946) observations about the health effects of separation and institutionalization on children helped convince generations of clinicians (and parents) of the potentially powerful role of early loss and events.[13] Fenichel (1945) believed that "many persons who have lost one of their parents

---

[13]Before they fade from memory, reports by psychoanalytically trained clinicians deserve to be credited for helping to launch scientific disciplines that have become important areas of basic research, including developmental neurobiology and developmental psychoneuroimmunology (see Kandel, 1999). In the early animal studies, "handling" was termed "gentling," reflecting the prevailing view (or bias) that handling conferred health benefits (Robert Ader, personal communication, October 1998). Also omitted from most textbook accounts of the literature on hospitalism is the fact that Ferenczi (1929) speculated about the physical health consequences of the early caregiver relationship before Spitz's (1946) "observations." Another detail that seems to fade with time is the controversy over how Spitz reported his data (Pinneau, 1955a, 1955b; Spitz, 1955).

early in childhood show signs of oral fixation" (p. 394). Oral fixation or excessive dependency may confer an increased vulnerability to depression, which in turn may lead to enhanced risk for physical morbidity and mortality.

There is probably no "statute of limitations" on risk associated with early loss. The effects of early events continue to be felt in older adulthood (Andersson & Stevens, 1993; Krause, 1993; Murphy, 1982), when spousal bereavement is more common. For example, Krause found that parental loss prior to age 16 decreases feelings of personal control in older adulthood primarily by affecting educational attainment and increasing financial strain. A decreased sense of personal control may increase risk for disease, perhaps especially in older adults (Rodin, 1986).

Klein (1940/1948) argued that "the child goes through states of mind comparable to the mourning of the adult[;] . . . this early mourning is revived whenever grief is experienced in later life" (p. 311). Findings from one study are consistent with this notion. In a comparison of 21 people who had been widowed by suicide for more than 4 years prior to death and 14 who had been widowed for less than 4 years, the latter were more likely to have a history of early loss or separation from a parent. They were also more likely to have histories of psychiatric treatment and substance abuse (Duberstein et al., 1998). Because of their histories or propensities, some people are more affected by specific life events than are others. Those who take their lives within 4 years of such an event are probably acting in the midst of complicated grief, which may be tied to their childhood. With rare exceptions, most suicides among those who had been widowed for more than 4 years are unrelated to complicated grief.

In emphasizing early objective events such as a loss or separation, I do not mean to dismiss the significance of early subjective experiences. From an empirical perspective, however, early subjective experiences can be operationalized only in prospective studies beginning in childhood. Because of logistical constraints, prospective studies of the relationship between early subjective experiences and morbidity following spousal bereavement are unlikely to be published in the near future. Even if the logistical barriers were removed, the interpretation of the findings would be suspect, given the likelihood of sample bias.

Kagan (1994, 1998) warned against overinterpreting the significance of early life events; traumatic events in childhood do not inevitably lead to pathology in adulthood. These arguments, grounded in science and offered with moral authority, are convincing. However, animal research shows that brief and prolonged early separations from one's mother have immunological (Coe, Rosenberg, Fischer, & Levine, 1987; Lubach, Coe & Ershler, 1995) and neuroendocrine consequences (Ladd, Owens, & Nemeroff, 1996) that could result in long-term health implications (see Ader, 1983; Hofer, 1984, 1996; and Kandel, 1999). In comparison with control rats, maternally deprived rats appeared to oversecrete certain chemicals in response to electrical shock, suggesting that they were more sensitive or reactive to stress (Ladd et al., 1996). This finding, among others in the developmental psychobiology literature, may help explain why there are elevated rates of early loss in psychiatric patients (Agid et al., 1999). Obviously, Kagan and others are correct when they argue that early loss does not inexorably increase risk for psychopathology. It is possible that loss confers direct effects on health outcomes, but in the majority of cases, the effect is likely indirect, mediated by economic hardship and decreased educational attainment. It is unwise for clinicians to ignore their patients' early life histories. There is simply too much evidence suggesting that even in older adults, past is frequently prologue.

Ambivalence and unconscious affect. In the psychoanalytic literature on bereavement, the term *ambivalence* and its cognates have been used to refer to (a) the nature of the relationship between the deceased person and bereaved person, (b) a personality trait arising from "real experiences" or "constitutional factors" (Freud, 1917/1957, p. 251), and (c) a complex blend of emotions. No matter how the term is used, ambivalence is invariably formulated as contributing to a bad outcome.[14] For brevity's sake, most of my comments in this section refer to ambivalent emotions because that domain may be most amenable to empirical investigation.

---

[14]Although it is generally believed that ambivalence forebodes a worse bereavement response in the long term, research suggests that in some contexts, the opposite pattern may hold true: Grief may precede a worsening of ambivalence (Bonanno et al., 1998).

When seemingly incompatible emotions are juxtaposed, such as sadness and joy, one is said to feel ambivalent. After a loss, this mixed state may be more frequently observed among people who tolerated an ambivalent relationship with the deceased person. Bonanno, Notarius, Gunzerath, Keltner, and Horowitz (1998) coded facial expressions in the context of a narrative interview designed to elicit comments about participants' experiences of bereavement. Participants whose facial expressions shifted from sadness to anger across a narrative unit were more ambivalent about the deceased person than were those who did not show this sequence of facial expression. These researchers also found that participants who felt more ambivalent about their partner also reported worse physical health (Bonanno et al., 1998).

Emotional ambivalence may also be part of a more universal and primeval pattern. Freud (1915/1957) noted that primeval man experienced a degree of satisfaction in the death of his or her kin, "since in each of the loved persons there was also something of the stranger [who had] aroused in him hostile feelings" (p. 293).[15] In certain contexts, one may feel genuinely saddened but also somewhat relieved that "death came to somebody else, not oneself" (Fenichel, 1945, p. 395). This may be especially true of deaths in the military, concentration camps, and prisons. Writing about his experience following his release from the concentration camp at Auschwitz, Levi (1988) observed that "leaving pain behind was a delight for only a few fortunate beings, or only a few instants, or for very simple souls; almost always it coincides with a phase of anguish" (p. 71). Bowlby (1980) discussed a different type of emotional ambivalence: Citing cases of fighter pilots who recklessly courted death after becoming convinced that they would die in action just as their friends did, he noted that "in each one of these boys, it was not hard to find the angry thought or the selfish thought that gave them satisfaction in their friend's death" (p. 167). Similarly, perhaps people who felt imprisoned in their marriages and those whose battles with a spouse verged on nuclear family

---

[15]Freud (1915/1957) went so far as to say that this "conflict of feeling at the death of loved yet alien and hated persons" (p. 293) formed the basis for the evolution of intellectual culture: "Of this conflict of feeling psychology was the first offspring" (pp. 293–294).

warfare are most vulnerable to ambivalence and its adverse health consequences.[16]

Speaking the unspeakable; articulating the anger, relief, or self-satisfaction that follows the death of another; or experiencing the amalgam of joy and guilt on realizing that one is alive at another's expense or simply because one is lucky may be therapeutic. This is difficult to accomplish. Lindemann (1944) noted that many bereaved individuals feel angry and hostile, "which to them seems absurd, representing a vicious change in their characters and to be hidden as much as possible" (p. 145). Moreover, some individuals are not very adept at labeling their emotions, some emotions do not have corresponding labels in natural language, and there are social constraints placed on emotional ventilation.

Social contexts can permit or constrain the expression of ambivalence (Lepore et al., 1996; Raphael, 1983). People whose social networks encourage an expression of the ambivalence avoid depression (Raphael, 1983). Those who do not permit themselves to express the ambivalence or whose social network stifles such expression may suffer the consequences. Physical symptoms are greater among widows who felt that they had not been permitted to express their feelings following their husband's death (Maddison, 1968). There may be a broader principle at work here, one that posits a link between physical symptoms and the free expression of personal concerns (see Smyth & Greenberg, chap. 4, this volume). HIV may progress more rapidly in gay men who remain "in the closet" or who are "half in and half out" than in those who are "out" (Cole, Kemeny, Taylor, Visscher, & Fahey, 1996).

Emotional ambivalence may have direct physiological concomitants. Darwin (1872/1998) noted that the facial expressions typical of adult grief reflect a tendency to scream like an infant and an inhibition of the same. The simultaneous expression of an "in-

[16]Sadly, the term *survivor guilt* has become all too familiar in the decades following World War II. The English language does not have a word to describe the experience that Levi (1988) had following the war that he "might be alive in the place of another, at the expense of another; I might have usurped, that is, in fact, killed" (p. 82). The term *guilt* does not do justice to Levi's internal experience. Ambivalence is preferable, but it is still too imprecise and unsatisfactory.

stinct" and its inhibition are reflected in the contorted facial expressions of grief that result from the simultaneous contraction of antagonistic muscles. Parkes (1987) described this expression as similar to "that of a person looking upwards toward a bright light —someone attempting to shield their eyes from the light by lowering the eyelashes but, at the same time, to look at the light by raising the brows" (p. 62; also see Darwin, 1872/1998, p. 187).

Darwin (1872/1998) noted that people tend to wring their hands when they are in the throes of acute grief. He thought this was odd. Violent shaking of the hands connotes a desire to act, when in fact nothing can be done to recover the lost one. Darwin ascribed this behavior to the principle of unconscious antithesis: Some gestures or expressions betray an opposite emotion. (Has Darwin's influence on Freud been underestimated?) Hand wringing, a call to action, actually betrays an inner sense of helplessness. The individual simultaneously experiences two incompatible emotions. Should this persist beyond some timepoint, it may have psychophysiological effects. Some bereavement symptoms may reflect neuroendocrine and sympathetic nervous system contortions or seizures, analogous to driving a car when the parking brake is engaged. One part of the nervous system behaves in one manner, while another part behaves differently. Internal desynchronization of biocircadian rhythms may exacerbate the mortality risk in widows with pre-existing conditions such as ischemic heart disease (cf. Osterweis et al., 1984); this desynchronization may be mediated by the unusual blends of emotions that characterize affective ambivalence.[17]

Conscious ambivalence may be avoided by conscious idealization of the deceased person (Raphael, 1983). The dissociation between conscious expressions of idealization and unconscious ambivalence may represent repression. Research that relies exclusively on self-report measures does not capture this phenomenon. Overcoming this methodological problem is difficult, as is redressing the overreliance on assessments of discrete emotions rather than

[17]Similarly, mixed affective states (Jamison, 1993) or unusual combinations of emotions (Duberstein et al., 1996) may be especially common in the suicides of younger people.

the complex and unusual blends that define ambivalence. Parkes (1987) observed that the "pain of pining and the pleasure of recollection are experienced as a bitter sweet mixture of emotions, 'nostalgia' . . . the two components seem to be experienced simultaneously" (pp. 79–80). Scientific research on emotion has blossomed over the past 2 decades, much of it premised on the assumption that a limited number of discrete emotions are defined in terms of facial expression and perhaps autonomic psychophysiology. Nostalgia and other complex loss-related emotions are not on that list. Freud (1930/1961) acknowledged that some emotions may not lend themselves to physiological examination: "It is not easy to deal scientifically with feelings. One can attempt to describe their physiological signs," but because this may not always be possible, "nothing remains but to fall back on the ideational content which is most readily associated with the feeling" (p. 12). Darwin (1872/1998) himself believed that some emotions, such as jealousy, do not bear "any outward sign" (p. 82). As long as they equate emotion with facial expression and autonomic psychophysiology, emotion researchers will not be able to do justice to the complexity of emotional experience in everyday life (Efron, 1985; Kagan, 1994), let alone during bereavement.

Identification and identification symptoms. Although identification symptoms may not be directly relevant to BRM, they are occasionally seen in clinical practice and ought to be considered in future research on the health consequences of bereavement. Psychoanalytic theorizing on how and why identification symptoms develop has been strained and tortuous.[18] At the core of this the-

---

[18]Abraham (1924/1948) claimed that the mourner identifies with the lost object to preserve the relationship with the deceased person. "The process of mourning thus brings with it the consolation: 'My loved object is not gone, for now I carry it within myself and can never lose it' " (p. 437). Freud (1917/1957) argued that grief work requires that libido be withdrawn from the object. Lindemann (1944) used a different metaphor but abided by the same principle when he remarked that grief work would lead to an "emancipation from the bondage to the deceased" (p. 143). How can one emancipate oneself from an introject? Fenichel (1945) cleverly (but perhaps incorrectly) solved this puzzle by arguing that "for a normal person it is easier to loosen the ties with an introject than with an external object" (p. 394). Identification symptoms result when this otherwise normal and adaptive process is undermined.

orizing lies the assumption that identification is a normative and adaptive process. For example, Fenichel asserted that "a hysterical woman (who) takes over her father's illness . . . is vainly attempting to free herself of him" (p. 221). He may have been making a veiled reference to Anna O. (Breuer & Freud, 1893/1955) but was clearly basing his argument on the assumption that identification was a normative and adaptive process that could become pathological under some circumstances.

Bowlby (1980) attacked this premise; he argued that "identification is neither the only, nor even the main, process involved in mourning[;] . . . no systematic data have ever been offered to support the idea that identification with the person lost is central to the mourning process" (p. 30). Parkes (1987), a colleague of Bowlby's, stated that "there was nothing to suggest that identification is a necessary part of the process of recovery" (p. 122). However, both Bowlby and Parkes conceded that identification symptoms do, in fact, exist. "Many symptoms of disordered mourning, can, however, be understood as due to some unfavorable development of [identification] processes. One form of maladjustment . . . leads the bereaved to develop symptoms of the deceased's last illness" (Bowlby, 1980, p. 99). Elsewhere, Bowlby wrote that these symptoms are "often but not always . . . similar to the bereaved's last illness" (p. 167). This "mislocation" of the lost person is "completely unconscious" (p. 167). Parkes (1987) pointed to "a peculiar kind of hypochondriacal condition in which the patient develops symptoms" (p. 128) and "aches and pains in the site of a pain that had been prominent during the illness of the relative whose death preceded their onset" (p. 132).

Parkes (1987) carefully acknowledged that many physical problems presumed to be identification phenomena may be manifestations of grief. Heart palpitations commonly accompany anxiety. They ought not to be interpreted as identification symptoms simply because the deceased person had a heart condition. Actual physical difficulties could be misinterpreted as psychopathology. Parkes's sober approach lends greater credibility to the cases of identification symptoms he believes to be genuine. A woman lost her voice for 10 days after hearing the news of her husband's death. He had suffered two strokes, one of which left him mute. Another woman's father died following a stroke that left him paralyzed on the left side of his body. She had a dream in which she saw her father lying in his coffin. He reached up at her and 'stroked' (Parkes, 1987, p. 132) her left side. When she awoke, her left side was paralyzed. An hour later, the paralysis disappeared. Another woman claimed she began vomiting every morning. She reported that her father had that very habit, and said, "I do exactly the same things as my father" (p. 133). These identification symptoms need not appear during the bereavement period. Roy (1982) reported a case of a middle-aged man who developed neurological symptoms at the age that his father died of a stroke.

The existence of such pathological identification phenomena are incontrovertible. Recent research suggests that they reflect complicated grief (Prigerson et al., 1996), but their psychoanalytic interpretation remains open to debate. Lindemann (1944) also called attention to the "appearance of traits of the deceased in the behavior of the bereaved, especially symptoms shown during the last illness" (p. 142), but he did not believe they represented a pathology of identification. In a letter to Fliess, Freud (1950/1966) wrote of a tendency for people to punish themselves "in a hysterical fashion through the medium of the idea of retribution with the same states [of illness]" (p. 255) that had afflicted the deceased person.

Two decades before publishing "Mourning and Melancholia," Freud apparently viewed identification as a manifestation of self-reproach, the cardinal symptom of melancholia. He did not view hysterical identification as a product of normative mourning gone awry. Indeed, he minimized this interpretation as a "fragment cast up on the beach at last tide" (Freud, 1950/1966, p. 253). But perhaps he was correct; identification phenomena may most parsimoniously be ascribed to depression. They may, in addition, represent unconscious attempts to contain, hold, or incorporate the deceased person. They may even represent bizarre attempts to recover the lost person. Or they might simply betray a tendency to amplify or misinterpret otherwise normal visceral or peripheral sensations. Given that bereavement is likely to induce a fear of one's own death in those left behind, these symptoms may also represent somatic hypervigilance. The present data allow for no firm conclusions.

Parkes (1987) commented that "it is more than coincidence that the breakthrough to which Breuer's talking cure gave rise resulted from the investigation of a case of mental illness arising at the time of the loss of a father" (p. 23). More than 100 years after Anna O. sought treatment for symptoms she developed while caring for her dying father, it is a pity so little is known about identification symptoms in bereaved people.

Conclusion

Freud was a brilliant clinical observer. Long before the health and mortality effects of caregiving were empirically documented (e.g., Kiecolt-Glaser et al., 1991; Schulz & Beach, 1999; Vitaliano et al., 1996), he noted that sick nursing could lead to sleep deprivation, worry, self-neglect, and emotional suppression, which in turn could cause a decline in physical health (Breuer & Freud, 1893/1955). He could easily have taken this scenario one logical step further and argued that the decline in physical health portended a premature death. Documentation of increased mortality rates in widowed people had been available at least since the middle of the 19th century (Durkheim, 1897/1951), but Freud did not show much interest in this phenomenon. Freud (1905/1953) once acknowledged that "persistent affective states of a distressing or 'depressive' nature [as they are called], such as sorrow, worry, or grief [can cause] the walls of the blood vessels to undergo morbid changes" (p. 287), and he noted that "the major affects evidently have a large bearing on the capacity to resist infectious illness" (p. 287). Despite his medical training and early research in biology (Gay, 1988), Freud was more interested in psychogenic symptoms than in those with a more physical basis. Although Freud touched on an enormous array of topics, ranging from the arcane to the everyday, he showed surprisingly little interest in psychological aspects of physical health.

Freud crafted a cognitive psychology, not a health psychology. As a result, psychoanalysis has played no more than a bit role in the scientific story of bereavement and mortality. Still, with its emphasis on developmental history, the interpersonal dynamics of help seeking, and the complexity of emotional experiences, psychoanalysis can and ought to inform future research on these topics.

Perhaps the biggest contribution that psychoanalysis can make is to bring the individual to the forefront and let the situational determinants of bereavement course recede into the background. A psychoanalytic approach to bereavement, and BRM in particular, encourages research on personality and all it encompasses, including temperament traits, motives, fears, beliefs, and fantasies. Situational variables are important, but they should not drive the research agenda. Bereavement course among young women whose husbands committed suicide may differ substantially from those whose husbands died 2 years after a cancer diagnosis. Perhaps these differences can be ascribed to the extent to which the deaths were anticipated. But in all probability, the two groups differed substantially prior to the loss.

The tendency to ascribe a person's behavior to stable traits rather than situational vagaries is known as the "fundamental attribution error" (Heider, 1958). Its discovery remains one of the major accomplishments of social psychology. Bereavement researchers may be guilty of the reverse of this error, creatively striving to identify any number of situational characteristics associated with bereavement course and outcome and expending little effort at understanding the contribution of personality. It is sensible to look for situational determinants of outcome following a rare event, like the death of a spouse, but that does not mean that person variables are unimportant.

Aside from the fact that psychoanalytic thinkers have not systematically addressed the topics of BRM and morbidity, there are two major reasons why situational variables are emphasized. First, it is difficult to study the relationship between personality and bereavement outcome. Ideally, prospective (prebereavement) data collection is required, but this is a complex and expensive task requiring the use of either a community or a high-risk sample, such as spouses of seriously ill people. Each has obvious drawbacks. Emphasis on situational variables may thus be ascribed in part to frustration with the logistical and methodological obstacles to personality research. Parkes (1987) asserted that "personality factors deriving from genetic givens" (p. 159) contribute to the magnitude of grief, and, by extension, to bereavement outcome. But he also acknowledged that more research is needed before "we can do more than speculate" (p. 59) about that. Second, the ascension of the stress paradigm in the 1960s and 1970s served to minimize the apparent significance of personality variables. Attention was instead fixed on defining stress: Researchers made distinctions among major events, minor events, and hassles, and they made efforts to understand how people coped. Gradually, a story about the relationship between stress and health evolved, one that was coherent, persuasive, and could be adapted to fit the data on bereavement.

It is commonly assumed that the stress of bereavement leads to psychological disequilibrium or destabilization, which could lead to immune downregulation and neuroendocrine dysfunction, thereby increasing one's risk for disease and all-cause mortality. This hypothesis, or more precisely set of hypotheses that constitute a story, has intuitive appeal. It fulfills the desire for abstract ideas in scientific hypothesizing (Berlin, 1969; Kagan, 1998). But abstractions such as stress, disease, disequilibrium, and immune downregulation are not truths.

The assumption that a vague, colloquial construct like stress can be imported into the scientific lexicon without exacting a cost is problematic. Plaut and Friedman (1982) argued that the concept of stress-related disease has "severely inhibited the development of the field of study" (p. 275). The constructs stress and disease are both so abstract that juxtaposing them may compound the number of incorrect conclusions and speculations appearing in scientific journals. Parkes's (1987) frustration with stress research resonates:

> Human beings and animals of all shapes and sizes have been tricked, confined, terrified, mutilated, shocked, puzzled, embarrassed, challenged, stumped, overwhelmed, confused, or poisoned in the widest variety of experimental conditions in attempts to track down the consequences [of stress]. The outcome of all this work has not been negligible, but it has been disappointing. (p. 50)

In a word, the reason for the disappointment is context. Contextual influences make it impossible to answer the following question: "Does stress affect health?" Indeed, the premise of the question must be challenged. Animal research allows a degree of experimental control simply not possible in studies with humans. Moreover, the range of stressors used in animal studies might make those who conduct research with humans envious: restraint, surgery, loud noises, handling, shipping, exposure to noxious odors, and administration of electric shock. Still, even in rats, animals with a relatively simple nervous system, the relationship between stress and disease depends on the nature, timing, intensity, and duration of the stressor, and these relationships are further moderated by housing conditions (individual vs. group) and the species, strain, and sex of the animal (for a review, see Ader & Cohen, 1993).

To complicate matters even further, the nature of the disease must also be considered (Ader & Cohen, 1993). Justice (1985) argued that ongoing stress accelerates the growth of viral tumors but may inhibit nonviral tumors. The termination of stress may cause nonviral tumors to grow but may also inhibit viral tumors through immune enhancement. Stress increases one's susceptibility to the onset of some diseases, decreases vulnerability to others, and has no effect on the remainder (Ader & Cohen, 1993). For some diseases, stress may affect onset but not course or functional impairment. For others, stress may affect course or functional impairment but not onset. Distinctions among onset, course, relapse, remission, and functional impairment illustrate the manifold nature of the construct disease. Bereavement may increase all-cause mortality, but the evidence suggests that the effect is more specific than that. Bereavement increases cause-specific mortality, particularly deaths due to violence, ischemic heart disease, and some cancers, especially lung cancer (Martikainen & Valkonen, 1996a). These findings sound an important warning against the perfunctory use of vague, underspecified constructs, such as all-cause mortality.

Now it is time for psychodynamics and other life-course theories to move beyond the stress paradigm and define and identify more precisely who will succumb to particular diseases under certain circumstances. It might be useful to develop psychodynamic formulations and hypotheses of mortality following bereavement. Consider the following self-neglect formulation of BRM due to heart disease. People with pre-existing heart disease and a lifelong tendency toward depression because of genetically mediated physiology and early life events start to neglect their health. Perhaps they smoke more or begin to smoke again. They get inadequate sleep and may self-medicate with alcohol. They experience complex emotions, many of which cannot be put into words. Biocircadian rhythms are disturbed. A dependent yet irritable help-seeking style helps to alienate people in their social network. Now the aggrieved individual is no longer irritable; he or she is angry and begins oversecreting catecholamines. The person fleetingly experiences a wish to die, and the wish is realized. Similar formulations can and ought to be developed for deaths by suicide and lung cancer. Ideally, these formulations will lead to specific hypotheses and rigorous research.

Having begun this chapter with a brief case vignette, I conclude on a clinical note. Left unsaid amidst all the speculation about natural deaths precipitated by stress in the aggrieved person is the possibility that these deaths represent the product of deliberate, malignant self-neglect in a person with a vulnerability to depression. Widowed people who die of heart disease or lung cancer following their spouses' deaths may have identifiable, potentially lifelong, psychological vulnerabilities, as do those who die a violent death or an alcohol-related death. Noting that excess mortality in widowed people can be ascribed largely to suicide, cirrhosis, and cardiac arrest, Osterweis et al. (1984) observed that "all three conditions have clinical antecedents [depression, alcoholism, and cardiovascular disease] that could be detected before or very shortly after bereavement, thus identifying three high-risk groups for whom early intervention might be useful" (p. 33). Psychologists and other health care providers who see dying patients and their families in chronic and acute settings are confronted with anticipatory bereavement and therefore have the opportunity to intervene in a manner that may decrease BRM and morbidity. Many patients enter psychotherapy in the context of bereavement. Perhaps this chapter will help therapists be more vigilant about exploring and discussing the health-damaging effects of loss with their patients.

References

Abraham, K. (1948). A short study of the development of the libido, viewed in the light of mental disorders. In D. Bryan & A. Strachey

(Eds. & Trans.), *Selected papers of Karl Abraham M. D.* (pp. 418–501). London: Hogarth Press. (Original work published 1924)

Abraham, K. (1955). Psycho-analysis and gynaecology (H. Abraham & D. R. Ellison, Trans.). In H. Abraham (Ed.), *Clinical papers and essays on psychoanalysis* (pp. 91–97). New York: Basic Books. (Original work published 1925)

Ader, R. (1983). Developmental psychoneuroimmunology. *Developmental Psychobiology, 15,* 251–267.

Ader, R., & Cohen, N. (1993). Psychoneuroimmunology: Conditioning and stress. *Annual Review of Psychology, 44,* 53–85.

Agid, O., Shapira, B., Zislin, J., Ritzner, M., Hanin, B., Murad, H., Trudart, T., Bloch, M., Heresco-Levy, U., & Lerer, B. (1999). Environment and vulnerability to major psychiatric illness: A case control study of early parental loss in major depression, bipolar disorder and schizophrenia. *Molecular Psychiatry, 4,* 163–172.

Andersson, L., & Stevens, N. (1993). Associations between early experiences with parents and well-being in old age. *Journal of Gerontology: Psychological Sciences, 48,* P109–P116.

Assortative mating in man: A cooperative study. (1903). *Biometrika, 2,* 481–498.

Averill, J. R. (1968). Grief: Its nature and significance. *Psychological Bulletin, 70,* 721–748.

Avis, N. E., Brambilla, D. J., Vass, K., & McKinlay, J. B. (1991). The effect of widowhood on health: A prospective analysis from the Massachusetts Women's Health Study. *Social Science and Medicine, 33,* 1063–1070.

Bakan, D. (1968). *Disease, pain and sacrifice: Toward a psychology of suffering.* Boston: Beacon Press.

Barrett, A. E. (1998, November). *Marital trajectories and mental health.* Poster session presented at the annual meeting of the Gerontological Society of America, Philadelphia, PA.

Bartrop, R. W., Luckhust, E., Lazarus, L., Kiloh, L. G., & Penny, R. (1977, April 16). Depressed lymphocyte function after bereavement. *The Lancet,* pp. 834–836.

Bass, D. M., & Bowman, K. (1990). The transition from caregiving to bereavement: The relationship of care-related strain and adjustment to death. *The Gerontologist, 30,* 35–42.

Becker, E. (1973). *The denial of death.* New York: Free Press.

Bell, I. R., Jasnoski, M. L., Kagan, J., & King, D. S. (1990). Is allergic rhinitis more frequent in young adults with extreme shyness? A preliminary survey. *Psychosomatic Medicine, 52,* 517–525.

Berkman, L. F. (1995). The role of social relations in health promotion. *Psychosomatic Medicine, 57,* 245–254.

Berlin, I. (1969). *Four essays on liberty.* New York: Oxford University Press.

Bibring, E. (1953). The mechanism of depression. In P. Greenacre (Ed.), *Affective disorders: Psychoanalytic contributions to their study* (pp. 13–48). New York: International Universities Press.

Blatt, S. J., & Zuroff, D. (1992). Interpersonal relatedness and self-definition: Two prototypes for depression. *Clinical Psychology Review, 12,* 527–562.

Bock, E. W., & Webber, I. L. (1972). Suicide among the elderly: Isolating widowhood and mitigating alternatives. *Journal of Marriage and the Family, 34,* 24–31.

Bonanno, G. A., & Keltner, D. (1997). Facial expressions of emotion and the course of conjugal bereavement. *Journal of Abnormal Psychology, 106,* 126–137.

Bonanno, G. A., Notarius, C. I., Gunzerath, L., Keltner, D., & Horowitz, M. J. (1998). Interpersonal ambivalence, perceived relationship adjustment, and conjugal loss. *Journal of Consulting and Clinical Psychology, 66,* 1012–1022.

Bornstein, R. F. (1992). The dependent personality: Developmental, social, and clinical perspectives. *Psychological Bulletin, 112,* 3–23.

Bornstein, R. F. (1993). *The dependent personality.* New York: Guilford Press.

Bornstein, R. F. (1998). Implicit and self-attributed dependency strivings: Differential relationships to laboratory and field measures of help seeking. *Journal of Personality and Social Psychology, 75,* 778–787.

Bower, J. E., Kemeny, M. E., Taylor, S. E., & Fahey, J. L. (1998). Cognitive processing, discovery of meaning, CD4 decline, and AIDS-related mortality among bereaved HIV-seropositive men. *Journal of Consulting and Clinical Psychology, 66,* 979–986.

Bowlby, J. (1980). *Attachment and loss. Vol. 3: Loss.* New York: Basic Books.

Breuer, J., & Freud, S. (1955). Studies on hysteria. In J. Strachey, A. Freud, A. Strachey, & A. Tyson (Eds. & Trans.), *The standard edition of the complete psychological works of Sigmund Freud* (Vol. 2). London: Hogarth Press. (Original work published 1893)

Bruce, M. L., Kim, K., Leaf, P., & Jacobs, S. (1990). Depressive episodes and dysphoria resulting from conjugal bereavement in a prospective community sample. *American Journal of Psychiatry, 147,* 608–611.

Byrne, G. J. A., & Raphael, B. (1997). The psychological symptoms of conjugal bereavement in elderly men over the first 13 months. *International Journal of Geriatric Psychiatry, 12,* 241–251.

Cacioppo, J. T. (1994). Social neuroscience: Autonomic, neuroendocrine, and immune responses to stress. *Psychophysiology, 31,* 113–128.

Cacioppo, J. T., & Bernston, G. G. (1992). Social psychological contributions to the decade of the brain: Doctrine of multilevel analysis. *American Psychologist, 47,* 1019–1028.

Carnelley, K. B., Wortman, C. B., & Kessler, R. C. (1999). The impact of widowhood on depression: Findings from a prospective study. *Psychological Medicine, 29,* 1111–1123.

Caspi, A., & Bem, D. J. (1990). Personality continuity and change across the life course. In L. A. Pervin (Ed.), *Handbook of personality: Theory and research* (pp. 549–575). New York: Guilford Press.

Chen, J. H., Bierhals, A. J., Prigerson, H. G., Kasl, S. V., Mazure, C. M., &

Jacobs, S. (1999). Gender differences in the effects of bereavement-related psychological distress in health outcomes. *Psychological Medicine, 29,* 377–380.

Ciocco, A. (1940). On mortality in husbands and wives. *Human Biology, 12,* 508–531.

Cobb, S., & Lindemann, E. (1943). Neuropsychiatric observations. *Annals of Surgery, 117,* 814–824.

Coe, C. L., Rosenberg, L. T., Fischer, M., & Levine, S. (1987). Psychological factors capable of preventing the inhibition of antibody responses in separated infant monkeys. *Child Development, 58,* 1420–1430.

Cohen, S., Kaplan, J. R., Cunnick, J. E., Manuck, S. B., & Rabin, B. (1992). Chronic social stress, affiliation, and cellular immune response in non-human primates. *Psychological Science, 3,* 301–304.

Cole, S. W., Kemeny, M. E., Taylor, S. E., Visscher, B. R., & Fahey, J. L. (1996). Accelerated course of human immunodeficiency virus infection in gay men who conceal their homosexual identity. *Psychosomatic Medicine, 58,* 219–231.

Conner, K. R., Duberstein, P. R., & Conwell, Y. (in press). Domestic violence, separation, and suicide in young men with early onset alcoholism: Re-analyses of Murphy's data. *Suicide and Life-Threatening Behavior.*

Conwell, Y., Duberstein, P. R., Cox, C., Herrmann, J., Forbes, N. T., & Caine, E. D. (1996). Relationships of age and Axis I diagnoses in victims of completed suicide: A psychological autopsy study. *American Journal of Psychiatry, 153,* 1001–1008.

Cope, O. (1943). Management of the Coconut Grove burns at the Massachusetts General Hospital: Foreword. *Annals of Surgery, 117,* 801–802.

Cox, P. R., & Ford, J. R. (1964). The mortality of widows shortly after widowhood. *Lancet, 1,* 163–164.

Coyne, J. C., & Whiffen, V. (1995). Issues in personality as diathesis for depression: The case of sociotropy-dependency and autonomy–self-criticism. *Psychological Bulletin, 118,* 358–378.

Darwin, C. (1998). *The expression of the emotions in man and animals* (3rd ed., with introduction, afterword, and commentaries by P. Ekman). New York: Oxford University Press. (Original work published 1872)

Deutsch, H. (1937). Masked grief. *Psychoanalytic Quarterly, 6,* 12–22.

Dinges, D. F., Douglas, S. D., Zaugg, L., Campbell, D. E., McMann, J. M., Whitehouse, W. G., Orne, E. C., Kapoor, S. C., Icaza, E., & Orne, M. T. (1994). Leukocytosis and natural killer cell function parallel neurobehavioral fatigue induced by 64 hours of sleep deprivation. *Journal of Clinical Investigation, 93,* 1930–1939.

Duberstein, P. R., Conwell, Y., & Caine, E. D. (1993). Interpersonal stressors, substance abuse, and suicide. *Journal of Nervous and Mental Disease, 181,* 80–85.

Duberstein, P. R., Conwell, Y., & Cox, C. (1998). Suicide in widowed persons: A psychological autopsy comparison of recently and remotely bereaved older subjects. *American Journal of Geriatric Psychiatry, 6,* 328–334.

Duberstein, P. R., Conwell, Y., Seidlitz, L., Lyness, J. M., Cox, C., & Caine, E. D. (1999). Age and suicidal ideation in older depressed inpatients. *American Journal of Geriatric Psychiatry, 7,* 289–296.

Duberstein, P. R., Seidlitz, L., & Conwell, Y. (1996). Reconsidering the role of hostility in completed suicide: A life-course perspective. In J. Masling & R. F. Bornstein (Eds.), *Psychoanalytic perspectives on developmental psychology* (pp. 257–323). Washington, DC: American Psychological Association.

Durkheim, E. (1951). *Suicide: A study in sociology.* New York: Free Press. (Original work published 1897)

Efron, A. (1985). The sexual body: An interdisciplinary perspective [Special issue]. *Journal of Mind & Behavior, 6*(1–2), 314.

Ehlers, C. L., Frank, E., & Kupfer, D. J. (1988). Social zeitgebers and biological rhythms. *Archives of General Psychiatry, 45,* 948–952.

Ekblom, B. (1963). Significance of psychosocial factors with regard to risk of death among elderly persons. *Acta Psychiatrica Scandinavia, 39,* 627–633.

Elder, G. (1974). *Children of the Great Depression.* Chicago: University of Chicago.

Engel, G. L. (1961). Is grief a disease? A challenge for medical research. *Psychosomatic Medicine, 23,* 18–22.

Engel, G. L. (1980). The clinical application of the biopsychosocial model. *American Journal of Psychiatry, 137,* 535–543.

Epstein, S. (1993). Bereavement from the perspective of cognitive–experiential self theory. In M. S. Stroebe, W. Stroebe, & R. O. Hansson (Eds.), *Handbook of bereavement: Theory, research and intervention* (pp. 112–125). Cambridge, UK: Cambridge University Press.

Ewald, P. W. (1994). *The evolution of infectious illness.* New York: Oxford University Press.

Eysenck, H. J. (1990). Biological dimensions of personality. In L. A. Pervin (Ed.), *Handbook of personality theory and research* (pp. 244–276). New York: Guilford Press.

Fenichel, O. (1945). *The psychoanalytic theory of neurosis.* New York: Norton.

Ferenczi, S. (1929). The unwelcome child and his death instinct. *International Journal of Psychoanalysis, 10,* 125–129.

Field, T. (1998). Massage therapy effects. *American Psychologist, 53,* 1270–1281.

Freud, S. (1953). Psychical (or mental) treatment. In J. Strachey, A. Freud, A. Strachey, & A. Tyson (Eds. & Trans.), *The standard edition of the complete psychological works of Sigmund Freud* (Vol. 7, pp. 283–304). London: Hogarth Press. (Original work published 1905)

Freud, S. (1957). Contributions to a discussion on suicide. In J. Strachey, A. Freud, A. Strachey, & A. Tyson (Eds. & Trans.), *The standard edition of the complete psychological works of Sigmund Freud* (Vol. 11, pp. 231–232). London: Hogarth Press. (Original work published 1910)

Freud, S. (1957). Thoughts for the times on war and death. In J. Strachey, A. Freud, A. Strachey, & A. Tyson (Eds. & Trans.), *The standard edition of the complete psychological works of Sigmund Freud* (Vol. 14, pp. 273–300). London: Hogarth Press. (Original work published 1915)

Freud, S. (1957). Mourning and melancholia. In J. Strachey, A. Freud, A. Strachey, & A. Tyson (Eds. & Trans.), *The standard edition of the complete psychological works of Sigmund Freud* (Vol. 14, pp. 243–258). London: Hogarth Press. (Original work published 1917)

Freud, S. (1961). *Civilization and its discontents* (J. Strachey, Ed. & Trans.). New York: Norton. (Original work published 1930)

Freud, S. (1965). *The interpretation of dreams* (J. Strachey, Ed. & Trans.). New York: Avon Books. (Original work published 1900)

Freud, S. (1966). Extracts from the Fliess papers. In J. Strachey, A. Freud, A. Strachey, & A. Tyson (Eds. & Trans.), *The standard edition of the complete psychological works of Sigmund Freud* (Vol. 1, pp. 177–280). London: Hogarth Press. (Original work published 1950, written 1892–1899)

Friedman, S. B., Ader, R., & Glasgow, L. A. (1965). Effects of psychological stress in adult mice inoculated with Coxsackie B viruses. *Psychosomatic Medicine, 27,* 361–368.

Fromm, E. (1990). *Man for himself: An inquiry into the psychology of ethics.* New York: Holt. (Original work published 1947)

Gallo, J. J., Anthony, J. C., & Muthen, B. (1994). Age differences in the symptoms of depression: A latent trait analysis. *Journal of Gerontology, 49,* P251–P264.

Gay, P. (1988). *Freud: A life for our time.* New York: Norton.

Geschwind, N., & Galaburda, A. M. (1987). *Cerebral lateralization: Biological mechanisms, associations, and pathology.* Cambridge, MA: MIT Press.

Gorer, G. (1965). *Death, grief, and mourning in contemporary Britain.* London: Cresset.

Greenberg, R. P., & Bornstein, R. F. (1988). The dependent personality: I. Risk for physical disorders. *Journal of Personality Disorders, 2,* 126–135.

Hall, M., Baum, A., Buysse, D. J., Prigerson, H. G., Kupfer, D. J., & Reynolds, C. F., III. (1998). Sleep as a mediator of the stress–immune relationship. *Psychosomatic Medicine, 60,* 48–51.

Hamilton, M. (1960). A rating scale for depression. *Journal of Neurology, Neurosurgery, and Psychiatry, 23,* 56–62.

Hansson, R. O. (1986). Relational competence, relationships, and adjustment in old age. *Journal of Personality and Social Psychology, 50,* 1050–1058.

Haracz, J. (1984). Neural plasticity and the inclusion of biology in psychoanalytic metatheory. *Psychoanalysis and Contemporary Thought, 7,* 469–490.

Harlow, S. D., Goldberg, E. L., & Comstock, G. W. (1991). A longitudinal study of the prevalence of depressive symptomatology in elderly widowed and married women. *Archives of General Psychiatry, 48,* 1065–1068.

Hays, J. C., Kasl, S., & Jacobs, S. (1994). Past personal history of dysphoria, social support, and psychological distress following conjugal bereavement. *Journal of the American Geriatrics Society, 42,* 712–718.

Heider, F. (1958). *The psychology of interpersonal relations.* New York: Wiley.

Helsing, J. K., Comstock, G. W., & Szklo, M. (1982). Causes of death in a widowed population. *American Journal of Epidemiology, 116,* 524–532.

Helsing, K. J., Szklo, M., & Comstock, G. W. (1981). Factors associated with mortality after widowhood. *American Journal of Public Health, 71,* 802–809.

Herbert, T. B., & Cohen, S. (1993). Depression and immunity: A meta-analytic review. *Psychological Bulletin, 113,* 472–486.

Hinkle, L. E., Jr., & Wolff, H. G. (1958). Ecologic investigations of the relationship between illness, life experiences, and the social environment. *Annals of Internal Medicine, 49,* 1373–1388.

Hofer, M. A. (1984). Relationships as regulators: A psychobiologic perspective on bereavement. *Psychosomatic Medicine, 46,* 183–197.

Hofer, M. A. (1996). On the nature and consequences of early loss. *Psychosomatic Medicine, 58,* 570–581.

Hofmann, B., Lindhart, B. O., Gerstoft, J., Petersen, C. S., Platz, P., Ryder, L. P., Odum, N., Dickmeiss, E., Nielsen, P. B., Ullman, S., & Svejgaard, A. (1987). Lymphocyte transformation response to pokeweed mitogen as a predictive marker for development of AIDS and AIDS related symptoms in homosexual men with HIV antibodies. *British Medical Journal, 295,* 293–296.

Holmes, T. H., & Rahe, R. H. (1967). The Social Readjustment Rating Scale. *Journal of Psychosomatic Research, 11,* 213–218.

Hooper, J. (1999, February). A new germ theory. *Atlantic Monthly, 283,* 41–53.

Horowitz, M. J., Bonanno, G. A., & Holen, A. (1993). Pathological grief: Diagnosis and explanation. *Psychosomatic Medicine, 55,* 260–273.

Horowitz, M. J., Siegel, B., Holen, A., Bonanno, G. A., Milbrath, C., & Stinson, C. H. (1997). Diagnostic criteria for complicated grief disorder. *American Journal of Psychiatry, 154,* 904–910.

Horowitz, M. J., Wilner, N., & Alvarez, W. (1979). Impact of Event Scale: A measure of subjective stress. *Psychosomatic Medicine, 41,* 209–218.

Horsten, M., Ericson, M., Perski, A., Wamala, S. P., Schenck-Gustafsson, K., & Orth-Gomer, K. (1999). Psychosocial factors and heart rate variability in healthy women. *Psychosomatic Medicine, 61,* 49–57.

House, J. S., Landis, K. R., & Umberson, D. (1988). Social relationships and health. *Science, 241,* 540–545.

Ironson, G., Wynings, C., Schneiderman, N., Baum, A., Rodriguez, M., Greenwood, D., Benight, C., Antoni, M., LaPerriere, A., Huang, H.-S., Klimas, N., & Fletcher, M. A. (1997). Posttraumatic stress symptoms, intrusive thoughts, loss, and immune function after Hurricane Andrew. *Psychosomatic Medicine, 59,* 128–141.

Irwin, M., Daniels, M., Smith, T. L., Bloom, E., & Weiner, H. (1987). Impaired natural killer cell activity during bereavement. *Brain, Behavior, and Immunity, 1,* 98–104.

Irwin, M., Mascovich, A., Gillin, J. C., Willoughby, R., Pike, J., & Smith, T. L. (1994). Partial sleep deprivation reduces natural killer cell activity in humans. *Psychosomatic Medicine, 56,* 493–498.

Irwin, M., & Pike, J. (1993). Bereavement, depressive symptoms, and immune function. In M. S. Stroebe, W. Stroebe, & R. O. Hansson (Eds.), *Handbook of bereavement: Theory, research, and intervention* (pp. 160–174). New York: Cambridge University Press.

Irwin, M., Smith, T. L., & Gillin, J. C. (1992). Electroencephalographic sleep and natural killer activity in depressed patients and control subjects. *Psychosomatic Medicine, 54,* 10–21.

Jackson, S. W. (1986). *Melancholia and depression: From Hippocratic times to modern times.* New Haven, CT: Yale University Press.

Jamison, K. R. (1993). *Touched with fire: Manic-depressive illness and the artistic temperament.* New York: Free Press.

Janoff-Bulman, R. (1992). *Shattered assumptions: Towards a new psychology of trauma.* New York: Free Press.

Jemmott, J. B., III, & Locke, S. E. (1984). Psychosocial factors, immunologic mediation, and human susceptibility to infectious diseases: How much do we know? *Psychological Bulletin, 95,* 78–108.

Justice, A. (1985). Review of the effects of stress on cancer in laboratory animals: Importance of time of stress application and type of tumor. *Psychological Bulletin, 98,* 108–138.

Kagan, J. (1998). *Three seductive ideas.* Cambridge, MA: Harvard University Press.

Kagan, J. (with Snidman, N., Arcus, D., & Reznick, J. S.). (1994). *Galen's prophecy: Temperament in human nature.* New York: Basic Books.

Kagan, J., Snidman, N., Julia-Sellers, M., & Johnson, M. O. (1991). Temperament and allergic symptoms. *Psychosomatic Medicine, 53,* 332–340.

Kandel, E. R. (1999). Biology and the future of psychoanalysis: A new intellectual framework for psychiatry revisited. *American Journal of Psychiatry, 156,* 505–524.

Kaprio, J., Koskenvuo, M., & Rita, H. (1987). Mortality after bereavement: A prospective study of 95,647 widowed persons. *American Journal of Public Health, 77,* 283–287.

Katz, I. R., Beaston-Wimmer, P., Parmelee, P. A., Friedman, E., & Lawton, M. P. (1993). Failure to thrive in the elderly: Exploration of the concept and delineation of psychiatric components. *Journal of Geriatric Psychiatry and Neurology, 6,* 161–169.

Kiecolt-Glaser, J. K., Dura, J. R., Speicher, C. E., Trask, O. J., & Glaser, R. (1991). Spousal caregivers of dementia victims: Longitudinal changes in immunity and health. *Psychosomatic Medicine, 53,* 345–362.

Kiecolt-Glaser, J. K., & Glaser, R. (1988). Methodological issues in behavioral immunology research with humans. *Brain, Behavior, and Immunity, 2,* 67–78.

Kiecolt-Glaser, J. K., & Glaser, R. (1991). Stress and immune function in humans. In R. Ader, D. L. Felten, & N. Cohen (Eds.), *Psychoneuroimmunology* (2nd ed., pp. 849–867). San Diego, CA: Academic Press.

Kimzey, S. L. (1975). The effects of extended spaceflight on hematologic and immunologic systems. *Journal of the American Medical Women's Association, 30,* 218–232.

Klein, M. (1948). Mourning and its relation to manic-depressive states. In E. Jones (Ed.), *Contributions to psycho-analysis 1921–1945* (pp. 311–338). London: Hogarth Press. (Original work published 1940)

Korenman, S., Goldman, N., & Fu, H. (1997). Misclassification bias in estimates of bereavement effects. *American Journal of Epidemiology, 145,* 992–1002.

Kraus, A. S., & Lilienfeld, A. M. (1959). Some epidemiological aspects of the high mortality rate in the young widowed group. *Journal of Chronic Diseases, 10,* 207–217.

Krause, N. (1993). Early parental loss and personal control in later life. *Journal of Gerontology: Psychological Sciences, 48,* P117–P126.

Kreitman, N. (1964). The patient's spouse. *British Journal of Psychiatry, 110,* 159–163.

Kuo, C. C., Shor, A., Cambell, L. A., Fukushi, H., Patton, D. L., & Grayston, J. T. (1993). Demonstration of chlamydia pneumonia in atherosclerotic lesions of coronary arteries. *Journal of Infectious Diseases, 167,* 841–849.

Kuypers, J. A., & Bengston, V. L. (1973). Social breakdown and competence: A model of normal aging. *Human Development, 16,* 181–201.

Ladd, C. O., Owens, M. J., & Nemeroff, C. B. (1996). Persistent changes in corticotropin-releasing factor neuronal systems induced by maternal deprivation. *Endocrinology, 137,* 1212–1218.

Lepore, S. J., Silver, R. C., Wortman, C. B., & Wayment, H. A. (1996). Social constraints, intrusive thoughts, and depressive symptoms among bereaved mothers. *Journal of Personality and Social Psychology, 70,* 271–282.

Levi, P. (1988). *The drowned and the saved* (R. Rosenthal, Trans.). New York: Random House.

Lichtenstein, P., Gatz, M., & Berg, S. (1998). A twin study of mortality after spousal bereavement. *Psychological Medicine, 23,* 635–643.

Lichtenstein, P., Gatz, M., Pedersen, N. L., Berg, S., & McClearn, G. E. (1996). A co-twin-control study of response to widowhood. *Journal of Gerontology: Psychological Sciences, 51B,* P279–P289.

Lindemann, E. (1944). Symptomatology and management of acute grief. *American Journal of Psychiatry, 101,* 141–148.

Linn, M. W., Linn, B. S., & Jensen, J. (1984). Stressful events, dysphoric mood, and immune responsiveness. *Psychological Reports, 54,* 219–222.

Lopata, H. Z. (1980). Loneliness in widowhood. In J. Hartog, J. R. Audy, & Y. A. Cohen (Eds.), *The anatomy of loneliness* (pp. 237–258). New York: International Universities Press.

Lubach, G. R., Coe, C. L., & Ershler, W. B. (1995). Effects of early rearing environment on immune responses of infant rhesus monkeys. *Brain, Behavior, & Immunity, 9,* 31–46.

Lund, D. A., Caserta, M. S., & Dimond, M. (1993). The course of spousal bereavement in later life. In M. S. Stroebe, W. Stroebe, & R. O. Hansson (Eds.), *Handbook of bereavement: Theory, research and intervention* (pp. 240–254). Cambridge, UK: Cambridge University Press.

Lyness, J. M., Cox, C., Curry, J., Conwell, Y., King, D. A., & Caine, E. D. (1995). Older age and the underreporting of depressive symptoms. *Journal of the American Geriatrics Society, 43,* 216–221.

MacMahon, B., & Pugh, T. F. (1965). Suicide in the widowed. *American Journal of Epidemiology, 81,* 23–31.

Maddison, D. C. (1968). The relevance of conjugal bereavement for preventive psychiatry. *British Journal of Medical Psychology, 41,* 223–233.

Maddison, D. C., & Viola, A. (1968). The health of widows in the year following bereavement. *Journal of Psychosomatic Research, 12,* 297–306.

Maier, S. F., Watkins, L. R., & Fleshner, M. (1994). Psychoneuroimmunology: The interface between behavior, brain, and immunity. *American Psychologist, 49,* 1004–1017.

Manuck, S. B., Cohen, S., Rabin, B. D., Muldoon, M. F., & Bachen, E. A. (1991). Individual differences in response to stress. *Psychological Science, 2,* 111–115.

March, L. (1912). Some researches concerning the factors of mortality. *Journal of the Royal Statistical Society, 75,* 505–538.

Martikainen, P., & Valkonen, T. (1996a). Mortality after death of spouse in relation to duration of bereavement in Finland. *Journal of Epidemiology and Community Health, 50,* 264–268.

Martikainen, P., & Valkonen, T. (1996b). Mortality after the death of a spouse: Rates and causes of death in a large Finnish cohort. *American Journal of Public Health, 86,* 1087–1093.

Martikainen, P., & Valkonen, T. (1998). Do education and income buffer the effects of death of spouse on mortality? *Epidemiology, 9,* 530–534.

Masling, J. (1986). Orality, pathology, and interpersonal behavior. In J. Masling (Ed.), *Empirical studies of psychoanalytical theories* (Vol. 2, pp. 73–106). Hillsdale, NJ: Erlbaum.

Mazure, C. M. (1998). Life stressors as risk factors for depression. *Clinical Psychology: Science and Practice, 5,* 291–314.

McClelland, D. C. (1989). Motivational factors in health and disease. *American Psychologist, 44,* 675–683.

McClelland, D. C., Alexander, C., & Marks, E. (1982). The need for power, stress, immune function, and illness among male prisoners. *Journal of Abnormal Psychology, 91,* 61–70.

McClelland, D. C., Koestner, R., & Weinberger, J. (1989). How do self-attributed and implicit motives differ? *Psychological Review, 96,* 690–702.

McClintock, M. K. (1978). Estrous synchrony and its mediation by air-borne chemical communication (rattus norvegicus). *Hormones and Behavior, 10,* 264–276.

McEwen, B. S., & Stellar, E. (1993). Stress and the individual: Mechanisms leading to disease. *Archives of Internal Medicine, 153,* 2093–2101.

McKay J. R. (1991). Assessing aspects of object relations associated with immune function: Development of the affiliative trust–mistrust coding system. *Psychological Assessment, 3,* 641–647.

McKay, J. R., Luborsky, L., Barber, J. P., Kabasakalian-McKay, R., Zorilla, E. P., & Cacciola, J. S. (1997). Affiliative trust–mistrust and immunity in depressed patients receiving supportive–expressive psychotherapy. *Psychotherapy Research, 7,* 249–260.

Mendes De Leon, C. F., Kasl, S. V., & Jacobs, S. (1993). Widowhood and mortality risk in a community sample of the elderly: A prospective study. *Journal of Clinical Epidemiology, 46,* 519–527.

Mendes De Leon, C. F., Kasl, S. V., & Jacobs, S. (1994). A prospective study of widowhood and changes I: Symptoms of depression in a community sample of the elderly. *Psychological Medicine, 24,* 613–624.

Miller, G. E., Dopp, J. M., Myers, H. F., Stevens, S. Y., & Fahey, J. L. (1999). Psychosocial predictors of natural killer cell mobilization during marital conflict. *Health Psychology, 18,* 262–271.

Miller, L. (1998). Psychotherapy of crime victims: Treating the aftermath of interpersonal violence. *Psychotherapy, 35,* 336–345.

Mullan, J. T. (1992). The bereaved caregiver: A prospective study of changes in well-being. *The Gerontologist, 32,* 673–683.

Murasko, D. M., Weiner, P., & Kaye, D. (1988). Association of lack of mitogen-induced lymphocyte proliferation with increased mortality in the elderly. *Aging: Immunology and Infectious Diseases, 1,* 1–16.

Murphy, E. (1982). Social origins of depression in old age. *British Journal of Psychiatry, 141,* 135–142.

Murrell, S. A., Himmelfarb, S., & Phifer, J. F. (1988). Effects of bereavement/loss and pre-event status on subsequent physical health in older adults. *International Journal of Aging & Human Development, 27,* 89–107.

Nadler, A. (1997). Personality and help seeking: Autonomous versus dependent seeking of help. In G. R. Pierce, B. Lakey, I. G. Sarason, & B. R. Sarason (Eds.), *Sourcebook of social support and personality* (pp. 379–407). New York: Plenum Press.

Ness, D. E., & Pfeffer, C. R. (1990). Sequelae of bereavement resulting from suicide. *American Journal of Psychiatry, 147,* 249–285.

Newman, D. L., Caspi, A., Moffitt, T. E., & Silva, P. (1997). Antecedents of adult interpersonal functioning: Effects of individual differences in age 3 temperament. *Developmental Psychology, 33,* 206–217.

Norris, F. H., & Murrell, S. A. (1987). Older adult family stress and adaptation before and after bereavement. *Journal of Gerontology, 42,* 606–612.

Nuss, W. S., & Zubenko, G. S. (1992). Correlates of persistent depressive symptoms in widows. *American Journal of Psychiatry, 149,* 346–351.

O'Leary, A. (1990). Stress, emotion, and human immune function. *Psychological Bulletin, 108,* 363–382.

Osterweis, M., Solomon, F., & Green, M. (1984). *Bereavement: Reactions, consequences, and care.* Washington, DC: National Academic Press.

Overmier, J. B., & Murison, R. (1997). Animal models reveal the "psych" in the psychosomatics of peptic ulcers. *Current Directions in Psychological Science, 6,* 178–184.

Parkes, C. M. (1987). *Bereavement: Studies of grief in adult life* (2nd American ed.). Madison, CT: International Universities Press.

Parkes, C. M. (1993). Psychiatric problems following bereavement by murder or manslaughter. *British Journal of Psychiatry, 162,* 49–54.

Parkes, C. M., Benjamin, B., & Fitzgerald, R. G. (1969). Broken heart: A statistical study of increased mortality among widowers. *British Medical Journal, 1,* 740–743.

Parkes, C. M., & Weiss, R. S. (1983). *Recovery from bereavement.* New York: Basic Books.

Pearlin, L. I. (1989). The sociological study of stress. *Journal of Health and Social Behavior, 30,* 241–256.

Petitto, J. M., Lysle, D. T., Gariepy, J.-L., & Lewis, M. H. (1994). Association of genetic differences in social behavior and cellular immune responsiveness: Effects of social experience. *Brain, Behavior, & Immunity, 8,* 111–122.

Pinneau, S. R. (1955a). The infantile disorders of hospitalism and anaclitic depression. *Psychological Bulletin, 52,* 429–452.

Pinneau, S. R. (1955b). Reply to Dr. Spitz. *Psychological Bulletin, 52,* 459–462.

Plaut, S. M., & Friedman, S. B. (1982). Stress, coping behavior, and resistance to disease. *Psychotherapy and Psychosomatics, 38,* 274–283.

Potter, P. T., & Zautra, A. J. (1997). Stressful life events' effects on rheumatoid arthritis disease activity. *Journal of Consulting and Clinical Psychology, 65,* 319–323.

Prigerson, H. G., Bierhals, A. J., Kasl, S. V., Reynolds, C. F., III, Shear, M. K., Day, N., Beery, L., Newsom, J. T., & Jacobs, S. (1997). Traumatic grief as a risk factor for mental and physical morbidity. *American Journal of Psychiatry, 154,* 616–623.

Prigerson, H. G., Bierhals, A. J., Kasl, S. V., Reynolds, C. F., III, Shear, K. M., Newsom, J. T., & Jacobs, S. (1996). Complicated grief as a disorder distinct from bereavement-related depression and anxiety: A replication study. *American Journal of Psychiatry, 153,* 1484–1486.

Prigerson, H. G., Frank, E., Kasl, S. V., Reynolds, C. F., III, Anderson, B., Zubenko, G. S., Houck, P. R., George, C. J., & Kupfer, D. J. (1995).

Complicated grief and bereavement-related depression as distinct disorders: Preliminary empirical validation in elderly bereaved spouses. *American Journal of Psychiatry, 152,* 22–30.

Rado, S. (1956). *Psychoanalysis and behavior: Collected papers.* New York: Grune & Stratton.

Raphael, B. (1983). *The anatomy of bereavement.* New York: Basic Books.

Rees, W., & Lutkins, S. (1967). Mortality of bereavement. *British Medical Journal, 4,* 13–16.

Rodin, J. (1986, September 19). Aging and health: Effects of the sense of control. *Science, 233,* 1271–1275.

Roitt, I. M. (1997). *Essential immunology* (9th ed.). Malden, MA: Blackwell Science.

Roy, A. (1982). Hysterical neurosis. In A. Roy (Ed.), *Hysteria* (pp. 89–98). New York: Wiley.

Rush, B. (1962). *Medical inquiries and observations upon the diseases of the mind.* New York: Hafner. (Original work published 1812)

Rynearson, E. K. (1995). Bereavement after homicide. A comparison of treatment seekers and refusers. *British Journal of Psychiatry, 166,* 507–510.

Sapolsky, R. M. (1994). *Why zebras don't get ulcers: A guide to stress, stress-related disease, and coping.* New York: Freeman.

Schaefer, C., Quesenberry, C. P., & Wi, S. (1995). Mortality following conjugal bereavement and the effects of a shared environment. *American Journal of Epidemiology, 141,* 1142–1152.

Schleifer, S. J., Keller, S. E., Camerino, M., Thornton, J. C., & Stein, M. (1983). Suppression of lymphocyte stimulation following bereavement. *Journal of the American Medical Association, 250,* 374–377.

Schulz, R., & Beach, S. R. (1999). Caregiving as a risk factor for mortality: The Caregiver Health Effects Study. *Journal of the American Medical Association, 282,* 2215–2219.

Selye, H. (1951). The general adaptation syndrome and the diseases of adaptation. *American Journal of Medicine, 10,* 549–555.

Shea, J., Burton, R., & Girgis, A. (1993). Negative affect, absorption, and immunity. *Physiology & Behavior, 53,* 449–457.

Shepherd, D., & Barraclough, B. M. (1974). The aftermath of suicide. *British Medical Journal, 2,* 600–603.

Shurtleff, D. (1955). Mortality and marital status. *Public Health Reports, 70,* 248–252.

Siegel, R. E. (1968). *Galen's system of physiology and medicine.* New York: Karger.

Siggins, L. D. (1966). Mourning: A critical survey of the literature. *International Journal of Psychoanalysis, 47,* 14–25.

Smith, K. R., & Zick, C. D. (1996). Risk of mortality following widowhood: Age and sex differences by mode of death. *Social Biology, 43,* 59–71.

Spitz, R. A. (1946). Hospitalism: An inquiry into the genesis of psychiatric conditions in early childhood. *Psychoanalytic Study of the Child, 1,* 53–74.

Spitz, R. A. (1955). Reply to Dr. Pinneau. *Psychological Bulletin, 52,* 453–459.

Spurrell, M. T., & Creed, F. H. (1993). Lymphocyte response in depressed patients and subjects anticipating bereavement. *British Journal of Psychiatry, 162,* 60–64.

Stone, A. A., Cox, D. S., Valdimarsdottir, H., & Neale, J. M. (1987). Secretory IgA as a measure of immunocompetence. *Journal of Human Stress, 13,* 136–140.

Stroebe, M. S., & Stroebe, W. (1983). Who suffers more? Sex differences in health risks of the widowed. *Psychological Bulletin, 93,* 279–301.

Stroebe, M. S., & Stroebe, W. (1993). The mortality of bereavement: A review. In M. S. Stroebe, W. Stroebe, & R. O. Hansson (Eds.), *Handbook of bereavement: Theory, research and intervention* (pp. 175–195). Cambridge, UK: Cambridge University Press.

Stroebe, W., & Stroebe, M. S. (1987). *Bereavement and health: The psychological and physical consequences of partner loss.* New York: Cambridge University Press.

Survey of the Nordic countries: Happy family? (1999, January 23). *The Economist, 353,* 1–16.

Swigar, M. E., Bowers, M. B., & Fleck, S. (1976). Grieving and unplanned pregnancy. *Psychiatry, 39,* 72–79.

Taylor, S. E. (1983). Adjustment to threatening events: A theory of cognitive adaptation. *American Psychologist, 38,* 1161–1173.

Thompson, L. W., Gallagher-Thompson, D., Futterman, A., Gilewski, M. J., & Peterson J. (1991). The effects of late-life spousal bereavement over a 30-month interval. *Psychology and Aging, 6,* 434–441.

Tower, R. B., & Kasl, S. V. (1996). Depressive symptoms across older spouses: Longitudinal influences. *Psychology and Aging, 11,* 683–697.

Trinchieri, G. (1989). Biology of natural killer cells. *Advances in Immunology, 47,* 187–376.

Turvey, C. L., Carney, C., Arndt, S., Wallace, R. B., & Herzog, A. R. (1999). Conjugal loss and syndromal depression in a sample of elders aged 70 years or older. *American Journal of Psychiatry, 156,* 1596–1601.

Umberson, D., Wortman, C. B., & Kessler, R. C. (1992). Widowhood and depression: Explaining long-term gender differences in vulnerability. *Journal of Health and Social Behavior, 33,* 10–24.

Vitaliano, P. P., Scanlan, J. M., Krenz, C., Schwartz, R. S., & Marcovina, S. M. (1996). Psychological distress, caregiving, and metabolic variables. *Journals of Gerontology: Psychological Sciences, 51B,* 290–299.

Von Dras, D. D., & Siegler, I. C. (1997). Stability in extraversion and aspects of social support at midlife. *Journal of Personality and Social Psychology, 72,* 233–241.

Waldron, I., Hughes, M. E., & Brooks, T. L. (1996). Marriage protection and marriage selection—Prospective evidence for reciprocal effects of marital status and health. *Social Science & Medicine, 43,* 113–123.

Westen, D. (1998). The scientific legacy of Sigmund Freud: Toward a psychodynamically informed psychological science. *Psychological Bulletin, 124,* 333–371.

Wolinsky, F. D., & Johnson, R. J. (1992). Widowhood, health status, and the use of health services by older adults: A cross-sectional and prospective approach. *Journal of Gerontology: Social Sciences, 47,* S8–S16.

Worden, J. W. (1991). *Grief counseling and grief therapy* (2nd ed.). New York: Springer.

Wortman, C. B. (1997, August). *Myths of coping with loss: Implications for prevention.* Paper presented at the 105th Annual Convention of the American Psychological Association, Chicago, IL.

Wortman, C. B., & Silver, R. C. (1989). The myths of coping with loss. *Journal of Consulting and Clinical Psychology, 57,* 349–357.

Wortman, C. B., Silver, R. C., & Kessler, R. C. (1993). The meaning of loss and adjustment of bereavement. In M. S. Stroebe, W. Stroebe, & R. O. Hansson (Eds.), *Handbook of bereavement: Theory, research and intervention* (pp. 349–366). Cambridge, UK: Cambridge University Press.

Wulsin, L. R., Vaillant, G. E., & Wells, V. E. (1999). A systematic review of the mortality of depression. *Psychosomatic Medicine, 61,* 6–17.

Yalom, I. D., & Lieberman, M. A. (1991). Bereavement and heightened existential awareness. *Psychiatry, 54,* 334–345.

Young, M., Benjamin, B., & Wallis, C. (1963). Mortality of widowers. *Lancet, 2,* 254–256.

Zajonc, R. B. (1985). Emotion and facial efference: A theory reclaimed. *Science, 228,* 15–21.

Zajonc, R. B., Adelmann, P. K., Murphy, S. T., & Niedenthal, P. M. (1987). Convergence in the physical appearance of spouses. *Motivation & Emotion, 11,* 335–346.

Zisook, S., Shuchter, S. R., Irwin, M., Darko, D. F., Sledge, P., & Resovsky, K. (1994). Bereavement, depression, and immune function. *Psychiatry Research, 52,* 1–10.

Zorrilla, E. P., McKay, J. R., Luborsky, L., & Schmidt, K. (1996). Relation of stressors and depressive symptoms to clinical progression of viral illness. *American Journal of Psychiatry, 153,* 626–635.

Author Index

Numbers in italics refer to listings in reference sections.

Subject Index

About the Editors

Paul Raphael Duberstein, PhD, is an associate professor of psychiatry and oncology at the University of Rochester School of Medicine and Dentistry (Rochester, NY), where he is affiliated with the Center for the Study and Prevention of Suicide. He received his PhD in clinical–community psychology from the State University of New York at Buffalo in 1991 and completed a postdoctoral fellowship in late-life psychopathology at the University of Rochester. Dr. Duberstein's research examines the relationships between personality and both mental and physical health, with a special emphasis on personality, loss, and suicidal behavior in older adults.

Joseph M. Masling, PhD, is an emeritus professor of psychology at the State University of New York at Buffalo. He has written numerous articles on interpersonal and situational variables influencing projective tests, and he has published widely on the empirical study of psychoanalytic concepts. Dr. Masling edited the first three volumes of the Empirical Studies of Psychoanalytic Theories book series (1983, 1986, 1990); coedited with Robert F. Bornstein the next five volumes, including *Psychoanalytic Perspectives on Developmental Psychology* (1996), *Empirical Studies of the Therapeutic Hour* (1998), and *Empirical Perspectives on the Psychoanalytic Unconscious* (1998); and received the Society for Personality Assessment's 1997 Bruno Klopfer Award for Lifetime Achievement in Personality Assessment.

psychosomatic
health
body